THE BROON·WINDSORS

CHRISTMAS AFTERNOON...

BBC Radio Ootside Broadcast Unit

RIGHT, MA'AM. WE'RE LIVE ON AIR FOR YOUR CHRISTMAS BROADCAST TO THE COMMONWEALTH IN TWO MINUTES.

GUID! IT'S A BRAW WEE SPEECH A'M GANNAE DELIVER THIS YEAR, AN ABSOLUT' STOATER.

I'LL JIST PRACTISE MA' OPENING LINES...

AHEM... MA HUSBAND AN' MA'SEL...

BANG! BANG! BANG! BANG!

WHIT THE...!?!

HOO THE DE'IL A'M AH SUPPOSED TAE DELIVER MA SPEECH WI THAT WEAN MAKIN' THAT DIN?!

SORRY, GRAN'MAW, WEE GEORGIE'S JIST TRYIN' OOT THE DRUM HE GOT FRAE SANTY CLAUS.

WELL GIT THE NOISY WEE SHITE OOT O' THE ROOM, OOR WULLIE. AH CANNAE DAE MA SPEECH WI' ALL THAT RACKET.

A'RICHT, KEEP YUR CROON ON.

AHEM... MA HUSBAND AN'...

SO YUR A WEE CACTUS, ARE YE? THAT'S AFFY INTERESTIN'. AN HOE LANG HAE YE BIN DAEIN' THAT FUR?

CRIVVENS! IF IT'S NAE WAN THING IT'S ANITHER...

HOO. OOR CHARLIE! STOAP BLETHERIN TAE THE HOOSEPLANTS WILL YE? AH'M TRYING TAE ADDRESS MA SUBJECTS, YE BIG-EARED GOWK, YE!

A'RICHT, MAW.

I DIDNAE KEN YE WIS BUSY WI' YIR MESSAGES.

AHEM!... MA HUSBAND...

BANG! BANG!

OCH! HELP MA BOAB!

BANG! BANG! BANG! BANG!

GOT THE STRIPY BAS! RICHT A'TWEEN THE EEN!

BRAW SHOOTIN' PAW

WILL YE KEEP THAE DIN DOON!

EH! AH'M AINLIE PLAYIN' TIGER HUNT THREE THOOSAND OAN THE AULD COMPUTER, HEN.

WELL DINNAE! AH'M TRYIN' TAE...

CHUP-A-CHUP! A-CHUP-A-CHUP!

FUR THE LOVE O' GORD!! WHIT NOO!?!

IT'S JUST OOR ANDREW MUCKIN' ABOOT IN HIS FREISH HELICOPTEE, MAW.

CHUP-A-CHUP! A-CHUP-A-CHUP!

STOAP THAT RACKIT, YE PIE-EATIN' BOABY HEID!!!

JUST HAUD YER WHEESHT FUR FUFTEEN MINUTES WHILE I DAE MA SPEECH! OR AH'LL BATTER THE LOT O' YE!

SORRY, GRAN'MAW. YE DAE YUR SPEECH AN' WE'LL A' LISTEN OAN THE WIRELESS.

RIGHT, YOUR MAJESTY. YOU'RE GOING LIVE IN 3...2...1....

CROAK!

HAW! HAW! HAW! SHE'S LOST HER VOICE AFTER A' THAT HOLLERIN' AN' BRAYIN'!

CROAK!

HAW! HAW!

THE GLAIKIT AULD FUD!

Snip! Snip!...Snip! Snip! Snip! It's

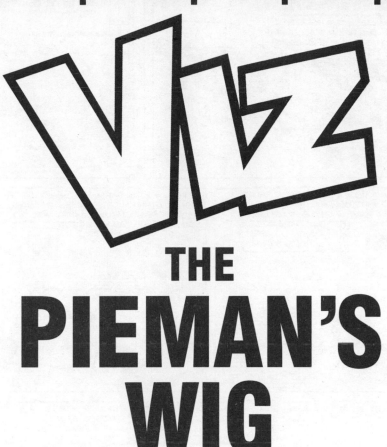

Viz

THE PIEMAN'S WIG

Unruly Tufts of Old Pelt Clipped from Issues 252~261

Dockyard Cats

Graham Dury and Simon Thorp

Unmown Creases

Mark Bates, Alex Collier, Terry Corrigan, Simon Ecob, Tom Ellen, Chad Elliott, Hunt Emerson, Barney Farmer, Ray Fury, Aidan Kelly, Lee Healey, Davey Jones, Marc Jones, Mathew Jones, Richard Milne, Alex Morris, Paul Palmer, Tom Paterson, Joe Shooman, Cat Sullivan, Kent Tayler, Ceri Thomas, Neil Tollfree, Nick Tolson, Katie Welsh and Stevie White.

Billy Goats' Chins

Dharmesh Mistry, Kerin O'Connor and Stephen Catherall

Published by Dennis Publishing Ltd
31-32 Alfred Place, London WC1E 7DP

ISBN 9 781781 066768
First Printing Autumn 2018

Subscribe online at www.viz.co.uk
Find us at facebook.com/vizcomic and twitter.com/vizcomic

ROGER MELLIE THE MAN ON THE TELLY

THANKS FOR STEPPING IN AT THE LAST MINUTE TO DO THE GRAND PRIX GRID WALK, ROGER

NO PROBLEM, TOM... A LITTLE HOLIDAY ABROAD, TWO GRAND A DAY AND ALL THE TOP TOTTY I CAN MANAGE... I SHOULD BE THANKING YOU!

NOW, WE'LL BE GOING LIVE IN A MINUTE, ROGER... YOU KNOW WHAT YOU'VE GOT TO DO, DON'T YOU?

OF COURSE, TOM... WHAT?

YOU JUST WALK ABOUT THE GRID, GRABBING PEOPLE AND TALKING TO THEM ABOUT THE RACE.

DON'T WORRY, I CAN PISS THIS STUFF IN MY SLEEP, TOM!

OKAY, ROGER... WE'VE GOT THIRTY SECONDS BEFORE WE GO ON AIR... LET'S HAVE A LITTLE PRACTICE!

RIGHT YOU ARE, TOM. ...HERE'S ONE...

HELLO, THERE, DARLING!.. 36, EH!?.. THEY LOOK BIGGER THAN THAT TO ME... 38 AT LEAST, IF I'M ANY JUDGE... ANYWAY, WHAT WILL YOU BE DOING DURING THE RACE?

ACTUALLY, FORGET THAT... WHAT WILL YOU BE DOING AFTER THE RACE?

NO, ROGER... IT'S THE DRIVERS YOU NEED TO INTERVIEW

THE DRIVERS!?... WHO THE FUCK WANTS TO LOOK AT THEM?... NO, IT'S THE BIRDS YOU WANT ON SCREEN, TOM... A NICE BIT OF GLAMOUR... GIVE THE BLOKES WATCHING A NICE SUNDAY AFTERNOON TENTPOLE.

THE DRIVERS, ROGER... OKAY?

IT'S YOUR CALL, TOM

LOOK... WE'RE ABOUT TO GO ON AIR.... 3..2..1...

...ACTION!

HELLO, AND WELCOME TO THE MAZOLA CIRCUIT IN MOLDOVA WHERE THE MOST HOTLY CONTESTED RACE IN THIS YEAR'S FORMULA ONE CALENDAR IS ABOUT TO BEGIN...

...AND I'M HERE ON THE STARTING GRID TO TRY TO GRAB A FEW WORDS WITH SOME OF THE DRIVERS...

...THIS ONE WILL DO... NUMBER 3.

PENSO CHE SARÀ UNA STRATEGIA DUE O TRE SOSTE, A SECONDA DEL TEMPO, NATURALMENTE!

E CHE I PNEUMATICI SI UTILIZZERÀ PER INIZIARE LA CORSA?

OUT THE WAY, LOVE... BRITISH TELLY.

SHOVE!

HEY, THIS IS A NICE CAR... HOW FAST DOES THIS FUCKER GO THEN, EH?

MI SCUSI! STAVO PARLANDO CON LA GIORNALISTA...

COME ON... IN ENGLISH!

E STATA QUI PRIMA

CUT, TOM... IT'S NO GOOD... HE DOESN'T SPEAK THE LINGO... I DID WARN YOU.

LET'S GO AND FIND US ANOTHER

ALRIGHT, PAL?.. BRITISH TELLY... IS THIS YOUR CAR, THEN?

YES

FAST, IS IT?

YES... ON THE STRAIGHT IT WILL DO AROUND 300 KILOMETRES AN HOUR

BRITISH TELLY... GIVE US THAT IN MILES.

ER... I THINK... ABOUT 200

FUCK ME! 200? MOST I'VE EVER DONE IS 130 ON THE M6 TOLL

NICE CAR... MIND, YOU WANT TO GET THEM CHANGED BEFORE YOU GO OUT...

BALD AS A PORN STAR'S FANNY

SIX POINTS ON YOUR LICENCE, PAL

ANYWAY... WHO DO YOU RECKON'S GOING TO WIN TODAY?.. ONLY I FANCY A BIT OF A FLUTTER

WELL, MAZOLA IS A LOW DOWNFORCE CIRCUIT, SO THAT WILL FAVOUR FERRA...

SCUSI...TV ITALIA... QUALCHE CONSIGLIO PER LA CORSA...SOLO IO VOGLIA DI METTER UNA SCOMMESSA SU...

WHAT THE FUCK!?

HEY! YOU CHEEKY FUCKER!.. I WAS HERE FIRST!

HAI AVUTO IL TUO TURNO... VAFFANCULO!

PER CUI LA VELOCITÀ PUÒ QUESTO BASTARDO ANDARE?

CIRCA 300 CHILOMETRI ALL'ORA

FOTTERMI!

OOF! YOU LITTLE BASTARD

SCENDERE IL MIO MICROFONO, BASTARDO

THUMP!

SMACK!!
PUNCH! FOOT!
OOF!

ROGER!.. WHAT THE **HELL** ARE YOU DOING?

HE FUCKING STARTED IT, TOM... HE FUCKING PUSHED IN

LEAVE IT, ROGER

LOOK!.. BERTIE ECCLESCAKE, THE HEAD OF FORMULA ONE IS OVER THERE, ROGER... GO AND SEE IF YOU CAN GET AN INTERVIEW WITH HIM... IT'LL BE A REAL COUP

RIGHTO

PIT LANE
AUTHORISED PERSONNEL... ONLY

MR. ECCLESCAKE!.. MR. ECCLESCAKE! A FEW WORDS FOR THE VIEWERS BACK IN BRITAIN, IF YOU WOULD...

YES, OF COURSE

NOW, BERTIE... MAZOLA IS ALWAYS THE JEWEL IN THE CROWN OF THE F1 SEASON... BUT WHAT THE VIEWERS WILL WANT TO KNOW IS... WHEN THE RACE IS OVER AND YOU ARE BOTH BACK IN THE MOTORHOME...

...WHICH ONE GOES ON TOP, EH!?.. IS IT YOU, OR THE MISSUS?.. A COUPLE OF THINGS TELLS ME IT'S PROBABLY HER... AM I RIGHT, BERTIE?

HEH! HEH!.. BET I AM, YOU DIRTY OLD SOD.

JESUS!..

ER...MR. ECCLESCAKE... I'M SO SORRY... I DO APOLOGISE... I'M AFRAID... ROGER... ERM... HASN'T BEEN WELL LATELY...

MISERABLE OLD SOD... IF I HAD HIS MILLIONS AND A WIFE WITH THEM KNOCKERS, I'D NEED PLASTIC SURGERY TO GET THE FUCKING SMILE OFF MY FACE.

I THINK WE'D BETTER GO...

RIGHTO, TOM... HEY, LOOK!.. TELL YOU WHAT, I'LL GET IN THIS CAR AND DO MY FINAL PIECE TO CAMERA. THEN I'LL SPIN THE WHEELS AND DRIVE OUT OF SHOT.

WHAT!?.. **NO!**

IT'S ALRIGHT, TOM...NOBODY WILL MIND. I'LL ONLY DRIVE IT A FEW YARDS.

ROGER! **STOP!**

COME ON, IT'LL BE A FANTASTIC SIGN OFF, THIS. FUCKING CRAMPED, MIND.

OKAY, START THE CAMERA

SO, FROM ME, ROGER MELLIE, ON THE STARTING GRID OF THE MOLDOVIAN GRAND PRIX, IT'S TIME TO GO RACING...

...GENTLEMEN... **START YOUR ENGINES!**

WHERE DO YOU TURN THE FUCKING THING ON, TOM?

...ET CE COURS EST CELEBRE DU SUR LES FREINS

OUI, C'EST VRAI...

VROOOOOM!
CRUMP! CRUMP!
CRUMP! CRUMP!
BANG!

THERE'S NO FUCKING **STEERING WHEEL!** I MEAN, HOW YOU SUPPOSED TO STEER THE FUCKER WHEN THEY'VE TAKEN THE STEERING WHEEL OUT?

ANYWAY, DON'T WORRY, TOM... I'M WITH ADMIRAL MULTICAR

Sid the Sexist

TYNESIDE'S SILVER-TONGUED CAVALIER

TITS OOT!

SID IS VISITING HIS YORKSHIRE COUSIN SHANE FOR THE DAY...

BEEN STOOD 'ERE TWO FUCKIN' 'OO-AZ WAITIN' F'YEE T'TORN UP AN' GET A FUCKIN' ROOND IN.

HOO, SHANE. ABOOT TIME, MAN. AH'VE

AYUP SID.

HANG ABOOT... WOT THE FUCK ARE YUZ WEARIN', MAN.?

IT'S ME NEW JOB, SID. AH'M ONE O'THEM 'CHARITY MUGGERS', THA KNAWS.

Y'KNAW, WOT STOPS FONK ON'T STREET AN' TEKS THEH BRASS FER A GOOD CAUSE.?

OH AYE.?

WELL Y'LOOK A REET FUCKIN' KNOB-'EAD IN THAT LUMINOUS PONCHO, SHANE. HO! HO!

THA CAN LAFF ALL THA WANTS, GEORDIE.

AH'M SECURE IN'T KNOWLEDGE AS 'OW A'M EARNIN' ME PARKIN, WHILST DOIN' SUMMAT GOOD FER 'UMANITY.

AYE. WOTEVAH.

PLUS, AH'M SHAGGIN' CRUMPET LEFT, REET AN' FUCKIN' CENTRE! HEH HEH!

Y'WOT?!

AH'M TELLIN' THEE, SID... AS SOON AS THA PUTS T' PONCHO ON, THA'S BEATIN' OFF FANNY WI' A SHITTY STICK.

HOO'S THAT WORK, THEN, SHANE?

THINK ABAHT IT, GEORDIE. THIS 'CHARITY MUGGER' JOB IS JUST LICENCE T'GAW UP AN' TALK T'ANY LASS THA WANTS, IN'T IT..?

THA STARTS CHATTIN' T'EM AN' THEY THINK THA'S REET BIG-'EARTED 'COS THA WORKS FERRA FUCKIN' CHARITY.

THA GETS 'EM T'FILL AHT THEH DETAILS ON FORM, AN' WALLOP, THA'S GOT THEH PHONE NUMBEH, SO THA CALLS 'EM OOP LATER FER A FOOK! THA SHOULD TRY IT, OUR SIDNEY.

NEE CHANCE. YUZ WOULDN'T CATCH SIDNEY SMUTT STANDIN' ABOOT AALL DEE HANDIN' OOT FLUAZ IN A LIME GREEN FUCKIN' PONCHUR!

NEXT DAY...

...WELL IT'S GREAT TO HAVE YOU ON BOARD, MR. SMUTT. BASICALLY, ALL YOU'VE GOT TU DO IS TRY TU TALK TO AS MANY PEOPLE AS POSSIBLE AND GET THEM TO SIGN UP FOR A £2 PER MONTH DONATION BY FILLING IN THIS FORM.

JUST STOP THEM WITH A BIG SMILE AND SAY, "HI, I'M SIDNEY. HAVE YOU GOT 5 MINUTES FOR A QUICK CHAT?"...OKAY?

AYE. REET Y'ARE PET. SOONDS CANNY.

SHORTLY...

HEH HEH! 'ERE WE FUCKIN' GAN!

HOWAY, PET. ME NAME'S SIDNEY. D'YEZ HEV FIVE MINUTES F'...

SORRY, NO.

FUCK'S SAKE!

REET. AH'LL JUST HEV TU WORK ME CHARM ON THIS BORD INSTEAD, I S'PURSE.

HI HINNY. ME NAME'S SIDNEY BUT YEEZ CAN CALL US BIG C...

AH, EXCELLENT! I'D BEEN HOPING TO BUMP INTO ONE OF YOU CHARITY CHAPS TODAY.

I'D LIKE TO SIGN UP FOR A MONTHLY DONATION, PLEASE.

FUCK'S SAKE, MAN. YUZ'VE JUST MADE ME MISS A FUCKIN' CRACKA THERE..!

EXCUSE ME..!?

CAN YUZ KEEP MOVIN', BONNY LAD? YUZ'RE 'CRAMPIN' ME FUCKIN' STYLE 'ERE.

BUT I'D LIKE TO SIGN UP TO HELP CATS. I WANT TO GIVE YOU MY DETAILS!

AH DIVVEN'T WANT YOUR DETAILS, PAL. AH'M TRYIN' T'GET A SHAG OOT O' THIS!

THIS IS DISGRACEFUL. GIVE ME THE FORM. I'LL FILL IT IN MYSELF!

OI! GERROFF ME CLIPBOARD, Y'SPECKY TWAT!

I WANT TO FILL IN THE FORM!

DON'T YOU CARE ABOUT CATS?

CATS? NAH, MAN. AH'M JUST USIN' THIS JOB T'GET INTO BORDS' KNICKAZ.

AH COULDN'T GIVE A FLYIN' FUCK ABOOT CATS, MAN.

:COUGH:

THISSUN COULDN'T GIVE A FLYIN' FUCK ABOOT CATS, GIRLS.

GUMPH!

LATER...

NOW MR SMUTT, WE MAY HAVE TO KEEP YOU IN OVERNIGHT, I'M AFRAID. THE CLIPBOARD REALLY IS LODGED QUITE FIRMLY UP YOUR BACK PASSAGE.

...the 1970s Pla

SCHOOLDAYS are supposed to be the happiest days of our lives, but sadly for today's kids nothing could be further from the truth. With the constant pressure of SATS tests, the ever-changing demands of the national curriculum to keep up with, and the constant threat of cyber-bullying and revenge porn in the classroom, life for the schoolchildren of 2016 is anything but happy. Of course, it wasn't always like this; things were different just a few short decades in the past. Let's take a journey back in time to the carefree days of the mid-1970s and drop in on a typical comprehensive during mid-morning break to see what's going on in...

1 A boy being good-naturedly 'ragged' by his chums, who are hanging him from the chainlink fence by his shoelaces because he is ginger.

2 A teacher on his way to the staffroom for a smoke, pretending he can't see a boy being good-naturedly "ragged" by his chums, who are hanging him from the chainlink fence by his shoelaces because he is ginger.

3 A boy benefiting from the character-building experience of having his shoes thrown onto the roof of the science block by some larger pals.

4 A new boy being quizzed about his favourite football team. He must think carefully because if he names the wrong club he'll be given a dead arm. And also if he gives the right answer.

5 A boy being good-naturedly 'kicked in' to congratulate him for getting full marks in a maths test.

6 A boy having his glasses stamped on after committing the unforgivable playground crime of needing glasses.

7 A burly fifth former asking a first year politely if he wouldn't mind lending him his dinner money.

8 A teacher on his way to the stockroom for a whisky, pretending he can't see burly fifth former asking a first year politely if he wouldn't mind lending him his dinner money.

9 Two boys whose friendly discussion about whether one of them is wearing gay shoes has escalated into a genial bout of fisticuffs.

10 The head of PE, who is running over to break up the fight, hoping to get a few crafty kicks and punches in himself.

11 A boy who forgot to bring in his games kit this morning, and is now enjoying a refreshing and invigorating 20 laps of the playground in his pants.

12 A boy getting his feet stamped on because he's got new shoes.

13 A boy being forced to eat a dogdirt as punishment for being on free dinners.

14 A boy being pushed against a wall on which the word "OM" has been thickly chalked.

15 A lively football match. Unusually, this game has no offside rule, no throw-ins, no teams and no apparent scoring system. Fouling is actively encouraged as a mob of dozens of players pursue an old tennis ball up and down the playground. Other than that, normal FIFA rules apply.

16 The only female teacher in the school being subjected to a barrage of good-natured, ribald comments courtesy of a hormone-fuelled mob of youths whose balls have just dropped.

17 A round of "British Bulldog", a traditional playground game which gives the smaller pupils a chance to join in the rough and tumble against a mob of much heavier schoolmates.

18 A junior entrepreneur whose dad runs a newsagent's shop, selling individual pages from girlie mags to his classmates for 5p each.

19 Two policemen turning up to start investigat who has burnt the library down this time.

20 A sensitive child who can be easily goaded an amusing fit of rage, being goaded into a amusing fit of rage by several older pupils.

21 Several boys who have been caught smokin behind the bike sheds and who are having cigarettes confiscated by a teacher. These will lat be placed in the staffroom "Free Ciggies" box.

oys' School ground

Several boys who have been caught masturbating behind the bike sheds and are ng their dirty books confiscated by a teacher. se will later be placed in the staffroom "Free rmags" box.

Someone who has been found to be in possession of some sweets, generously ring them with some burly older boys.

A boy enjoying a "barber's scrub" - the playground tradition whereby someone who just had his hair cut is held in a headlock by a h bigger boy who then rubs his knuckles hard and fast across his newly shorn cranium while as many other boys as care to join in kick him as hard as they can up the backside and in the stomach.

25 A teacher solving a dispute between two pupils by using the time-honoured method of cracking their heads together.

26 A boy being pushed against a wall on which a crudely-drawn ejaculating phallus has been thickly chalked.

27 A line of boys who were caught talking during Assembly and/or running in the corridor, and who are waiting outside the head's office where they will shortly be beaten repeatedly with a stick across the bare buttocks by a grown man, a process that he claims, somewhat disingenuously, will hurt him much more than it will hurt them.

28 Some mischievous pupils who have sneaked back into the chemistry lab and lit the gas taps.

29 A boy shinning up the drainpipe of the science block to try and retrieve his rucksack while his laughing pals good-naturedly try and dislodge him by throwing clods of earth and stones.

Next week - *Spotlight on the Past visits a Victorian Asylum for Unmarried Mothers*

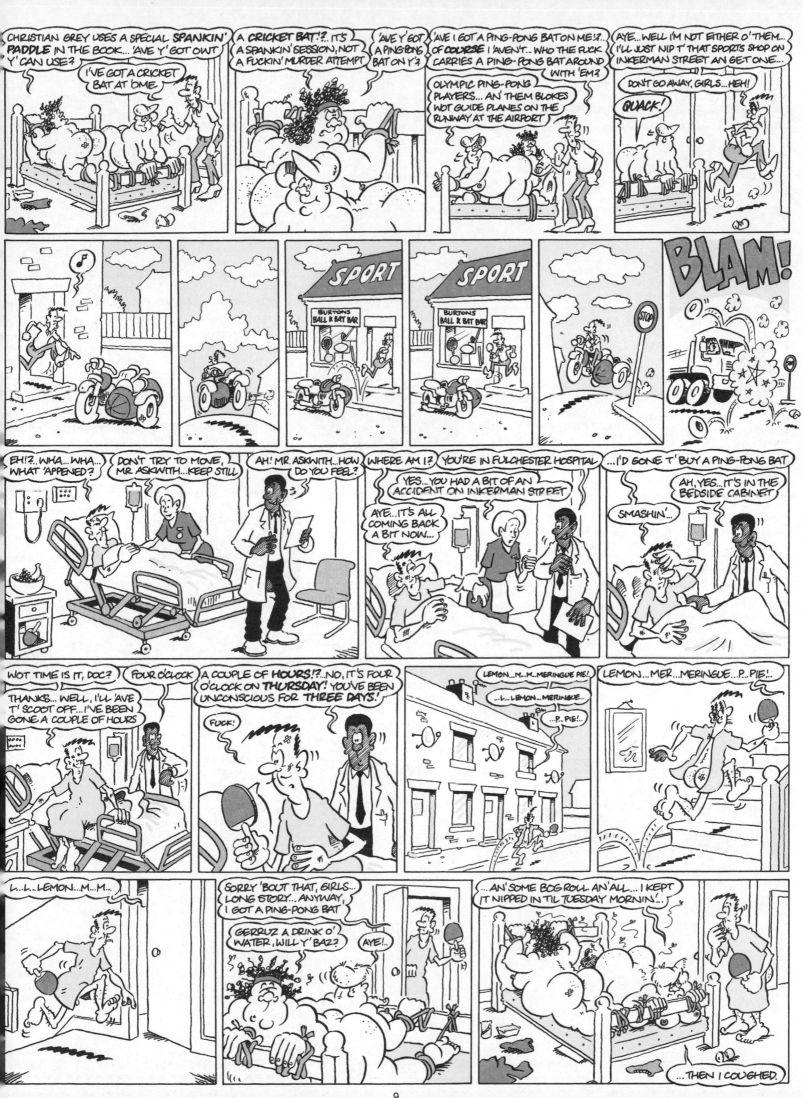

LeTTERbOcks

email: letters@viz.co.uk

THE World Health Organisation has now said it's bacon what gives you cancer. But when I went down to the shops, all the warning stickers were still on the fags. Not very organised if you ask me.

Twig, Leeds

I'VE never understood loan sharks. Whenever I've lent money to someone, I'm always too embarrassed to ask for it back. I lent £200 pounds to my father-in-law to get a motorised wheelchair a year ago, and he's never even so much as mentioned it since. Those loan sharks never seem to have that problem though, so perhaps threatening to break his legs is the way to go.

Tarquin Voltaire, Leeds

I WAS disgusted to see a young couple snogging the other night, and thought to myself, "for fuck's sake, get a hotel room." It was only then that I realised that they had in fact gotten a room, and I was a peeping Tom hiding in the wardrobe.

Monty Plywood, Tooting

I WENT to Edinburgh by train on Saturday and was disturbed to find that they provide an emergency stop handle in the toilet. Could any readers please let me know what sort of emergency could occur in the lavatory that would be helped or resolved by stopping the train? Let's face it, we've all had some pretty catastrophic toilet visits from time to time but what would possess you to draw attention to such an event by calling the train to a halt?

Col Percy Fawcett, email

I JUST ordered a chicken and an egg off of Amazon. I'll let you know.

Ross Kennet, England

I THINK Richard Dawkins missed a trick when he foolishly let the catchphrase "I don't believe it!" go to Victor Meldrew. Professor, ethologist, evolutionary biologist or whatever, he could have been right up there with the Janette Krankie and her "Fandabidozi" thing if he'd boxed a bit more clever.

H Ramrod, Cromer

STAR LETTER

HOW come Norwich Cathedral charges £140 for cars parked without permission on its property when every Sunday they say the Lord's Prayer which states "Forgive us our trespasses as we forgive those who trespass against us"? There's nothing in the Lord's Prayer about charging a hundred and forty quid to have your car unclamped. I bet they are not serious about God's kingdom coming and His will be done either.

Alan Heath, Poland

PERHAPS if Sir Tim Berners-Lee had organised the internet alphabetically in the first place, then everything would be much easier to find and there would be no need for all this so-called 'Googling.'

Sarah Emily Kristan, Harlow

HOW is it that whenever you see a duel on films or on telly, the blokes are always wearing frilly, ruffled shirts? They're just asking for trouble in my opinion. I know if I went out of a night dressed like that round our way, it would definitely kick off.

Jack Bumblebum, Manchester

I WAS thinking of writing to the Queen to ask her for my centennial birthday telegram. I'm only 39 but surely she won't be around when I'm 100, so she may as well do it now. I'll just stick it in a drawer for a few years.

Pierre Farrimond, Bolton

JOHN Lennon famously said "All you need is love." However he also said, "I am the eggman, I am the walrus, goo goo ga joob." I for one will be taking his words of wisdom with a very large pinch of salt in future.

Mark Wilson, Leicester

SOMEONE told me that if you open a tin of baked beans upside down, you don't get all the juice at the top. But I just got all dizzy and couldn't see what I was doing. What a load of shit that was.

Grant B Warner, New Zealand

I BET if someone killed me it wouldn't lead to a world war. Once again it's one rule for muggins here and another rule for minor Austrian royals who lived a century or so ago.

Wootsy, London

WHAT with so many of your readers writing in to regale the rest of us with their tales about the length of a fart they once did, or who they'd do first if the Saturdays or some other girl band came round demanding a portion when their missus was out, or how many shits they managed to do on Boxing Day, I'd say most of your readers have pretty poor taste and aren't afraid to tell the world about it. I once put both toilets at my parents' place in Wales out of action for an entire afternoon after a prawn vindaloo and garlic nan supper the night before, but why would I feel the urge to advertise something like that in your comic? I wasn't particularly proud of it, and if anything I would probably want it forgotten.

George Hill, Tenby

I SHARE the same name as miserable former Queen bassist, John Deacon, although sadly, not his wealth. Do any of your other readers share names which were a great conversation starter down th[e] pub in 1986 but less so now?

John Deacon, Amwlc[h]

FOR the attention of people on diets - trus[t] me, you don't "just have to look at the cream cakes for the weight to pile on." The weight goes on when you stuff them in your mouth and swallow them.

Tim Buktu, Timbukt[u]

I'M getting tired of this Schrödinger's ca[t] debate. Schrödinger himse[lf] died in 1961, so the chance[s] of his cat still being alive must be pretty slim.

Stuart Bonna[r], Scarboroug[h]

WHEN I was younger I often heard the witty phrase "you can stick you[r] whistle up your arse, ref" from the terraces. I have been wondering for years if a referee has ever had a whistle up his arse, and if he did, did it make a whistle noise when he farted? I don't need to know how it got up there, just whether it whistled when he farted.

Tim Buktu, Timbukt[u]

I KNOW the Berlin Wall coming down in 1989 was always going to be a big deal. However, watching all those weedy students struggling with sledgehammers had me shouting at the TV. Surely if they had gotten Fred Dibnah involved with proceedings, th[e] whole affair would have bee[n] much more entertaining. A few quirky asides and subtle northernisms as he set about the task, grinning with his usual good humour, would have made much better television, I reckon.

Brampton Carlisl[e], Aglionb[y]

RUDDY 'ARD KIPLING

TIK TAK TIK

KREAK

RAAARGH!

SHORTLY AFTER...

NOW... WHERE WAS I?

TIK TAK

JESUS CHRIST!

—Tayler—

I'M not scared of ghosts, because if you're not scared of them, then they won't come and visit you.

A Wetpants, Nobshire

I DON'T know why dairy farmers complain about the low price of milk. It's not like they have to drill for milk in the middle of the sea and then refine it. All they do is pull a cow's tit and voilà.

Jamie Cuffe, Isle of Man

I AM currently employed as a lavatory attendant, but I fancy a career change and would be interested in becoming a poet. Could any of your readers tell me exactly what is involved?

Chester Urine, Truro

Well readers, can you help Mr Urine? Are YOU a poet? If so, what hours do you work, and how much do you get paid? How many weeks holiday do you get, and how many days can you have off without a doctor's note? And how do you get the job in the first place? Write in and tell us, and we'll pass the information on to Mr Urine.

THEY say it's bad luck to open an umbrella indoors. However, when I did so last week and accidentally cut my mother-in-law in the eye, on the way to A&E I found a quid down the side of the car seat.

Will Mylchreest, Leamington Spa

THAT *Apprentice* house is rubbish. It's only got one phone and that's right at the bottom of the stairs, so when it rings someone has to run down in their pants to

What would the celebrity short-arses do if they were...

TALL FOR A DAY?

JUST imagine being a famous short-arse and then waking up one morning to discover you'd been granted 24 hours of tallness! We asked four pint-sized megastars how THEY would spend the day if they were suddenly average height or above.

Tom Cruise, *small actor*

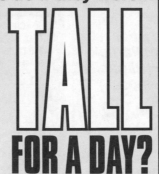

Not being pint-sized for 24 hours would be a nightmare for me, as all my stuff is designed for someone of minuscule stature. I would no longer be able to fit in my trailer, which is the size of a large breadbin, so I'd have to eat lunch in the cafeteria with all the extras and crew. Plus, all the planes you see me flying or blowing up or jumping off in films are Airfix models, so I'd have to shell out for some real ones. The only bonus would be that I'd finally be able to reach the scud mags in the newsagent, so I'd probably just take the day off acting in order to stock up on some filth.

Richard 'The Hamster' Hammond, *small petrolhead*

When I'm driving cars I normally have to sit on a few copies of the Yellow Pages and wear enormous platform shoes so I can see over the steering wheel and reach the pedals. So if I were tall for a day, I'd probably enjoy driving around barefoot with my arse touching the seat, just as nature intended. I would also sort myself out a new nickname that was more suited to my larger stature. Maybe Richard 'The Hammerhead Shark' Hammond, or Richard 'The Hammoth' Hammond (like 'Mammoth' but with an 'H')? I'd probably spend a fair chunk of the day thrashing that one out, to be honest.

Declan 'Dec' Donnelly, *small TV presenter*

I think I'd use my 24 hours of tallness to laud it over my co-presenter Anthony 'Ant' McPartlin, who is also famously short-arsed. I'd do stuff like balance my pint on his head, or ask him how the weather was down there, or put his *Britain's Got Talent* script on a shelf that was just slightly too high for him to reach. And if he got pissed off and tried to attack me, I'd do that thing you see in films where I hold his head at arm's length while he furiously swings air punches at my chest.

Bono, *small twat*

If I was tall for a day? That's an easy one. I'd go on Nemesis at Alton Towers as many times as I could in 24 hours. We always go to Alton Towers for The Edge's birthday, but I am never allowed on Nemesis due to the height restrictions. So, I'm forced to watch as The Edge, Larry Mullen and the other one have the time of their lives, whilst I go on the fucking Frog Hopper over and over again. So, yeah, I reckon I'd spend my one day of tallness whizzing about gleefully on Nemesis until the clock struck midnight and it was time for me to return to my regular, short-arsed size again.

answer it. You'd think with all of Lord Sugar's money he'd have one in every room, and even one in the khazi.

Richard Devereux, Hereford

I'VE just had an email from Paypal with the subject "Your Account Going To Limiet Please Reslove It Before Limiet." I'd better log in as advised and sort that out.

Christina Martin, Walton on Thames

HAS anybody else wondered why the star constellation Orion has a 'belt' hanging between his legs. Is this really the first thing that popped into our

forefathers' minds as they shared stories around the campfire? Yeah, right.

Calum Grant, Banbury

ANDREX Washlets, them wet bog roll things, are brilliant for really giving your ring a good clean.

Neil, Liverpool

✱ *Thanks for your letter, Neil. But so we are not accused of crass, commercial product placement, let us say that their are many other moist wipes available on the market, all of which are very good at removing clag and leaving your nipsy lemon fresh.*

A LOT of people say that Hull, the former UK City of Culture, is quite dull. They clearly do not not know that it was actually the birthplace of John Venn, the inventor of the Venn diagram.

Violet Rommel, Humberside

WANT two pieces of toast in the morning? Make three in case you drop one, thus rendering it inedible. If all three pieces survive and you still only want two, simply throw one on the floor to render it inedible.

Phil O'Meara, London

A COUPLE of bungee cords make excellent braces for the denim trouser wearer, hooking neatly into the reinforced belt loops.

Mike Stand, Redcar

SAVE money on *Game of Thrones* boxsets by watching porn at ten minute intervals during *Lord of the Rings*.

Johnny Lad, Stoke

MAKE the neighbours think you've recently purchased a trampoline by going into the back garden and repeatedly throwing your children in the air.

Will Mylchreest, Leamington Spa

A FROZEN odd sock makes an ideal boomerang substitute. A slightly larger odd sock makes an ideal bag or sheath for your frozen sock substitute boomerang.

Brian Penk, Gloucester

RECREATE the experience of being on a cruise ship by walking around the house wearing one platform shoe and sleeping in the cupboard under the stairs.

Will Mylchreest, Leamington Spa

NEXT time you get any junk mail, carefully cut out the address panel from the envelope and put it in your wallet or purse. In no time at all you will have collected a selection of pre-printed 'business cards' on a variety of materials.

John Bedlington, Beamish

MUSICIANS. Record a cover version of a classic 1980s pop hit at about half the tempo, using only an acoustic guitar and singing in a melancholic way. Hey presto! You've created a lucrative TV advert theme tune.

Mike Tatham, St. Andrews

TIPS

OK. THE BLANKET AND THE BASKET **ARE** ALLOWABLE EXPENSES ALTHOUGH I'M NOT HAPPY WITH YOU TRYING TO CLAIM DEPRECIATION ON **EITHER** OF THEM. BUT THE SQUEAKY TOY?!? **SERIOUSLY!?!** ON WHAT PLANET CAN THAT **POSSIBLY** BE A WORK-RELATED EXPENSE?!?

BAD DOG. / BAD DOG! / WHIMPER! / WHINE!!

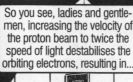
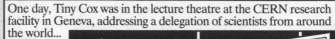

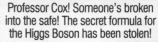

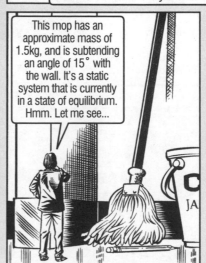

If I can apply the same force to the mop shank, I should be able to push it to a vertical position...

Gnnn! It's moving!

There! It's straight up. Now, just one more Newton of force and I'll be able to move the mop's centre of gravity outside a line perpendicular with its base, causing it to topple...

Kolchinsky! Stop!

There! Done it! It's time for gravity to turn that potential energy into kinetic energy!

Waah! Oof!

And that's why I love physics!

Well done, Professor Cox. Your unrivalled knowledge of mechanics, static systems, forces and moments has saved the day.

These plans are going straight back in the safe.

The head of CERN was the next to speak.

Thanks to you, the secret of the Higgs Boson is safe and the free world can breathe easy once again.

I was only doing what any scientist would have done.

Well, you may be only six inch tall, but when it comes to courage and science, you're a giant. And we're going to throw a party tonight in the CERN ballroom to toast your bravery.

The celebrations went on late into the night, with music provided by top pop band D:Ream...

♪♫ Thiiiiiiiiings... can only get better-er-er...! ♫♪

WELL DONE PROFESSOR TINY COX

...with someone very special on keyboards!

The End

LOVE ON THE ROCK

Seaman Preston recalls his 40 year sex-filled career as a lighthouse keeper

PRESTON Chorley-Standish has been in charge of the Loxley Head lighthouse, 20 miles off the East Yorkshire coast, since 1975. The dazzling beam sweeping out from the top of his isolated, waveswept home, visible for over 50 miles in every direction, has long been a welcome sight for sailors at sea. Warning of a treacherous submerged outcrop of rocks, over the years it has prevented countless shipwrecks and saved an untold number of lives.

But Preston is the last of a dying breed. For Loxley lighthouse is the final beacon in British waters to be automated, meaning that a full-time keeper is no longer required to switch on the light each night. And now, as Chorley-Standish prepares to bid a last, fond farewell to the 150ft granite tower where he has lived and worked for the last four decades, he speaks exclusively to us about a career that was - *amazingly* - often wilder than the storm-tossed seas that crashed around the rocky outcrop he called home!

lighthouse

"Most people probably think that the life of a lighthouse keeper is one of quiet solitude and loneliness," he told us. "... Endless hours spent polishing the lenses, playing clock patience and listening to the Shipping Forecast. But in reality, nothing could be further from the truth. Most nights in my lighthouse it was like party central, with the booze flowing like water and wall-to-wall crumpet."

Get your rocks off: Rocks like these led a flotilla of females to Preston's door.

"That might sound like the wild imaginings of some sex-starved loner who has spent the best part of his life sat on his own in the middle of the sea. You believe that if you want,

but it's simply not true. These things really happened, and I know because I was there."

"The other people involved might deny what I'm saying, but then they would, wouldn't they? They are liars, pure and simple. The plain truth of the matter is, life as a lighthouse keeper consisted of sex, sex, sex... and then more sex. Beautiful women were constantly hammering on my lighthouse door, demanding to be satisfied. And for forty years I was only too happy to oblige. In fact, I actually used to look forward to my annual three months shore-leave with the missus as a chance to give my poor old chopper a rest."

Chorley-Standish, 59, found out on his very first day as a lighthouse keeper that the quiet, solitary life he was expecting was going to be anything but.

royle

"I was eighteen years old, and it was my first day in the job. The retiring keeper was showing me the ropes - where the switch was to turn the light on and all the other things I'd need to know, such has how to switch it off again. After thirty seconds, he said goodbye and left. That was it, I was on my own. I was going to be here, twenty miles out at sea, for the next nine months, so I made myself a cup of tea and a pot noodle, got out my *Puzzler* magazine and set-to on a wordsearch.

Five minutes later, there was a knock at the door. I assumed it was the old keeper who had forgotten something, but when I went to answer it I got the surprise of my life. For standing there on the step was a gorgeous, scantily clad woman. Tied up by the jetty at the foot of the rock was a small lifeboat. "Please can I come in?" the woman asked. I invited her

Keeping it up: Chorley-Standish's lighthouse keeper's job wasn't as solitary as it sounds.

inside, got her out of her wet clothes and sat her by the stove to warm her up as she told me her tale.

addams

It turned out she was a dancer on a ferry, which had sunk after hitting an old WW2 German mine in the middle of the North Sea. She had somehow managed to scramble onto a lifeboat but had been the only survivor and had been drifting helplessly at the mercy of the tides and current for three weeks until finally spotting my lighthouse and paddling her way towards it with the last vestiges of her strength.

I gave her a cup of tea and what was left of my pot noodle, which she hungrily wolfed down. When she had finished, she looked like a new woman. The colour had returned to her cheeks and the warm glow of the fire outlined every inch of her supple dancer's body, from her pert, swelling breasts to her long, lithe legs. As she put down her mug she looked me up and down, licking the spoon suggestively.

"You know, food and drink isn't the only thing I've been without for

the last three weeks," she pouted. Of course, I knew what she was talking about. I was a red-blooded lighthouse keeper after all. I had already seen to her thirst and hunger, and now it was time for me to satisfy another of her bodily cravings. Full of pot noodle and tea, she took my hand and gently led me up the circular stairs up to my little round bedroom, where we indulged in the wildest sex I could have ever imagined. Even though, as I say, I definitely didn't imagine it.

partridge

The powerful hundred foot waves that crashed against the lighthouse all that night were nothing compared to the waves of ecstasy experienced by me and my shipwrecked lover. Her cries of passion as I did it to her over and over again drowned out the boom of the swell. In the morning, as the sun rose over the rolling breakers outside, we made love once more before going downstairs for a romantic cup of tea and a pop tart.

Over breakfast, she told me she was leaving. After asking me which direction Grimsby was, she climbed back into her lifeboat and bobbed off in the vague direction of the Hum-

14

ber Estuary. As I watched her vanish over the horizon and out of my life, I was filled with sadness. But my sadness quickly turned to horror when I realised that amidst the previous evening's frantic throes of passion I had completely forgotten to switch the light on.

Fortunately, when I checked, no boats had run aground on the rocks overnight, so that was alright."

Preston's sex-filled first night on Loxley Head had certainly been an eventful one. But as he was to learn, it was hardly exceptional. The very next day, he had just heated up a box of microwave smokey fries when he heard a thundering clatter from the roof of his lighthouse.

manson

"I quickly bounded up the stairs and out onto the balcony just in time to see a bright orange helicopter settling down on the rooftop landing pad. I realised with relief that it was merely my monthly supplies being delivered. I waved to the pilots, and they clambered down from the cockpit and came inside. In the kitchen, as I made a brew and put another couple of boxes of chips in the microwave, they unzipped their bulky buoyancy suits and took off their helmets.

My jaw nearly hit the floor as I turned to talk to them. For standing there in the room were two of the most gorgeous, sexy women I'd ever seen. As they shook their heads to release their long golden tresses, allowing them to cascade across their shoulders in slow motion, they looked more like some of the voluptuous centrefolds in the magazines the previous keeper had left than helicopter pilots.

As we sat in the little round kitchen enjoying our tea and fries, we could hear the wind picking up outside. So much so that as night fell, when the girls got up to leave, there was a proper gale blowing outside. Up on the roof, their helicopter was rocking from side to side as the powerful gusts tore at its rotor blades. It was clear that it was now far too dangerous for them to take off back to the mainland.

temple

"There's only one thing for it, we'll just have to stay the night," said one of the sexy girls. "That's fine by me," I replied. "The only thing is, there's only one bed in the lighthouse."

"That's fine by us," the twins said in unison. I just remembered they were identical twins.

The next thing I knew, we were stripping off in my little round bedroom. Soon, their sexy lingerie lay strewn all over the floor along with my big jumper and boots, and we were all stark naked. Every five seconds, their nubile bodies were illuminated in blinding relief as the one million candle power beam of the Loxley Head light swept through the bedroom win-

dow, flashing out its warning of peril to nearby shipping. Suddenly, the twins stopped and sighed.

"We can only do it in the dark," they said. "Would it be okay to turn the light off?" I was thrown into a quandary. On the one hand, turning a lighthouse off at night is against every regulation in the Trinity House rulebook. It's the first thing they teach you on the lighthouse keeping course. But knowing that those two sexy helicopter pilots were lying naked in my bunk, just waiting for me to do them, was too much of a temptation for a red-blooded man to resist. I reached out the side of the bed and flicked the switch. The light may have been turned off, but the twins were turned on alright. And it was electrifying.

Tanks a million: Oil tanker crash could have cost Preston his job.

As darkness filled the room, the three of us began hungrily exploring each other's bodies in my little bed, frantically driving each other to ever greater heights of passion as the force ten gale raged outside.

bassey

Not being able to see seemed to intensify our other senses. The girls may have been unable to get their chopper up that night, but I had no such trouble, I can tell you. And as we reached a shattering simultaneous climax, I could have sworn the whole lighthouse shook on its foundations.

In the morning, I realised that the lighthouse had indeed shook on its foundations during the night. But it was nothing to do with my threesup. With the light switched off, a giant Panamanian oil tanker had run aground on the rocks, splitting its hull wide open. As I stood on the step and surveyed the damage, my heart sank. The sea was coated with a thick, black slick of tarry crude, dotted with dead and dying seals, gulls and puffins as far as the eye could see.

I got a proper roasting for that one, I can tell you."

williams

The oil tanker disaster had taught Preston a valuable lesson, and he vowed never again to let his sex life compromise his professional responsibilities. But that isn't to say that there weren't many more episodes when temptation was put in his way.

"I remember this one day, I had finished my dingbats book and I was just thinking about opening a couple of Peperamis for tea when there was a knock at the door. Standing on the step were four women wearing rowing all-in-ones that left very little to the imagination. They were all attractive thirty-somethings - proper milfs who looked like they knew a trick or two. It was cold that day and I couldn't help noticing that their nipples were standing out through the sheer cloth. I asked them if they'd like to come in and have a cup of tea in the lighthouse.

They told me that they were four bored housewives from Yorkshire who had decided to row the Atlantic. However, they had got as far as Loxley Head before running out of supplies, and they had called in to see if I would sell them some food. I said that I could give them enough pot noodles, pop tarts and bags of Bombay mix to get them to Antigua. But I explained that money was of no use to me, as there was nothing to spend it on on my solitary island home in the middle of the North Sea.

crabtree

The milfs had a quick confab. "Perhaps there's some other way we could pay you for our provisions," one of them said, winking at the others. Before I knew what was happening, they had taken their all-in-onesies off to reveal their sexy cougar bodies. There they stood, clad in their underwear, stockings and suspenders. Giggling, they began to drag me up the spiral stairs to my bedroom. I say drag me - to tell the truth I wasn't protesting too much.

Once inside, we got down to action. I'm too much of a gentleman to recount exactly what we got up to in there. Suffice to say, they may have arrived as a 'coxless four', but that all changed in my bedroom, I can tell you. Loxley Head lighthouse was designed to survive hundred foot waves crashing over it and we certainly tested its foundations to the limits that night.

thornley

The next morning, after a traditional hearty lighthouseman's breakfast of tea and cheesestrings, the milfs set off again, their boat filled to the gunwhales with all the provisions they would need to get them to the other side of the pond - jars of haribos and bombay mix, a big box of monster munch and a catering-size bag of marshmallows. They had certainly earned it, I thought, as I patted my flat knackers.

I couldn't have been more pleased when I heard those ladies eventually reached Antigua, after rowing nearly five thousand miles. But I had to chuckle to myself when, at their press conference, they claimed to have made the trip in one continuous row. They somehow omitted to mention

their overnight stop-off at my lighthouse lovenest."

NEXT WEEK, Preston recalls the time when a lifeboat full of Swedish strippers arrived at the door after their trawler was sunk by a Russian submarine caught in its nets. "Two minutes later, a container full of Bacardi Breezers lost overboard from a Chinese cargo ship washed ashore, and it was party time at Loxley Rock."

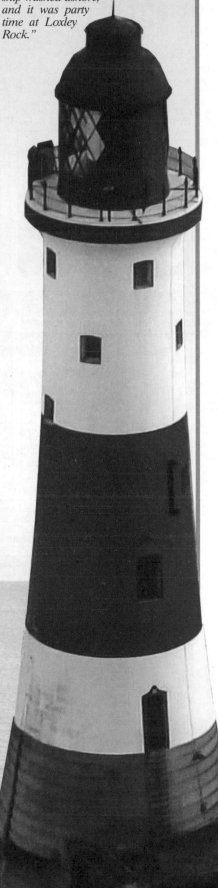

FRU'T'BUNN
The MASTER BAKER & HIS GINGERBREAD SEX DOLL

SATURDAY NIGHT...

FRUBERT DEAR, ARE YOU READY TO TAKE CHELSEA AND ME TO THE PICTURES..?

FRUBERT! WHAT ON EARTH ARE YOU DOING WITH ALL MY CLOTHES?

OH...ERM...NOTHING, DEAR. I'M JUST GOING TO TAKE SOME STUFF DOWN THE CHARITY SHOP.

...BUT THAT'S MY FAVOURITE DRESS! AND I ONLY BOUGHT THIS BLOUSE THIS AFTERNOON!

GOD, YOU'RE SELFISH, WOMAN! DON'T YOU THINK THERE COULD BE SOME POOR, DOWNTRODDEN LADIES OUT THERE WHO MIGHT NEED THESE CLOTHES A LITTLE BIT MORE THAN YOU DO, NOREEN.?

WELL...I SUPPOSE SO...

AND YOU KNOW WHAT THEY SAY...CHARITY BEGINS AT HOME!

YES, BUT YOU DID SAY YOU'D TAKE US TO THE PICTURES TONIGHT, FRUB...

GREAT, SO WE'RE AGREED. I'M OFF TO OXFAM. DON'T WAIT UP.

SLAM!

HEH-HEH! OXFAM MY RANDY OLD BAKER'S ARSE! I'M ACTUALLY MEETING THREE GINGERBREAD HOTTIES FOR A LITTLE GAME OF STRIP POKER!

VROOM!

LATER, AT THE BAKERY...

JESUS, THIS IS HOT! I'M ALREADY AS HARD AS A MONTH-OLD SCONE AND I HAVEN'T EVEN DEALT A CARD YET!

RIGHT, GIRLS, YOU KNOW THE RULES...WHOEVER LOSES A HAND HAS TO REMOVE ONE ITEM OF CLOTHING!

ACES HIGH, I'LL DEAL FIRST... HEH-HEH-HEH!

ONE HOUR LATER...

RATS' COCKS! I CAN'T BELIEVE I LOST AGAIN!

YOU MUST BE CHEATING! HOW THE HELL DO YOU KEEP GETTING SUCH GOOD CARDS?

WHAT'S THAT YOU SAY.? SINCE I'VE GOT NO MORE CLOTHES TO TAKE OFF, I'LL HAVE TO DO A FORFEIT? WHAT KIND OF FORFEIT.?

I'LL HAVE TO GO TO THE ALL-NIGHT GARAGE AND GET SOME MORE DORITOS, YOU SAY? HUH! THAT DOESN'T SOUND TOO TAXING.

WHAT'S THAT YOU SAY... I'LL HAVE TO DO IT NAKED? OH, BLOODY HELL.. I DON'T KNOW ABOUT THAT GIRLS...

I MEAN...WHAT IF SOMEBODY SAW ME..?

WHAT'S THAT.? IF I'LL DO IT, YOU PROMISE TO LET ME WIN A FEW HANDS WHEN I GET BACK, YOU SAY.? HEH-HEH! ALRIGHT THEN, BACK IN A TICK!

SLURP!

AW, IT'S SUCH A SHAME THAT DADDY COULDN'T COME TO THE PICTURES WITH US, CHELSEA. BUT HE WAS DOING SOME VERY IMPORTANT DELIVERY WORK FOR A LOCAL CHARITY.

IMAGINE THAT - GIVING UP HIS SATURDAY NIGHT TO HELP THE NEEDY. HE'S A VERY KIND AND DECENT MAN, IS YOUR DADDY.

DADDY! DADDY!

HEY DIDDLE DIDDLE, WE'RE ALL ON THE FIDDLE

Britain Becomes World Capital of Tax Dodges & Benefit Fraud

THE LEAK of the so-called "Panama Papers" - damning secret documents revealing the myriad ways that the mega-rich use offshore havens to shield their fortunes from the Inland Revenue - recently brought the topic of tax evasion to the fore. Top celebrities including a galaxy of household names suddenly found their dubious dealings coming under intense public scrutiny. Following several carefully worded denials, even former Prime Minister *David Cameron* was eventually forced to admit that he too had benefitted by stashing his millions in a 'shady' offshore scheme run by his late father.

Taxation Nation: We sent our undercover reporter Mahatma Macaroon to blow the lid of unscrupulous Brits on the make.

But despite dominating the head-lines, celebrities' tax shenanigans are small beer compared to the whole-sale fiddling perpetrated by the man in the street. For it seems that every one of us is on the take, playing fast and loose with Britain's notoriously lax tax laws. We sent *Viz* Reporter of the Year *Mahatma Macaroon* under-cover to check out the seedy under-belly of the UK's Delboy economy. And the flagrant abuses he discov-ered during his wide-ranging inves-tigation will shock every law-abiding British taxpayer to the core.

Ice Work if You Can Get It

We all like to hear the merry jingle of an approaching ice-cream van. It's as much a part of the traditional British summer's day as the thwack of leather upon willow, strawberries and cream at Wimbledon and mor-ris dancers on the village green. And when we hand over our hard-earned pennies to the man in the van, our 99 tastes all the better for knowing that a proportion of that money will go in tax, to be used for good causes like schools and hospitals. But is that what really happens? I decide to find out.

Disguising myself as a typical schoolboy with a blazer, cap and a catapult in the back pocket of my grey flannel shorts, I approach an ice cream van that has parked up in a nearby street and ask for a vanilla cone with hundreds and thousands and monkey blood. With a friendly wink and a smile, the vendor cheer-

EXCLUSIVE!

fully gives me my tasty treat and I hand over £1.50 in return.

But his previously sunny demean-our turns as icy as one of his lollies when I request a proof of purchase - including a VAT breakdown. Firstly, he says he can't provide a receipt, because he hasn't got a till in his van. When I tell him a hand-written cash invoice will do, he conveniently remembers he hasn't got a pen and paper with him either.

Then he tries to fob me off by pointing out that there's a long queue of people building up behind me. Only after I flatly insist that he has a legal obligation to provide all his customers with an official record of their purchase does he lock up his van and reluctantly venture to a near-by newsagent for a ballpoint pen and a note pad.

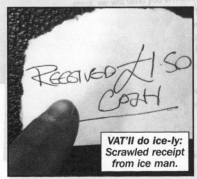

VAT'll do ice-ly: Scrawled receipt from ice man.

When he returns several minutes later, the queue has lost patience and gone and he grumpily writes

out my signed receipt: "Received £1.50 cash". I ask him to append his 16-digit VAT registration number and he claims it has slipped his mind. How convenient.

As he slams his van into first gear and drives off up the road, I wonder how much of my lolly will end up funding the National Health Service, our police force and our children's schools. Not much, I suspect. *He may have put hundreds and thou-sands on my cone, but it's the hun-dreds and thousands he is keeping hidden from the taxman that are making my monkey blood boil.*

No Vat in Me Kitchen

Britain's Inland Revenue inspectors scrutinise our tax returns with forensic attention to detail, but they can only

work with the information we give them. They rely on us to declare our income honestly and completely in order to do their job. But my next in-vestigation shows me just how easy it is to pull the wool over the taxman's eyes. Dressing myself up as a frail old lady, complete with grey wig, shawl, ear trumpet, bloomers and walking stick, I move into an empty flat.

Later that day, I knock on a neigh-bour's door and ask him - in a high-pitched, quavery voice - if he wouldn't mind popping round to change a light for me. The man cheerfully agrees to help, and ten minutes later he is standing on a chair in my kitch-en, putting a new bulb in.

Affecting an arthritic shake, I fiddle with my purse and offer to pay him, but my knight in shining armour gal-lantly refuses, assuring me it was no trouble.

CONTINUED OVER...

...CONTINUED

Nevertheless I insist on making him a drink to thank him.

Later, as he sits with me and enjoys a cup of tea and a slice of my home-made Victoria sponge, I tell

Light fingered: 'Good' neighbour kept impromptu job quiet from HMRC.

him all about my fictitious family - my late war hero husband, my son in Canada, my daughter in New Zealand and my grandchildren who, I tearfully explain, I never get to see. My neighbour eventually leaves, promising to pop in and check on me a couple of times a week. But little does he know that it's actually ME who will be checking up on HIM.

That cuppa and the slice of cake he has just wolfed down at my kitchen table would have set him back £5 in a high street cafe. A fiver for changing a lightbulb? Nice work if you can get it! And although it wasn't cash, it was still a payment in kind and is therefore a taxable benefit.

The next day I ring the Inland Revenue to see if our tea-swigging chum has declared his windfall in full. Surprise, surprise - I am told that all tax records are confidential and they are only able to discuss them with individual taxpayers, their accountants or assignees. I hang up, satisfied that I have PG-tipped off the authorities to this chancer's lucrative scam. *When it comes to cheating the authorities, he'll no longer get to have his cake and eat it.*

Hat's the Way to Do It

The country's dwindling band of ageing WW2 veterans battled like lions to keep Britain free from the Nazi menace. But now it seems there's another menace threatening them - the army of tax fiddlers who are stealing from the country they fought so hard to save.

For my next undercover sting I disguise myself as a D-Day hero, complete with regimental blazer and beret, khaki flannel trousers and a chestful of medals bought at a house clearance sale, and join my local branch of the British Legion. Very quickly, my fellow veterans accept me as one of their own and invite me to join them on a coach trip to visit the Normandy Beaches where so many of our brave comrades fell.

The long bus journey passes quickly as we reminisce about our experiences as frightened young conscripts seventy years ago, thrown into the frontline of the battle against Adolf Hitler's evil war machine. It's a very moving day and many a tear is shed as we stand on the sands in silent remembrance of those who never came back.

The mood lightens on the long drive home as we laugh, joke and sing our favourite wartime songs; even my fake passport barely elicits a second glance as we sweep through the Eurotunnel customs checkpoint. Half an hour from home, I stand up and begin making my way up and down the aisle of the coach, holding out my regimental beret to take a collection for our driver. The pound coins, fifty pees and twenty pences shower into my hat like confetti, and by the time we pull into the British Legion car park there must be the thick end of £15 in there.

The driver looks genuinely moved as I hand over the cash, which he stuffs into his trousers without even counting it. He clearly has no intention of declaring it as it is now mixed up with all the other change in his pocket. I make a mental note of his badge number, which I later phone in to the Inland Revenue's Whistleblowers Hotline. My comrades and I fought, many of us dying in the process, to defend the British way of life. In the immortal worlds of Winston Churchill, *we - the gallant few - had nothing but blood, toil, tears and sweat to give. This chump at the wheel is simply on the take.*

Give the Dogger a Bonus

Most people believe that any windfall that comes to them outside of their employment is tax-free. But this isn't the case. By law any income - other than a betting win where the tax has been paid on the stake - is subject to full duty at the prevailing rate and must be declared. And although many of us happily abide by the rules, abuse of the system is widespread.

I decide to put a cross section of the public to the test. Disguising myself as a dogger, complete with elastic-waisted jogging bottoms, a tracksuit top and Burberry cap, I make my way to a notorious local layby.

By the time I arrive at 2am, a small group of men has already gathered around the back of a Seat Alham-

Dog-gone!: Dirty doggers drove off with dodged tax.

bra, where an overweight man and woman in their mid-40s are having sex. Choking back the revulsion, I join the crowd of voyeurs - many of whom, I soon realise with disgust, are openly masturbating. In order to blend in and not blow my cover as an investigative reporter, I put my hand down my trousers and join in, shouting four-letter encouragement to the exhibitionist couple in the car and leaning in to get a better look at the sordid goings-on.

As the show and its seedy audience reach simultaneous climaxes, I look about me and realise that I'm going to have to play a long game to win my tax-fiddling quarry's confidence. Every night for the next three months I frequent all the local dogging spots, feigning enthusiasm for the tawdry car boot sex shows until I am eventually accepted as a member of the group. It's time to enact phase two of my sting operation.

At the next session, after ejaculating I surreptitiously drop a twenty pound note on the ground. As the crowd of grubby open air onanists pull up their trousers and leave, the woman who has just been having sex in the car spots the crisp twenty lying near her discarded leopardskin knickers on the grass.

She picks it up and shows it to me. *"Have you just dropped this, love?"* she asks me. *"No,"* I respond. *"Get in, it's my lucky night,"* she grins, stuffing the crisp purple note into her handbag. *"I trust you're going to pay the tax on that money,"* I venture. But the answer I receive from this 15-stone brassy blonde exhibitionist shocks me to my core. *"Like f*** I will,"* she cackles, her fag-raddled voice echoing round the car park.

I make a note of the car's registration number and mail it anonymously to HMRC. *It's one thing to have public sex in front of a group of masturbating strangers, but the way that this woman brazenly boasts about her dirty tax-fiddling plans shows that she is utterly without shame.*

NEXT WEEK: *Mahatma Macaroon goes undercover behind skips in the country's most notorious red light districts to find out if British punters are being short-changed on their handjobs.*

SPIV COAT SALES SOAR

BRITAIN is the black market capital of the world, with billions of pounds worth of 'dodgy' goods being sold every year on street corners, behind pubs and under tables. Everything from cigarettes to watches, from perfume to pirate DVDs, can all be bought with no VAT and no questions asked.

But while a black market economy is bad for Britain, costing the exchequer billions in lost tax revenues each year, not everyone is suffering. Because the country's spiv coat manufacturing industry is reporting record profits.

Sales of the loose, belted coats with dozens of inside pockets are at their highest for 50 years, according to Renton Carstairs, CEO of Carstairs Fashions, who specialise in gents' spiv outfitting.

"We produce a wide range of multi-inner pocket coats in a variety of styles," he told reporters. *"Our basic model has eighteen inner pockets, nine on each side, and at the top of our range we have a forty pocket knee-length model."*

"All our coats have a very easy opening action, and they can be quickly belted shut if the police are spotted," he added.

And according to Carstairs, all the coats are selling like smuggled tobacco. *"We haven't seen sales like these since the second world war,"* he said. *"And it's all thanks to Britain's army of wheeler-dealer Delboys and Arthur Daleys."*

Delboy

Demand for the coats is so high that many would-be spivs and wideboys are having difficulty getting their hands on one, and Carstairs called for patience. He told us: *"We have taken on more staff and the factory is currently working three shifts in order to meet demand."*

"Shops are constantly restocking and everyone who wants one will eventually get one. But if they can't wait, one of our warehousemen has stolen two hundred of them which he is selling for a fiver at time from the boot of his car behind the Fat Ox pub in Derby."

F·R·I·E·N·D·S WITH BENEFITS

Central perks of US sitcom stars exposed

THE STARS of hit nineties sitcom *FRIENDS* are living high on the hog courtesy of the lax British benefits system, it has been revealed. The US actors, who still pocket seven figure salaries a dozen years after the final episode aired, claim a variety of generous handouts from the UK authorities. *"I'll be there for you,"* sang THE REMBRANDTS in the famous theme song to the top-rated show that made them all rich. But it seems that these days it's hard-working British taxpayers who are there for this bunch of shameless millionaire scroungers.

COURTENEY COX

Age	51
Estimated personal wealth	$100 million
Housing Benefit claimed	£68.50/week

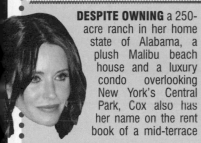

DESPITE OWNING a 250-acre ranch in her home state of Alabama, a plush Malibu beach house and a luxury condo overlooking New York's Central Park, Cox also has her name on the rent book of a mid-terrace council house on Hull's rundown Bransholme Estate. Thanks to clever accounting which keeps all her wealth safely locked up on the other side of the pond, she can truthfully declare to Humberside Borough Council that her UK earnings are zero. This means she is entitled to pocket nearly £300 each month in Housing Benefit.

MATTHEW PERRY

Age	46
Estimated personal wealth	$100 million
Benefits claimed	Free car + petrol

AS WISE-CRACKING Chandler Bing in *Friends*, Perry regularly managed to talk himself out of trouble. But in real life he's evidently managed to *talk himself into* a brand new £11,000 Ford Fiesta paid for by Joe and Joanne Muggins. The millionaire actor somehow managed to convince Motability Allowance assessors at Huddersfield Council into believing that he was unable to use public transport after his weight had ballooned to a whopping 50-stone, producing a doctor's note to back up his outsized claim. Just days later, he was handed the keys to the shiny, specially adapted motor, in which he is regularly seen driving round the West Yorkshire town. *With Friends like Perry taking advantage of us, who needs enemies?*

JENNIFER ANISTON

Age	47
Estimated personal wealth	$100 million
Jobseeker's Allowance claimed	£72.40/week

EVERYONE KNOWS that Aniston, recently voted one of the world's most beautiful women, regularly commands multi-million dollar fees from Hollywood moviemakers. But you might not realise that she also commands more than a tenner a day in Jobseeker's Allowance from Cricklewood Council. In a brazen bid to scam Britain's overly generous benefits system, the actress has signed on with a west London-based agent who regularly puts her forward for unsuitable roles - such as old men, ugly women and small children - in provincial theatre productions and low-rent TV dramas. In no danger of even being called for an audition, the glamorous multi-millionairess comedy star can safely trouser the cash and laugh all the way to the bank.

DAVID SCHWIMMER

Age	49
Estimated personal wealth	$100 million
Income support claimed	£57.90/week

SINCE JANUARY, Schwimmer has been picking up plaudits for his performances as Feste the Fool in *Twelfth Night* at London's National Theatre. But South Bank audiences might not be clapping so loudly if they knew that the actor has also been picking up nearly £60 a week in benefits for the last four months. With the play lasting just 2hrs 11minutes Monday to Friday, and with an extra Matinee performance on Saturdays, Schwimmer works for less than 15½ hours a week, comfortably under the government's 16-hour working week threshold for Income Support claimants. Never mind Feste, it is the British public that is being played for tools, *and just like in a Shakespeare comedy, nobody's laughing.*

LISA KUDROW

Age	52
Estimated personal wealth	$100 million
Benefits claimed	Free eye tests

KUDROW'S *FRIENDS* **CHARACTER**, ditzy blonde Phoebe Buffay, was famous for regaling the customers of Central Perc with her song *Smelly Cat*. But something definitely smells a bit fishy about the way she's been brazenly milking our hard-pressed National Health Service since the show was axed in 2004. Taking advantage of a little-known rule, Kudrow claims that her father once suffered from glaucoma, meaning that she is entitled to as many free eye tests as she likes. Secure in the knowledge that the tab will be picked up by generous British taxpayers, Kudrow regularly enjoys 4 or 5 eye tests a day, Monday to Friday. And at an eye-popping £20 a time, that's £500 we're forking out for the millionaire actress each week. *She must have seen us coming.*

MATT LEBLANC

Age	48
Estimated personal wealth	$100 million
Personal Independence Payment claimed	£139.75/week

LEBLANC PLAYED actor Joey Tribbiani in the series, where his catchphrase *"How ya doin'?"* regularly had viewers rolling in the aisles. But when the same question was asked of him by disability benefits assessors working for Dumfries and Galloway DHS, he told them he had a bad back that limited his mobility and stopped him working. He was duly awarded the maximum PIP allowance of nearly £140 a week. It's strange that LeBlanc's "bad back" doesn't seem to have stopped him hopping into a sports car and performing high-speed doughnuts round the Cenotaph. *Bad back? Brass neck more like.*

Do *YOU* suspect an American sitcom star of committing benefits fraud? Perhaps you've seen *The Big Bang Theory's* **JIM PARSONS** cleaning your neighbour's windows while receiving Unemployment Benefit. Or maybe *2½ Men's* **ASHTON KUTCHER** was claiming Incapacity Benefit when you saw him refereeing a football match. Dob them in to the *Viz Whistleblowers Hotline* and we'll do our best to get their nash took off them.

GOOD INVESTMENT...
...BAD INVESTMENT

ED SHEERAN, GINGER MUSICIAN, 25

BEST INVESTMENT

I BOUGHT a wheel of cheese at my local cash'n'carry. It was £20, which seemed like a lot of money at the time, but when I went to my local supermarket, slices of the same cheese were selling for £2.80 each. You could easily have got thirty slices out of my wheel, so I was quids in.

WORST INVESTMENT

I SPENT £2 million on a restaurant - Ed's Diner - twenty feet from the lip of the crater on Mount St Helens. Two days after the grand opening, the volcano went off and that was that.

TRACEY ULLMAN, FORMER COMEDIAN, 56

BEST INVESTMENT

WHEN I was in America, I bought a rusty Lincoln convertible for $10 at a yard sale. I only got it for spares, but when I checked the license plate it turned out it was the car that JFK got assassinated in - there was still a bit of his brain on the back seat. I sold it at auction the very next day for $10 million.

WORST INVESTMENT

I BOUGHT a torch at Home Bargains, but the second time I used it, the slidey switch on the side sprung off and wouldn't go back on again. I couldn't find the receipt so there was no point taking it back to the shop and I ended up throwing the whole thing in the trash. So that was £2.49 down the drain.

KENDO NAGASAKI, MASKED WRESTLER, 70

BEST INVESTMENT

I SPENT fifteen bob on a K-Tel Hair Magician home barber kit in 1969. Over the years it must have saved me more than two grand in haircuts. It makes a terrible job, leaving me with bald patches, tufts sticking up and an uneven fringe, but that doesn't matter as I wear my trademark ninja mask 24 hours a day so nobody ever sees the state of my barnet.

WORST INVESTMENT

WHEN the exotic pets import ban came into force in the early eighties, Mick McManus decided to set up a tortoise farm, and I invested £500 so as he could buy a breeding pair of tortoises, an incubator and some lettuce. Unfortunately, the man tortoise turned out to be gay, so he never got any eggs off the female. The business went bust and I lost my money.

FIONA BRUCE, ANTIQUES ROADSHOW HOST, 52

BEST INVESTMENT

ON A RECENT *Antiques Roadshow* shoot, I saw an old lady standing in a queue holding a vase. I told her it was rubbish but offered her £10 for it to take it off her hands. She accepted, and when I showed my purchase to ceramics expert Henry Sandon, he recognised it immediately as Ming and I later sold it at Sothebys for £15 million.

WORST INVESTMENT

I WENT to the BATA Shoe Museum in Toronto and they had one of Jimi Hendrix's shoes in a display case. A week later at a jumble sale in Smethwick I saw the other one from the pair on a stall priced just 50p, so I snapped it up. When I phoned the museum to see how much they'd pay for it, they said they didn't want it because they were a Shoe Museum, not a Shoes museum. So I was 50p down and left with a shoe I didn't want.

BILL TURNBULL, EX-BREAKFAST TV HOST, 60

BEST INVESTMENT

SOMEONE in my local bee-keeping club got stung to death and his widow was selling off all his old gear. I bought his bee-keeping suit off her for £5, and quickly located the hole in the arse of it where the bees had got in and stung him. It took me 3 minutes to darn it up and the suit was as good as new. A brand new suit would have cost me £300!

WORST INVESTMENT

I SAW a swarm of bees advertised for sale on the internet for £10. The seller was in Russia, which should probably have rung alarm bells, but they were so cheap I decided to buy them anyway. When they arrived a couple weeks later and I opened the box, I realised I'd be conned. They were wasps and therefore utterly worthless. In fact, I had to spend another couple of quid on a can of Raid when they got out and started building a nest in the living room curtains.

£°° Money Shots
Offshore Tax Havens Explained
with Harde Cashe the Financial Porn Star

" HI. HARDE CASHE here. Now I've made loads of money by putting my cock into women's fannies, but I've made even more by putting that money where the Inland Revenue can't get it. And while I often stick my cock in a shaven haven, one of the safest places I've found to stick my cash is an Offshore Tax Haven. We've all heard of them, but what exactly are they? Well, they are a legitimate means by which you can lower your tax liability. They are very complicated, but let me explain simply.

Imagine I ran a pizza shop in the UK, and one night I delivered some pizzas to three women having a slumber party. They'd invite me in and strip naked and I'd have oral sex with them one at a time whilst the other two pleasured each other. Then I'd fuck them all, one at a time whilst feeling the other two's tits. Then I'd do anal and end up shooting my load on their arses, after which they'd pay me £25 for the pizzas.

Because my pizza shop is registered in the UK, the profit from that £25 after costs would be liable for taxation at 25%, or 40% depending on my tax threshold. However, if I registered my pizza business in somewhere like the British Virgin Islands, even though my shop was physically in the UK and traded in the UK, I would not be liable to pay tax on any profits generated to HMRC. So when I delivered some pizzas to a women's prison, the attractive inmates would tell me that they hadn't had a man in months, before stripping me naked and performing oral sex on me. Then they'd push me back on a bed and I'd fuck each of them in turn in all sorts of positions including doggy, scissors, between the tits and reverse cowgirl. After I had shot my load on their faces while grimacing, they'd pay me £30 for the pizzas which would be taxed by the British Virgin Island authorities at a zero tax rate.

As I always say, when it comes to protecting your hard-earned money, you won't go far wrong if you stick to the porn actor's mantra: *It's Up, In, Out and Offshore.* *Harde x* "

Next week. The Financial Porn Star explains Hedge Funds

HMRC BUSSELL

the HOPELESSLY INCOMPETENT BUREAUCRATIC BALLET DANCER

DJ '16

NO CHEQUES PLEASE, WE'RE BRICKIES!

British builders prefer cash, says report

THE UK'S jobbing builders are increasingly eschewing cheque and credit card payments and insisting on cash, according to a new report. But contrary to what you might think, it's not an attempt to hide their profits from the tax authorities.

"It's a simple matter of convenience," says Nobby Gatepost, head of the UK Federation of Cash Only Builders. "If a customer pays me in folding notes, I can tuck it straight into my pocket where it's nice and safe and ready to be put through the books and declared as income when I get home."

"A cheque, on the other hand, could easily blow away in the wind or get torn when I'm clambering round on some scaffolding. Or I could simply lose it or drop it into a cement mixer," he told us.

EXCLUSIVE!

And Gatepost was equally dismissive of card-based payments. "I'd have to carry one of those little machines round with me all the time, wouldn't I?" he said.

"If I was up fixing a roof and I dropped one of them things, it could easily hit somebody on the head and kill them. It's simply not worth taking the risk, and that's why cash is king."

Gatepost pointed out that he also prefers his outgoings to be cash only, and his local builders' merchants are perfectly happy with this arrangement. He told us: "When I'm loading up my van with bags of cement, lengths of four-by-two and sheets of plasterboard, the last thing I need to be worrying about is whether I've remembered to bring my chequebook and a pen with me."

And he dismissed suggestions that his cash-only arrangement was a brazen attempt to avoid paying tax and VAT. "It all goes through the books, don't you worry about that," he told us. "Every last penny is accounted for, I can assure you."

"Mind I've had a terrible year. I don't think I've made anything," he added from his villa in Spain.

On the nail: Britain's jobbing builders prefer to be paid in cash.

Peake Practice

NOBODY likes paying tax, and many people go to great lengths to avoid having to hand over their hard-earned dosh to the Inland Revenue. But one British man has gone further than anyone else… by going into *SPACE!* Because the atmosphere 40 miles above the Earth's surface is not only gravity-free, it's also tax-free.

Astronaut **TIM PEAKE** made the headlines last year when he became the first Briton to step aboard the International Space Station. But what didn't make the news was that he would not be charged any tax or national insurance on his £258.67 per week salary for the duration of his inter-galactic mission.

space

"Working in space, Major Peake would be classed for tax purposes as a non-UK resident if he spent no more than 182 days directly over the UK in any one tax year," said HMRC spokesman Hector Toothbrush-Moustache. "His space station orbits the Earth

Tax heaven: Space is the place for tin-canny Major Tim.

Major tax loophole for spaceman Tim

once every 90 minutes, but does not always cross over the British Isles," he continued. "And when it does, it is only for two or three minutes at a time as it is travelling at more than 17,000mph."

"Major Peake would therefore be exempt from paying tax to HMRC in the UK," Toothbrush-Moustache added. "He is also exempt from paying national insurance while in orbit, although he may choose to make voluntary Class 3 contributions in order to remain entitled to a state pension when he retires from being an astronaut."

And Toothbrush-Moustache had more good news for Britain's Major Tim. "As a non-resident, he will also not be required to pay tax on any interest earned on savings in UK banks or building societies, providing he has filled in form R105 at his branch which will prevent tax being deducted at source," he said.

rhinestone

But if he's thinking about celebrating his windfalls, Peake may have to put the champagne on ice.

"Of course, Major Peake will be liable to pay tax in any of the countries that he floats over on his mission," said Toothbush-Moustache. "It's a simple matter of registering for tax liability in each individual country and filling out one of their self assessment returns. Major Peake will then pay tax at the prevailing rates proportional to the length of time he was working above that country in the tax year," he continued.

And he had this warning for Peake. "Make sure you return you self assessment forms to the various countries' revenue offices on time, as many of them issue a standard penalty for late submissions, usually around £100 local currency for the missed return date, then 5% of the tax due up to 30 days, then £10 per day thereafter."

PATH OF TRUTH

Are *YOU* an EVADER or an AVOIDER?

BRITAIN'S TAX LAWS are the most complicated in the world. It's unlikely that anyone, even a tax accountant, is familiar with every clause and sub clause of the 20,000, closely typed pages that set out all the rules. And to complicate the problem, the rules are constantly changing as threshold levels are changed, old loopholes are closed and new ones are opened.

Tax avoidance - playing the system to minimise your tax bill - is perfectly legal. *Tax evasion* - breaking the rules to hide your money from the taxman - is a criminal offence. But with such a complicated system, it's easy to unwittingly fall foul of the rules and find yourself on the wrong side of the law. So follow our simple Path of Truth to discover if, when it comes to paying tax, you are an *EVADER* or an *AVOIDER*.

YOU win the meat raffle at your local social club. Do you estimate the value of the meat and inform the authorities so they can raise your tax or lower your benefits accordingly?

What's a meat raffle?

No

THE private investment company you own pays you a £1million bonus. Do you set up an offshore trust fund, naming your wife as sole beneficiary, and pay the bonus into that via a wholly owned subsidiary company in the form of unit trust cash equivalents?

HOW DID YOU DO?

Yes

You are a tax *AVOIDER.* Don't ever complain about the length of hospital waiting lists or overcrowded classrooms. Cheating the Inland Revenue like you do means our hard-pressed doctors, nurses and teachers must try to do their jobs with less resources. Your selfish actions are bringing this country to its knees. *Shame on you.*

Well done, you are a tax *EVADER.* You understand the value of money and know how to make it work for you. Your knowledge of economics and fiscal matters helps to keep the wheels of Britain's financial engine room turning. Without people like you, the country would grind to a halt in poverty. *Award yourself a knighthood.*

No Specs Please, We're British Tax Inspectors!

TAX avoidance is estimated to cost the Treasury a fortune each year, with companies such as Amazon, Starbucks and Google coughing up a paltry pittance in tax despite raking in billions of pounds in profit.

And, according to a new report put out by an independent think tank, Inland Revenue tax inspectors are powerless to act because they literally can't see what's going on right under their noses. "Over 82% of tax inspectors wear glasses," the report's author Dr Chedwyn Buttifant told us.

"Even if they squint really hard through their thick geps, they still can't see the loopholes that big businesses are blatantly exploiting to dodge tax."

Dr Buttifant, head of the influential Adam Ricketts Institute, called for a radical re-think of recruitment policy at HMRC. He told us: "All employees should be required to have 20/20 vision so that they can spot the financial sleight of hand these companies are using to get away without paying their dues."

present

"As things stand at present, rich multinationals are easily able to run rings round these speccy four-eyed officials. Because of their thick glasses, they literally can't see what's going on and it's costing the country a fortune in lost tax revenue."

Short-Sighted Taxmen Costing UK Dear ~report

The report highlights many instances where businesses have exploited the poor eyesight of Inland Revenue employees.

humphries

"Facebook's accountants, for example, fill in their tax returns using really small writing, a thin nib and very watery ink," said Dr Buttifant. "It would take a tax inspector with the eyes of a hawk to read the amounts they've written in the boxes and work out what they owe."

"With four out of five HMRC staff peering dimly through the bottoms of coke bottles, it's no wonder Facebook gets away with paying less tax each year than a fucking postman," he added.

 STOP EVERYTHING! IT'S AN ABSOLUTE DISGRACE! WOMEN'S VOICES ARE NOT BEING HEARD!

WELL YOURS IS MILLIE. JESUS, I'M TRYING TO READ HERE.

 WHAT DO YOU MEAN, MILLIE?

THIS!

 HAVE YOU EVER NOTICED HOW ALL COMIC BOOK SUPERHEROES ARE MEN? WITHOUT EXCEPTION...

WELL, NOT ALL OF THEM...

 ALL OF THEM! SUPER MAN! SPIDER MAN! BAT MAN! THERE ARE LITERALLY NO WOMAN SUPERHEROES!

WHAT ABOUT WONDER-WOMAN... CAT WOMAN... ATOM GIRL.?

 AS I SAY, THERE ARE NO WOMAN SUPERHEROES! NOT A SINGLE ONE!

 WELL IT'S TIME FOR CHANGE. I'M GOING TO CREATE THE WORLD'S FIRST SUPER "SHE"-RO!

 SHE'S GOING TO BE A STRONG, INDEPENDENT WOMAN WHO DOES THINGS FOR HERSELF.

 DAVE. GO AND GET ME SOME PENS AND PAPER.

 LATER...

YAWN! YOU STILL AT IT, MILLIE?

 YES. I'VE BEEN UP ALL NIGHT WORKING ON MY RADICAL FEMINIST COMIC.

 HOW ARE YOU GETTING ON?

FANTASTIC! THE IDEAS ARE SIMPLY POURING OUT OF ME, JANE.

LOOK...

 MENSTRO-WOMAN? IS THAT ALL YOU'VE COME UP WITH?

NO. OF COURSE NOT. I'VE DONE A DRAWING OF HER TOO.

 SHE FIGHTS FOR LGBLT RIGHTS ONCE A MONTH, USING THE POWER OF HER RADIO-ACTIVE OVARIES.

RAAARSH!

 WHAT DO YOU THINK, JANE? GIVE ME YOUR HONEST OPINION.

IT'S VERY GOOD, MILLIE.

DO YOU REALLY LIKE IT?

 I DO, BUT WHAT WOULD BE REALLY GOOD WOULD BE IF SHE HAD A SIDE-KICK, YOU KNOW, A YOUNG NEPHEW OR A...

A MAN?! I'M NOT HAVING A MAN IN MY COMIC STRIP JANE. I TOLD YOU, IT'S ALL ABOUT GIVING WOMEN A VOICE!

 WELL, IT WOULDN'T HAVE TO BE A...

NO! I'M GOING TO NO-PLATFORM YOU!

 THIS IS MY HOME. IT IS A SAFE SPACE WHERE I SHOULD NOT BE FORCED TO LISTEN TO YOUR VILE, LESBO-PHOBIC RHETORIC.

BUT MILLIE, YOU ARE MY LODGER. I'M ALLOWED TO EXPRESS MYSELF IN MY OWN HOUSE, SURELY?

NOT WHEN IT IMPINGES ON MY RIGHT TO STOP YOU FROM DOING SO.

 FREE SPEECH IS NOT A LICENCE TO SAY WHAT YOU WANT, JANE.

BUT SURELY...

 SHUT UP!!

If there's something strange in the neighbourhood of your bedroom, who ya gonna call?...

THE VIZ
GHOST BUST-a-MATIC
Bedside Paranormal Activity Detector

ARE YOU being kept awake by ghosties and ghoulies and things that go bump in the night? The UK is the world's most haunted country, with an estimated 6 spooks or more for every man, woman and child in the land. Every night, millions of Britons are kept awake by paranormal activity and strange goings-on of one sort or another. Whether it's the *glowing figure of Mary Queen of Scots* walking through the wall, a *platoon of Roman soldiers* cut off at the knee as they march across the landing, or an *horrific, screaming ghoul* rattling its chains on the stairs and filling the house with the rank stench of death and decay, they disturb our sleep, leaving us cranky and irritable in the morning and tired throughout the day.

But now it's time to reclaim the night and put a stop to spirits putting the willies up us once and for all. We've teamed up with excitable *Most Haunted* presenter and ghost expert **YVETTE FIELDING** to bring you this fantastic free *Viz Ghost Bust-a-Matic*.

Fearless former *Blue Peter* presenter Yvette has been travelling the country and busting ghosts on her top-rated TV show for more than 13 years and less than 14 years. And now she's packed all the knowledge and expertise she has gained while spending countless nights wandering round buildings with the lights turned off into this amazing piece of paranormal kit. She told us: *"I ain't afraid of no ghosts, and neither will you be if you use the Viz Ghost Bust-a-Matic!"*

Keep the *Viz Ghost Bust-a-Matic* by your bedside and next time you are woken at the witching hour by a malign supernatural presence, the Ghost Bust-a-Matic's user-friendly interface will quickly allow you to identify what it is that is haunting you and - more importantly - how to get rid of it... *quick!* Remember the drill: *Identify... Read up... and Bust!* It's as easy as 1,2,3!

AFFIX THIS TAB TO PENCIL

DRACULA

NOSFERATU

SEXY VAMPIRE

POLTERGEIST

ZOMBIE

WRAITH

AFFIX THIS TAB TO PENCIL

Dracula
There are many ways to get rid of a Dracula. If the sun has already risen, simply open the curtains and it will combust whilst making a noise like a big pan of bubble and squeak. Alternatively, make a cross from any two straight objects in your bedside table drawer, eg. a candle and a neck massager, and brandish it at the Dracula until it turns into a bat and flies back out of the window. If all else fails, drive a sharp wooden stake through its heart. The Dracula will disappear, leaving just its cloak in a heap on the floor.

Nosferatu
Nosferatus are a more ancient form of Dracula and can be recognised by their bald heads, pointy teeth and overgrown fingernails. Whilst they can be combatted using the same techniques you would use against a Dracula, they can also be warded off by reading a bit out of the Bible at them. Alternatively, if you keep your false teeth in a glass of water by the bed, quickly turn it into Holy Water by saying a Hail Mary over it and flick it over your unwanted nocturnal visitor. It will burn him like acid.

Sexy Vampire
These bloodthirsty sucubuses usually appear in pairs, and can be recognised by their low-cut night-dresses, over-the-top make-up and heaving Confessions film-style cleavages. Ladies, if these appear in your room you can go straight back to sleep, because they only will only ever attack a man, whom they will mesmerise with a softcore lesbian show before sinking their fangs hungrily into his neck. They can be warded off with a simple clove of garlic kept in the top pyjama pocket or a crucifix hung over the bed.

Frankenstein
Made by mad scientists using body parts gathered from graveyards, execution sites and morgues re-vivified by the power of a raging storm, Frankensteins are simple-minded monsters who don't know their own strength. If one turns up in your bedroom, chances are he's escaped from his master's castle and is confused. If possible, try to calm him down by singing beautifully or playing the violin. If this fails and he becomes agitated, smashing things with his arms, drive him downstairs and out of the front door with a flaming torch.

Mummy
Is there a groaning, bandage-wrapped figure standing at the end of your bed? Chances are it's a mummy - the restless remains of an Egyptian Pharaoh, bent on enacting an ancient curse placed on those who deign to disturb its eternal rest. So, if you're an archaeologist or a museum curator who's just taken delivery of a new sarcophagus, you need to act fast. Throw it off its guard by chanting a hieroglyphic incantation from the Egyptian Book of the Dead and then throw a paraffin lamp at it. It'll go up like a fucking rocket.

Werewolf
These lycanthropic monsters live normal lives except if it's a full moon, when they transform into ravenous, fur-covered beasts bent on slaking their bloodlust on innocent townfolk. And if you find one climbing in through your bedroom window, you'd better take care because if it bites you, you'll become a werewolf too. Shooting it with a bullet of the purest silver is the surest way to

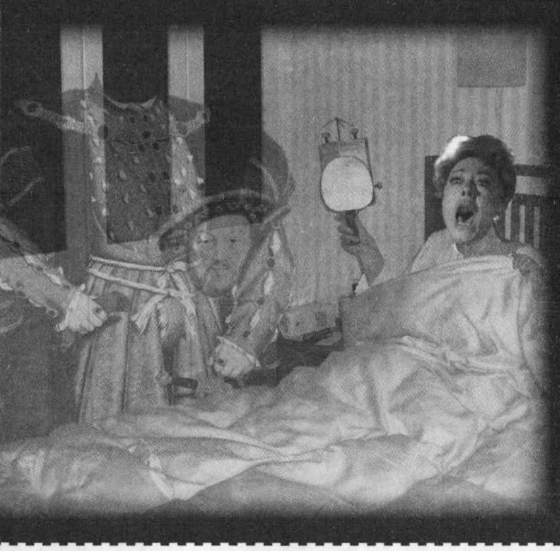

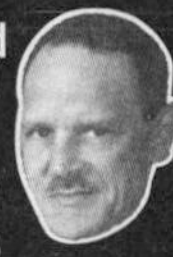

THE VIZ COMIC AND YVETTE FIELDING
GHOST BUST-a-MaTIc

EEK! It's a fucking... ✂ GNW !

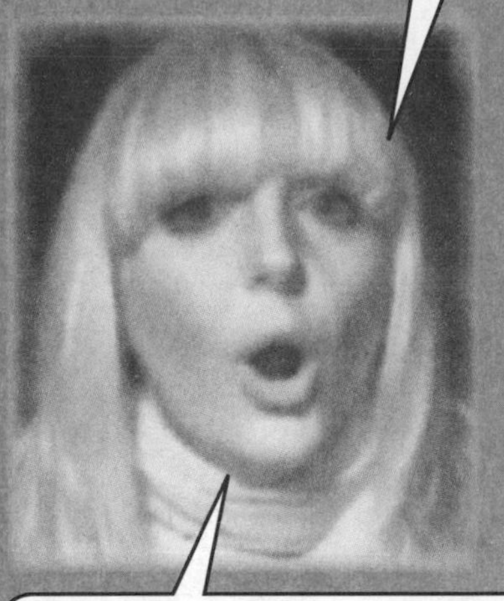

✂ GIW

After the Ghost Bust-a-Matic interface is stuck to the box, cut out and remove the ghost nomenclature window (GNW - top), the ghost identification window (GIW -centre) and the ghost busting information window (GBIW - bottom).

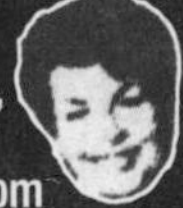

Here's how to BUST IT!

Step 1: *Identify...*
Step 2: *Read up...*
Step 3: *Bust!*

✂ GBIW

HOW TO USE: As soon as a spectre manifests itself in front of you, point your Viz Ghost Bust-a-Matic at it and wind the vertical knob until a picture of it appears in the identification screen and refer to Yvette's speech balloon to discover the type of phantom you are dealing with. Now, turn the horizontal knob until the name of your ghost and instructions for how to deal with it appear in the ghost busting information window. It's time to bust your ghost!

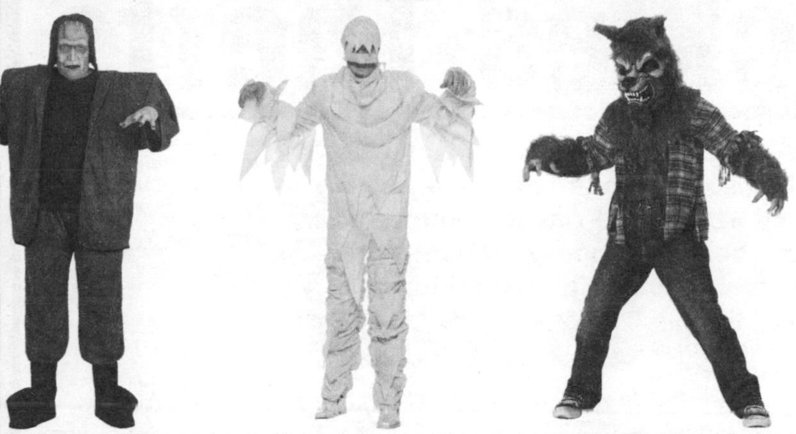

ENSTEIN

MUMMY

WEREWOLF

AFFIX THIS TAB TO OTHER HALF

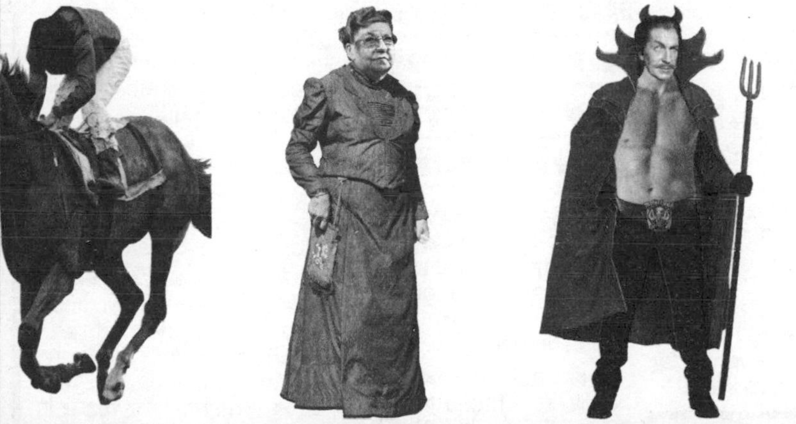

LESS HORSEMAN

GREY LADY

BEELZEBUB

AFFIX THIS TAB TO PENCIL

INSTRUCTIONS You will need: An empty cardboard box (eg. Economy size soap powder, teabags etc.) An old table tennis bat. 4 pencils, 4 squash bottle tops, Plasticine. Cut out the various pieces and assemble the Viz Ghost Bust-a-Matic as shown in the diagram. Wind one end of the ghost data strip onto one pencil and fix the other end to a second pencil as shown in the diagram. Do the same with the information strip. Mount the pencils in holes in the side and top of the Viz Ghost Bust-a-Matic box as shown. Stick the bottle tops onto the end of the pencils using the Plasticine. Bend three pipe cleaners and put them in the top to look like ghost-detecting antennae...

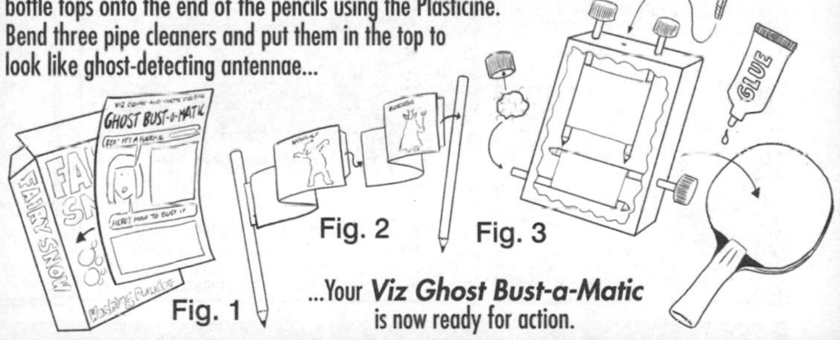

Fig. 1

Fig. 2

Fig. 3

...Your *Viz Ghost Bust-a-Matic* is now ready for action.

ZOMBIE

beaten to death by their masters, hanged monks, and witches who were burned at the stake. If the wardrobe door begins banging and things start flying round the room, exorcise your poltergeist by lighting some incense in a thurible and saying some Latin. The door will bang a bit more violently during the exorcism, until it suddenly stops and whatever was flying around drops to the floor. Job done.

ZOMBIE

Whilst not strictly ghosts - zombies are merely corpses of the recently dead re-animated by a foul contagion or voodoo sorcery - it is nevertheless a little disconcerting when one of these decomposing, groaning ghouls shuffles into your bedroom with its rotting arms outstretched and one of its eyes dangling on its cheek. Thankfully, they are easy to get rid of. Give it a sharp blow on the bonce with the nearest heavy object. Once zombies' brains are destroyed they can no longer hurt you and you can get a well-earned forty winks.

WRAITH

Wraiths are common-or-garden ghosts, the ones that look like a sheet with two holes cut out for the eyes. They are the souls of people who died suddenly. Unable to comprehend what has happened to them, they are condemned to exist in an unearthly limbo suspended between this world and the next. If one floats through the wall going "woo", explain that it is okay to go towards the light place where it will find eternal peace. Nine times out of ten this does the trick. Alternatively, pop your head under the covers for 5 minutes until it goes away.

HEADLESS HORSEMAN

The bad news is there's very little you can do to get rid of one of these noisy phantoms, especially if your house was built on the site of an ancient inn at a crossroads where Dick Turpin was beheaded. The good news is, they only appear once a year - on the anniversary of their death. And also on Halloween. On these nights, simply book yourself into a Travelodge. If you book well in advance you should be able to get a very good deal, perhaps including a free continental breakfast.

GREY LADY

Grey ladies are OAP ghosts who warn homeowners of impending disasters, sometimes by fiddling with the radio until a portentous report of a plane crash or rail disaster comes on, or sitting weeping over a newspaper report of a motorway pile-up that has yet to happen. Announce in a loud, clear voice: "Begone, old woman, for you are not welcome in this house." This will usually keep your property grey lady free for up to six months. NB. You might like to cancel all travel plans for the next week or so in case she was right.

BEELZEBUB

The Lord of Darkness, Satan, Lucifer, He Who Walks Backwards, Old Nick ... call him what you will, you don't want the Devil in your room, especially if you've got to be up for work. But if your teenage kids have been messing with a Ouija board or playing their Judas Priest records backwards, then you could easily find yourself face to face with the Antichrist himself. To send the Beast back where he came from, throw salt in his eyes. If that doesn't work, play a Judas Priest record the right way round, as that's enough to get rid of anybody.

AFFIX THIS TAB TO PENCIL

Major Misunderstanding

UM, EXCUSE ME, I WONDER IF YOU COULD HELP ME...?

CERTAINLY MADAM!

IT'S THESE 'CHOCLO' BARS — I CAN'T TELL IF THEY CONTAIN NUTS.

I'M BUYING TREATS FOR A CHILDREN'S PARTY, YOU SEE, AND ONE OF THE KIDS MIGHT HAVE AN ALLERGY...

YOU CAN'T BE TOO CAREFUL NOWADAYS, CAN YOU?

NOW LET'S SEE, IT OUGHT TO TELL YOU ON THE WRAPPER SOMEWHERE...

THERE'S NORMALLY A LITTLE WARNING, ISN'T THERE? THERE SHOULD BE...

TSK.

BUT I CAN'T SEEM TO FIND ONE ON HERE...

I'M SORRY TO INTERRUPT YOU BOTH, BUT I AM ACTUALLY A CUSTOMER.

I'M SORRY?

YOU KNOW — A CUSTOMER. YOU MAY HAVE HEARD OF US — WE ARE THE PEOPLE THAT YOU ARE IN FACT EMPLOYED TO ASSIST.

I REALISE IT'S VERY HARD FOR YOU TO TEAR YOUR EYES AWAY FROM YOUR MOBILE PHONES FOR A FEW SECONDS.

DOUBTLESS YOU'RE PLAYING A VERY IMPORTANT GAME OF SPACE INVADERS, OR WATCHING A HILARIOUS VIDEO OF AN ELDERLY PENSIONER BEING "HAPPY-SLAPPED".

BUT IF I CAN DRAG YOUR ATTENTION INTO THE REAL WORLD FOR JUST A MOMENT, PERHAPS ONE OF YOU COULD TELL ME WHERE THE GENTLEMAN'S RELISH IS KEPT?

THEN YOU CAN GO BACK TO YOUR "SEXTING."

ON SECOND THOUGHTS I'LL JUST FIND IT MYSELF.

IF IT'S NOT CONTAINED WITHIN ONE OF YOUR LITTLE OBLONG SCREENS THEN I DON'T SUPPOSE YOU'LL EVEN BE AWARE OF ITS EXISTENCE.

FUCKING LYRE

IN THE CHANGING ROOM...

HMM... DO YOU THINK THIS MAKES MY BUM LOOK BIG?

ABSOLUTELY NOT!

Office Vigilante Tackles Thefts

A DEPARTMENT in Tennent & Lowe Solutions Ltd has seen a 60% reduction in fridge-based crime after one woman took a stand by pinning up a stridently discouraging note in the kitchen.

Team manager *Eleanor Gay* has to use a special kind of yoghurt for improved digestive transit. But over the past few weeks, Ms Gay discovered that a light-fingered colleague at the Oswestry-based consultancy business had been helping themselves to her mid-morning snack from the staffroom fridge.

yoghurt

Following repeated thefts, Ms Gay decided to inform her line manager about the situation.

"I went straight to the top and told Mr Lowe," she told co-worker Eileen Driscoll, 51. "I told him that someone had been having it away with my special yoghurt for improved digestive transit."

EXCLUSIVE!

Reduction in fridge crime after no-nonsense note pinned up in office kitchen

Ms Gay continued: "I told him that if it had been a one-off, I wouldn't have minded, but it was now a regular occurrence. I told him he had to do something."

"He said he would, but he didn't. I mean they say they will, don't they. But they don't," she added.

plant

Frustrated by the lack of action from her boss, Ms Gay decided to take matters into her own hands and put a notice on the fridge. And the 42-year-old filing clerk didn't mince her words.

"I put: *'The yoghurt for improved digestive transit is NOT for use of anyone. Please buy YOUR OWN!!!!!'*" she told Mrs Driscoll.

"I underlined the word 'not' and put five exclamation marks on the end," she said. "I also cut a picture of a policeman out of a magazine and stuck that at side of it. I think that

Freeze!: The fridge where Ms Gay placed the note.

must have made the yoghurt thief reconsider their actions, because after I stuck it up the rate of thefts dropped by quite a bit."

cooking

Senior management at the company praised Eleanor for her initiative in dealing with the situation.

"Ms Gay's actions certainly seemed to have worked," said Hector Voldermort, head of HR at the firm. "Since she put the notice up, she has seen a marked decrease in the number of her digestive yoghurts being taken."

bag of nuts

Ms Gay told her friend that, although she is pleased with the reduction in the theft rate, she is now planning to implement a 'zero tolerance' approach to yoghurt pilfering.

"I won't be happy until there are no fridge crimes being perpetrated in my department of Tennent & Lowe Solutions," she said.

"I'm going to trial a system whereby I write my initials on my special yoghurt pots with a sharpie. If that doesn't work, I'm going to ask Mr Lowe if I can have my own little fridge on my desk," she added.

WHY is it that caffeine addicts are allowed to indulge their habit on the Tube in the morning, yet I can't have my eye opener can of high strength lager? I'm a taxpayer as well, you know.

Wootsy, Southend

THE family of that British astronaut who went into space said they were proud and happy, even though they wouldn't see him for months and he wouldn't be home for Christmas. Yet when I was sentenced to eight months in prison for kicking someone in the head, my wife didn't show the same support. In fact she even got a bit angry.

Keith Queef, email

OVERWEIGHT, under-talented singer Meatloaf sang "I'll do anything for love... But I won't do that." As an Australian relative of Mr Logic, I feel obliged to point out that the set of phenomena contained in 'anything' most certainly comprises 'that' and that Meatloaf is therefore being disingenuous in his quest to get his end away.

Ed Wombat, Melbourne

DO other readers think, as I do, that aircraft should be equipped with an emergency stop handle in the toilet? It's a standard feature in trains as I pointed out in my letter on page 10. If one of your toilet visits has ever necessitated stopping a train, you will appreciate how much more this facility is needed when 35,000 feet in the air.

Percy Fawcett, Durham

HOW come it's okay for Lord Attenborough to have a whole TV series, *The Hunt*, showing nothing but cougars and things ripping the throats out of wildebeests for his and our enjoyment? But if a couple of lads on a housing estate take their terriers to a badger's sett for a bit of fun they end up in the pokey? Once again, it's one rule for Oxbridge graduates and another for the rest of us.

Brucie Bonus, St. Leonards on Sea

WHY don't they make seats on mobility scooters a bit more comfortable? I've never seen an even vaguely happy person on one of those things. Maybe a nice soft cushion might cheer them up a bit.

N S Fletcher, Pitchester

ACCORDING to various newspapers, a researcher has discovered Adolf Hitler's medical records, which confirm that he did indeed only have one testicle. However no such confirmation has been forthcoming concerning Himmler, and since Goebbels had six children, it is inconceivable that he had no testicles at all. Whoever wrote that song really needs to get their facts straight.

Geoffrey Bunglebear, Rainbow

WHY don't they stagger rush hour to cut down on congestion? I think it would be good if people with surnames beginning with the letters M-Z stayed at work for an extra half hour in order to ease the journey home for those with surnames beginning A-L.

Franklyn Anderson, London

IF I had a time machine, I wouldn't go back and kill Hitler as a baby. I'd go back to 1980 dressed as the hottest princess ever, and cavort in front of Prince Charles. He'd marry me instead of Lady Di, which would save her from being killed by the Duke of Edinburgh. Lady Di would now still be driving around in her Austin Metro, which I'd service every 6 months for a purely nominal charge, providing I can keep the used engine oil.

Ian Andrews, Hastings

WHY is it that in this day and age, we have to see professional footballers 'warming up' at the side of the pitch by running around and doing exercises? Surely with the millions that some of these clubs have, you'd think they could afford to put a couple of Calor gas heaters in the dugout.

Rosemary Flatbread, Hull

I SEE a lot of people are excited by the return of *Robot Wars* on TV, and rightly so. Personally, I can't wait to see two metal boxes slowly nudge each other until one just stops, accompanied by a painfully histrionic commentary.

Boris Scrumramp, Scarborough

WHEN you think about it, mayflies must have some really good chat up lines. They only live for a day and during that time they have to pull a female, give her all the patter, get their end away and then fuck off. No mean feat because they are right ugly little bastards, in my opinion.

Morton Bjornssen, Hull

MAGNUMS and Cornettos are certainly shrinking. Who can deny the impact of global warming now?

Razzle Bathbone, Muscat

WHY is it that Bolivians always wear hats that are too small for them? Come on, Bolivians, you only have to put a tape measure round your bonce before you buy a hat. It's not rocket science.

Ely Trump, Barnsley

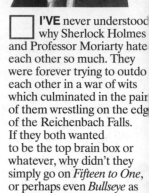

I'VE never understood why Sherlock Holmes and Professor Moriarty hate each other so much. They were forever trying to outdo each other in a war of wits which culminated in the pair of them wrestling on the edge of the Reichenbach Falls. If they both wanted to be the top brain box or whatever, why didn't they simply go on *Fifteen to One*, or perhaps even *Bullseye* as non-dart throwers?

Mick McM, Derby

THE BBC Big Band has 40% of its name dominated by the letter 'B'. Can any of your readers think of another musical ensemble that has a name comprising a high percentage of the same letter? For instance ZZ Top or something?

R Harvey, Ipswich

* *Well, readers, the gauntlet has been well and truly flung. Can YOU think of a band whose name has a higher proportion of one particular letter in it than the BBC Big Band's 40%? Other than Santana (42.857%), Weezer (50%) and A-Ha (66.667%), Write in and let us know at the usual address.*

WHENEVER I see the woman smiling in the Senokot advert, I just think to myself that she's just enjoyed a really big shit.

Peter Crompton, Sunderland

PEOPLE who say Mars bars are fattening are talking rubbish. The daily suggested calorific intake is 2600 for a man and 2000 for a woman, yet there are only 260 calories in a normal-sized Mars bar. This means I could eat 10 of the buggers a day and my wife could put away the best part of eight and neither of us would put on an ounce.

Hampton Redwood, Plumstead

ROLLOVER BEETHOVEN

THEY say there's far more chance of being struck by lightning than winning the lottery. Well my mate Daz is an electrician and he's been electrocuted 27 times and he doesn't even play the lottery. Somebody really should have a word with these so-called boffins.

Richard Carroll, London

WHY do people always say, "I wouldn't do that if I were you"? If they were me then they WOULD do it, because they were me and I decided to do it. Whatever it is. Probably something filthy, knowing me.

Mervyn Pissflaps, Bristol

WHY do vampires insist on sleeping in coffins? It must be murder on their backs. They are immortal and from the look of their clothes, castles and servants, they clearly have a few bob. So come on vampires, why not invest in a nice divan with a memory foam mattress?

Chris Powell, Stafford

DAVID Attenborough is always banging on about how great lions are. He even said they were social animals. Well, the hyena that they were ripping apart in his wildlife programme the other night might beg to differ, I reckon.

Horace Tremlow, Poole

WHY is it in films or telly programmes, blokes who are up on the battlement of a castle during a siege always fall forward and out of the castle to their deaths if they get hit by an arrow? Surely it would be wiser to fall backwards into the castle and hope that there's a doctor or at least a first aider knocking about.

Lemons Windsor, Truro

AFTER I got sacked for sexual harassment, my mate said I probably shouldn't have been so lecherous. I know hindsight is a wonderful thing, but I love looking at arses.

James Wallace, Belper

Mme. Miriam

Worried by hubby's use of tongue

Dear Miriam

My husband has always been an attentive and grammatically accurate lover but recently he has become more distant and very sloppy in the use of his French.

During recent lovemaking, he talked dirty to me in French, but used German sentence structure and got the tense wrong which just didn't seem right to me. I challenged him about it afterwards but he brushed over it and then went all quiet.

I love him very much and don't want to lose him but I can't accept him learning a third language.

D. Arsecrack, Leeds

Mme. Miriam says...

A loss of interest in using the correct verb tense is usually the first sign that your husband might be attempting to become trilingual.

Next time you are making love, surprise him by telling him you want to use a strap-on double dong, in German. If he shows any reaction, then your suspicions of a third language may be confirmed and I'm afraid divorce could be the only solution.

HOW come ghosts spend all their time trying to put the shits up people? They must have an awful lot of time on their hands, that's all I can say. And if they don't like my comments on here, they can fucking haunt me if they dare. I don't even believe in ghosts anyway, so good luck to them with that.

J Geilsband, Norfolk

I WATCHED some relationship expert on the telly the other night and she reckoned that chocolate is an aphrodisiac. I always thought that the whole 'Toblerone up the arse,' thing was an urban myth, but maybe I got it wrong. It just goes to show, I don't know everything.

Roger Plywood, Leeds

WE'RE a man short for our 5-a-side football team tonight and I was just wondering if any of your readers fancied a game? If they could bring a blue shirt that would be great.

Moono, Ipswich

✻ *Well, readers. Do you fancy a game of five-a-side, live in or near Ipswich and have a blue shirt? If so, drop us a line and we'll pass your details on.*

OVER the years, NASA must have wasted billions of dollars adapting their rockets to accommodate the monkeys, dogs, rats and spiders that they've sent up into space. Why don't they just use giraffes? They're practically the same shape as a rocket and so would fit neatly inside without the need for expensive modifications. Besides which, they're fuck all use down here as you can't ride them and they die when they fall over. Come on, NASA, it's not rocket science!

Nickers, Batley

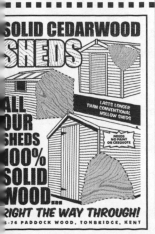

TOP TIPS

PREVENT the fur around your dog's anus from becoming matted with faeces by inserting a cook's piping bag into the animal using the handle of a wooden spoon. Then simply choose a nozzle to produce whichever profile of stool you prefer.

B Woodhouse, Heaven

RECREATE the nostalgic effect of listening to old fashioned 'long-wave' radio whilst actually listening to digital radio, by constantly rustling crisp packets next to your ears.

Trevor Broadbank, e-mail

VISITORS to Chester Zoo. Despite being sensationally trumpeted as 'wowing visitors', the elephant shrews are considerably smaller than expected.

Ben, Rigsby

TURN a dull day at the office into your own private Martin Scorsese film by loudly playing Motown songs on your phone and telling difficult clients to "go fuck their mothers."

Violet Rommel, Humberside

INSTEAD of spending an extra few pence on smoked cheese next Christmas, simply buy yourself a lump of basic cheddar and prop it up over your ashtray for a couple of hours.

Ted Belter, Dukinfield

COUNTDOWN. Save space on your set by only installing the half of the clock that you use.

Alasdair, Edinburgh

INVITED to a fancy dress party and can't think of an idea for a costume? Simply turn up in your normal clothes and tell partygoers that you have come as the bass player from Oasis.

Lance Dinkly, Manchester

TIRED of constantly straightening picture frames? Simply pop a few beer mats under one side of all the furniture in the room, adjust the skirting boards a bit and remove the top hinge from any doors. Hey presto! No more wonky-looking pictures.

David Herron, Sunderland

CONVINCE people you are Donald Trump by balancing a cat on your head and acting like a cunt.

Kevin Caswell-Jones, Gresford

ASPIRIN tablets painted blue make an ideal replacement for Viagra, if you don't mind not being able to achieve an erection.

Gerry Paton, London

BROKEN kettle? Make tea by putting a cup of water in a crisp packet and popping it into the toaster.

Hampton Bumwad, Croydon

IT MIGHT WELBY

With the Archbishop of Canterbury, *Justin Welby*

EACH WEEK the popular Church of England figurehead offers vague, ambiguous answers to **YOUR** theological questions...

Dear Justin, **MY** beloved pet rabbit Mr Flopsy died yesterday. At first, I was utterly distraught, but then it suddenly hit me: I shouldn't be sad at all, should I, because I'll see Mr Flopsy again in Heaven when I pass over. That's right, isn't it?

Mrs Ada Zanzibar, Cheam

● *Justin says: "It might Welby, Mrs Zanzibar. I reckon that the chances of you seeing Mr Flopsy again in Heaven depend on three things: 1. That you led a clean, pure, sin-free life; 2. That Mr Flopsy led a clean, pure, sin-free life; and 3. That animal Heaven and people Heaven are the same place. You'll know the answers to 1 and 2 better than me, but to be totally honest with you, I'm not 100% on 3. I can check this afternoon and get back to you."*

Dear Justin, **IN HER** 1987 hit *Heaven Is A Place On Earth*, the American singer Belinda Carlisle claims that Heaven is a place on Earth. Do you think it actually is?

Mrs Ethel Marzipan, Scholes

● *Justin says: "It might Welby. From what I can gather, Mrs Marzipan, the Bible generally seems* to imply that Heaven is an ethereal place, located way above the clouds on another astral plane altogether. But that said, I suppose it is technically possible that Ms Carlisle is correct, and that Heaven can in fact be found somewhere on this planet. I'll have a flick through the New Testament this evening and see if there's anything in there that can clear this one up once and for all."

Dear Justin, **THERE'S** a bloke in my office who's quite religious, and he told me the other day how he believes that Jesus is our saviour, and he died for our sins but was then reborn, only to ascend to Heaven forty days later and sit at the right hand of God for all eternity. No offence, but that sounds like a load of old shite to me.

Fat Baz, Orpington

● *Justin says: "It might Welby. To be honest, Mr Baz, I've always taken it as read that all that stuff actually happened. However, now that I hear myself say it out loud, it does sound a bit far-fetched. I don't know. I'll ring around a few of the other archbishops tomorrow and see what they reckon."*

HAVE YOU got a burning ecumenical inquiry that you would like an uncertain or hazy response to? Write in to:
Justin Welby, c/o Viz Comic
PO Box 841, Whitley Bay, NE26 9EQ

New Role for Gove

Cabinet Minister signs lucrative cosmetics deal

TORY Secretary of State for the Environment *Michael Gove* has been named as the new face of Rimmel Lip Gloss after signing a lucrative $5 million 3-year deal with the upmarket cosmetics brand.

The 51-year-old MP for Surrey Heath said he was delighted by the new appointment, which will see him feature in magazine advertisements and on billboards.

wet-look

"Rimmel's silky-smooth lip gloss gives

Pout-ilicious: Gove's Boy next door looks

me the wet-look, smoochable lips that my wife, poisonous *Daily Mail* columnist Sarah Vine, just can't resist," Gove told *Cosmopolitan* magazine.

"And its guaranteed round-the-clock coverage me ans my delectable 3D-licious pout looks back-row ready 24 hours a day," he added.

Drill Sergeant JUMBO

Young Jumbo Williams was the luckiest boy in Barnton, for his uncle was an eccentric inventor who had built him his own platoon of miniature remote control soldiers that were under his command...

4:30 am...
Snore!
ZZZZZZZ!
ZZZZZZZ!

Suddenly...
WAKEY WAKEY! RISE AND FUCKING SHINE, YOU 'ORRIBLE SHOWER OF FUCKING SHITE!...
HANDS OFF COCKS! I WANT YOU ON PARADE IN TWO MINUTES FLAT! DO YOU FUCKING HEAR ME!

GET A FUCKING MOVE ON YOU LAZY-ARSED BUNCH OF FUCKIN' FAIRIES!
TWO FUCKING MINUTES! HAVE YOU GOT THAT!?

HUP! TWO! HUP! TWO! LEFT! RIGHT! LEFT! RIGHT!
COME ON, FUCKIN' STEP TO IT YOU TWINKLE-TOED COCKSUCKERS!

HA' TEN...
...SHUN!

What the fuck!?!...
Jumbo, quick! A petrol tanker has swerved through the barriers of Barnton flyover...
...it's dangling over the edge!...

Nice to see you, private, so glad you could join our little parade. I'm terribly sorry we started without you... if it wasn't convenient you should have said and we could have held it this afternoon...
...but you're here now, and if you wouldn't mind, I'd be very grateful if you'd shoulder your rifle...
...One of your soldiers would be light enough to climb into the cab without tipping it over and pull it into reverse!

MARCH
LEFT TURN
STAND AT EASE
DROP RIFLE
ATTENTION
RIGHT TURN
EYES RIGHT
CLICK!

CLATTER!

YOU CLUMSY LITTLE SHIT HEAD! IF YOU EVER DROP YOUR GUN AGAIN I WILL SHOVE MY HAND DOWN YOUR THROAT, I WILL PULL YOUR BOLLOCKS INTO YOUR MOUTH AND I WILL MAKE YOU CHEW THE FUCKING THINGS...
...DO YOU HEAR ME, PRIVATE!?
Sir! Yes, sir!

NOW EVERY LAST ONE OF YOU SPINELESS PISS BUBBLES DROP AND GIVE ME FIFTY!
NOW!

ONE!...TWO!...THREE!...FOUR!...FIVE!...AND YOU CAN GIVE ME A HUNDRED TO GET SOME OF THAT FAT OFF, YOU FAT FUCK...
...YOU 'ORRIBLE TWO-TON SACK OF SHIT! I DO NOT LIKE FAT FUCKS IN MY PLATOON...
...WHAT DO I NOT LIKE!?!
Jumbo, please... the petrol tanker!
Sir! Fat fucks, sir!

NEXT WEEK: As the tanker slips closer to disaster, Jumbo makes his platoon run up and down a pile of sand in full kit, before ordering them to clean the toilets with a toothbrush.

35

THE BRAGGS are the socialist firebrands who help keep the red flag flying. Working class hero *Billy*'s anti-Tory protest songs have roused picket line rabbles for decades, whilst lifelong Labour stalwart *Melvyn* strives tirelessly to dismantle Britain's outdated class system. They're both famous champions of the Left, but which one is the leftier of the two? We put them through their paces, scrutinising their left wing credentials to find out once and for all...

BILLY or MELVYN
Which is the Leftiest Bragg?

Lowliness of Birth .... ROUND 1 .... Lowliness of Birth

2 | 8

BORN in the grimy backstreets of Barking, Essex, the son of a humble hat maker who manufactured flat caps for workers, Billy might at first glance seem to have this first round sewn up. But it's possible that his father also turned out silk toppers and straw boaters for the braying Hooray Henrys of nearby Eton, perhaps even providing titfers for toffee-nosed public schoolboys such as *Boris Johnson*, *David Cameron* and *Tom Parker-Bowles*.

ALTHOUGH he is now a member of the Hampstead glitterati, Melvyn's parents were as common as muck. Born in a 2-up 2-down hovel in the slums of Carlisle, his father was a mechanic with oil in his fingernails, while his mother toiled for a pittance as a seamstress. The family later took over a backstreet alehouse in Wigton, Cumbria, where Melvyn spent his childhood emptying working class hockle and phlegm out of the spittoons for a farthing a week. A high-scoring round for the low-born *South Bank Show* presenter.

Common-ness of Name........ ROUND 2 ....Common-ness of Name

1 | 9

ALTHOUGH nowadays he prefers to go by the working class monicker of "Billy," he was actually christened *Stephen William Bragg*. With such a hoity-toity triple-barrelled name, he joins the aristocratic likes of *Simon Sebag Montefiore*, *Tara Palmer Tompkinson* and *Norman St. John Stevas*.

WHEN called to speak in the House of Lords, Bragg is formally addressed as *His Grace Baron Bragg of Wigton in the County of Cumbria*. But he was born plain old 'Melvyn,' and at school this was often shortened to the distinctly working class 'Mel' or 'Braggsy,' so once again it's a high-scoring round for the adenoidal *In Our Time* host.

Roughness of Education....... ROUND 3 ....Roughness of Education

2 | 8

THE *Between-the-Wars* singer failed his eleven-plus and never went to university; on the face of it, solid left wing credentials for any would-be militant. However, whilst attending Northbury Junior in Dagenham, his teacher Miss Tindall appointed 8-year-old Billy as class milk monitor - a non-elected position of power and privilege which any self-respecting socialist radical would have turned down flat.

AFTER attending grammar school, Melvyn won a scholarship to Oxford University's Wadham College, where he read Modern History. The dreaming spires of such an elite institution may seem an unlikely setting for a left wing education, but Wadham is widely renowned as the most working class of the Oxford colleges, boasting amongst its alumni two time World Darts Champion *Jocky Wilson*, "my arse" actor *Ricky Tomlinson* and "Gertcha!" musicians *Chas and Dave*.

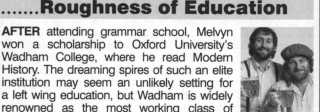

Snubbing the Queen........... ROUND 4 ....Snubbing the Queen

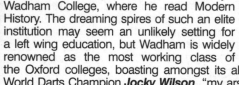

2 | 10

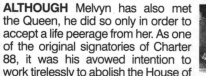

ANY Trotskyist worth his salt is committed to smashing the monarchy. Yet in 1981, fired up with patriotic fervour, Billy had a spell in the army when he signed up for a tour of duty in the Queen's Hussars, pledging an oath of allegiance to the crown and swearing to protect the British Empire with his life. The forelock-tugging troubadour later compounded this hypocritical sycophancy by shaking hands with Her Majesty after appearing at a Royal Variety Performance.

ALTHOUGH Melvyn has also met the Queen, he did so only in order to accept a life peerage from her. As one of the original signatories of Charter 88, it was his avowed intention to work tirelessly to abolish the House of Lords from within. After nearly two decades of Melvyn toiling away on the upper house's red leather benches in his ermine robes and coronet, that undemocratic, archaic bastion of privilege must now be just about ready to tumble into dust.

Anti-Thatcherite Songs........ ROUND 5 ....Anti-Thatcherite Songs

2 | 6

DURING his long career as a Stalinist singer-songwriter, Billy has written countless toe-tapping ditties that attack the late Iron Lady. For example, the song *Thatcherites* - from his 1997 album *Bloke On Bloke* - is an excoriating attack on the eponymous capitalist PM's economic legacy. However, any brownie points he might have been expecting to accrue are swept away by the fact that, when the record's lyrics are searched for on the internet, pop-up adverts for mail order Thai Brides and pornographic DVDs appear all over the screen, showing Billy up in his true colours as just the sort of capitalist misogynist he pretends to rail against.

IN November 2015, Melvyn was the headline act at the Chorleywood Literary Festival. Unfortunately, a cursory internet search failed to reveal what he did while he was on stage. He may, as usual, have read a few passages from his latest arse-numbing potboiler of a novel. But for all anyone knows, Bragg could have broken with convention and performed a series of self-penned protest songs attacking Margaret Thatcher for crushing the unions, privatising the public sector and destroying the country's industrial infrastructure, accompanying himself on a battered acoustic guitar and mouth organ. We have to give him the benefit of the doubt.

How Did They Do?

9   **41**

"BILLY, DON'T be a hero," sang shit group Paper Lace back in the 1970s. And Billy Bragg is certainly no working class hero after getting the trouncing of his life off his bunged-up namesake. With a paltry 9 out of a possible 50, the colours seem to have run for this dyed-in-the-wool red wedger.

GOOD LORD! It's a case of "Full Bragging Rights" to Melvyn, as he "South Banks" 41 "Karl Marx" following some Lenin-tastic lefty footwork across the full five rounds of the competition, proudly claiming his rightful crown as the Leftiest Bragg in all the land.

Next week: *Krankie versus Clitheroe versus Osmond: Who's the Best Little Jimmy?*

Victorian Dad

...AND THUS WE GIVE OUR THANKS FOR THIS THY BOUNTIFUL GIFT FOR WHICH NONE OF US ARE WORTHY, YET, **WRETCHES** THOUGH WE BE, YOU DEEM US DESERVING OF YOUR MUNIFICENCE...

...BY LOADING SO, OUR LOWLY TABLE WITH YOUR GRACIOUS BOUNTY OF WHICH WE, IN OUR SMALLNESS AND INSIGNIFITUDE ARE UNMERITORIOUS...

YAWN! (STIFLE!)

...YET FOR WHICH WE HUMBLY COWER IN OUR SINFUL GRATITUDE...

...AMEN!

AMEN!

AND **WHAT** IS THAT BEVERAGE, BOY? IT IS **TOO CLOUDY** TO BE WATER...

...THE **ONLY DRINK** THE LORD DEEMS FITTETH TO SUP.

IT'S GINGER BEER, DAD!

EGAD!! BEER! THE DEVIL'S BREW... **HERE!** AT MY TABLE!

I HAVE **SPAWNED A SOT!**... A **SOT** AND AN **INEBRIATE!**

OW!

YOU SHALL REJOIN THE PATH OF TEMPERANCE, BOY, BUT FIRST WE MUST PURIFY YOUR BLOOD OF THE MYRIAD FOUL INTOXICANTS THAT COURSE THERETHROUGH

TOMORROW WE SHALL TRAVEL TO **HARROGATE**, THERE TO PARTAKE OF THE EFFERVESCENT AND HEALTH-GIVING WATERS OF THE SPA

NEXT DAY... FOLLOW ME TO THE PUMP ROOM, FAMILY. AND LOOK TO YOUR POCKETS... THE RAILWAY TERMINUS IS A VERITABLE **LODESTONE** FOR THIEVES, CUTPURSES AND THE FILTH OF HUMAN SOCIETY

AHA! HERE WE ARE!

GOOD DAY TO YOU, MADAM... FOUR GLASSES OF YOUR LIFE-AFFIRMING AQUA-VITAE, IF YOU WILL

IT'S FOUR POUND FOR ADULTS, TWO-FIFTY FOR CHILDREN, OR YOU CAN GET AN ALL DAY FAMILY TICKET FOR TEN POUND

WHAT!?! CHARGING FOR WATER!? HOW **DARE YOU**, MADAM?... IT'S A **BLASPHEMY!**

I SHALL PAY NOT A **FARTHING!**

FOR DOES NOT THE LORD CAUSE THE RAIN TO FALLETH FROM THE SKY, AND THE RIVERS TO RUNNETH OVER THE EARTH THAT WE, IN OUR PALTRINESS MAY DRINK FREELY THEREOF?

COME, FAMILY... LET US LEAVE THIS VILE TEMPLE OF MAMMON

AHA! WE SHALL TRY THIS ESTABLISHMENT

FOUR GLASSES OF YOUR LIFE-GIVING WATERS, MY GOOD MAN

TAKE YOUR PICK, SIR

HMM!... I DO OWN THAT I WAS UNAWARE THERE WAS SUCH AN ARRAY OF SPA WATERS...

...LET ME SEE... A GREEN VESPA... ANGEL FACE... CORPSE REVIVER... ROYAL ARRIVAL... SALTY DOG... HARROGATE NIGHTS... THREE WISE MEN...

SUCH INTERESTING NAMES

I SHALL SAMPLE THEM **ALL**, AT WHICH POINT I SHALL ADVISE WHICH IS THE MOST EFFICACIOUS... ...SPA KEEPER... I SHALL BEGIN WITH A GLASS OF **HARROGATE NIGHTS**, IF YOU WOULD BE SO KIND

COMING UP

FEAR NOT... IT SHALL NOT BE LONG BEFORE YOUR BODIES ARE PURGED OF THE DIABOLIC SUBSTANCES WHICH LUCIFER HIMSELF HAS TEMPTED YOU TO IMBIBE

THERE YOU GO, SIR.... ONE HARROGATE NIGHTS

FORMIDABLE

SLURP!

HMM!... VERY INTERESTING. ONE CAN CERTAINLY TASTE THE SULPHOROUS IONS AND RICH MINERAL OXIDES... HMM! MOST PALATABLE... MOST PALATABLE INDEED

NEXT, I SHALL SAMPLE THE BUSH-WACKER, FOLLOWED BY THE SINGAPORE SLING

CERTAINLY, SIR

SHORTLY... WILL HE BE OKAY, MUM?

YES... I'M SURE HE'LL FIND HIS WAY HOME

OY! WHAT'S YOUR GAME?

AAGH! GO **FUCK YOURSELF!** I'M HIC TAKING THE F.. F.. FUCKIN' WATERS, AN' NO PEELER'S GOIN' T' HIC STOP ME!

SO FUCK OFF AN' BLOW Y'WHISTLE, TIT-HEAD!

Drunken bakers

Free Christmas cake?

Is it free?

Yeah.

Fucking ten-bob *twats*.

Ain't enough to cut our throat on price any more, oh no –

– now, *now* the bastards are giving the shit away for nothing!

You, *mate*, have fucked every craftsman baker in the *ARSE* – happy?

That shut the bloody prick up.

I reckon we should try it.

Soon

Maybe, if people get to taste a proper Christmas cake...

...everything will be alright again.

Pass us some brandy.

Is there brandy?

I could go a brandy.

For the cakes.

Haven't we a drop in?

I'd be very surprised.

Any joy?

No.

I suppose we could use some of the Teacher's...

Sod off! There's only two dozen and they're to see us through 'til Boxing Day.

Here, I found this in the black bin.

Fuck knows how come we never drunk it.

GEOFF'S VODKA

I know. The first glass knocked us blind for a day.

Come from that bloke who set up behind the old fish market.

He was on the front of the paper a week later.

Them two boys died...

Ahhhhhh.

Mind, they'd have been lightweights.

Once the cake sops it up and the fruit's oozed a bit...

It'll just be vodka.

Next day

BAKERY

BWAWWK! Me eyes!!

I'm blind!

I really didn't think that that would happen.

Gasp!

The Cat in the Hatton Garden Heist?

Millineried millionaire: Kay in one of his hats, yesterday.

IN FEBRUARY, six men were jailed for their part in last year's daring Hatton Garden robbery, in which an estimated **£200 million** of valuables were stolen from safety deposit boxes in London's diamond district. However, a seventh member of the gang, known only by his nickname of "Basil" is still at large.

Many underworld sources believe that the mysterious fugitive may have escaped with a fortune in diamonds that are still unaccounted for more than a year on from the audacious haul. And with no fresh evidence as to his identity and whereabouts, Scotland Yard now fear that Basil, whoever he may be, may never be arrested and brought to justice.

basil

But now an Oswestry music fan believes he may be able to put a name and face to the grainy CCTV footage of the elusive seventh member of the Hatton Garden gang. "In my opinion, the evidence points to Basil being none other than JK out of Jamiroquai," says Darren Margarine. "I've been to the police, so he'd better look out. The net is closing in on him."

rosemary

The unemployed dad of three's interest was first piqued when he read a magazine feature about the acid jazz pop singer's flamboyant lifestyle. He told us: "In the article, Jay Kay said he lived in an eleven bedroom mansion, owned sixty-eight performance cars and a helicopter, and there was a picture of him stood by a lake that he owned, and it had an island in the middle. A fucking island!"

"Where the fuck's the money for all that come from? His last record came out six years ago and only got to number 76 in the charts."

"The Bay City Rollers had dozens of number ones and they're stacking shelves in Morrisons these days."

parsley

Margarine's suspicions were further aroused after watching an edition of *Crimewatch* which featured a dramatic reconstruction of the 2015 heist. "I noticed that Basil was

Funkmeister Kay fingered for bank holiday diamond blag

`06:10 05/04/2015`

Virtual insanity: The east wing of one of Kay's mansions in the UK and (left) the elusive Hatton Garden 'Basil'

wearing a hat, and I remembered another bit from the article in which Jamiroquai boasted about his large collection of hats," he said.

"I immediately rang the number on the screen and asked to be put through to the incident desk at Scotland Yard. However, when I gave them the name Jay Kay out of Jamiroquai in connection with the incident, they just put the phone down on me. When I called back, they put the phone down on me again."

dill

With detectives unwilling to follow up his leads, Margarine decided to post his incriminating dossier of evidence against Kay up on a website, which has now had nearly 150 views. "I am determined to unmask Basil as Jamiroquai and claim a substantial reward," he told us.

"There's 200 million quid missing and I know who's got it. I will not rest until Jay Kay out of Jamiroquai is behind bars where he belongs."

pashana bedhi

However, last night, following a letter from solicitors acting on behalf of Sony Records, the website had been taken down. In its place was a message signed by Mr Margarine which read: "There is no evidence whatsoever linking the musician Jay Kay, real name Jason Luís Cheetham, with any illegal acts, including, but

not restricted to, safety deposit box theft and the receiving of stolen goods. I unreservedly withdraw any suggestions I have made to the contrary and hereby apologise for any distress I may have caused to Mr Kay, his representatives, assignees and agents."

Bin Juice

Un parfum de Ricky Tomlinson

CAN SOMEONG JUMP ON A TILL, PLEASE?

BASH! SMASH! CRUNCH!

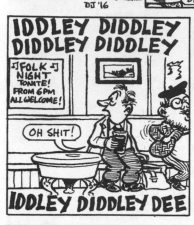

Nick Clegg's BARKERS' EGGS

"Hi Lib Dem leader Nick Clegg here. Oops, sorry, *former* leader. The leader's that other bloke now, isn't it, whatshisname. Anyway, now I'm not a political party leader any more, I've got plenty of time to pursue my hobbies and interests. And one thing I'm particularly interested in is **DOGS' EGGS**. Which is just as well, as I had plenty of the ruddy things pushed through my letterbox when I formed that coalition government. Christ they took some clearing up, I can tell you. Anyway, judging by my mailbag, it looks like *Viz* readers are as **"barking"** mad about these offensive little parcels as I am. So without further **"adoo-doo"**, let's have a look at some of the best canine kak correspondence that's landed on my shitty doormat this week. **"** *Nick x*

WE ALL know that dog shit causes blindness, right? But what's the one thing blind people need? Dogs. Don't get me wrong, I'm not saying that our furry canine friends are expelling sight-decimating turds simply to keep themselves in regular employment. But I am saying it's a happy little 'coincidence,' isn't it? I can't go into further detail on a public forum such as this, but if you want to know more, meet me by the dog shit bins in Regent's Park at 1.30pm this afternoon. Wear a brown carnation in your lapel. We are through the looking glass here, people

Anonymous, London

WHATEVER HAPPENED to bullies making puny children eat dog dirt off lolly sticks? It used to happen all the time in my day, but here in 2016, schoolyard predators seem to be more interested in 'cyber-abusing' their victims online than force-feeding them canine excrement. Come on, bullies, get off your arses and start making kids eat dog dirt off lolly sticks again.

Barnaby Extricate, Salisbury

WHY OH why don't dog-owners simply sellotape a plastic bag around their pet's anus before taking them out for a walk? That way, the dog's turds would drop neatly into the bag, without the owner having to get his or her hands dirty cleaning them up, or worse, simply walking off and leaving the faeces to befoul and soil our green and pleasant pavements. I think any dog-owner who doesn't sellotape a plastic bag around his pet's anus before taking them out for a walk should be jailed for up to two years.

Oliver Reaction, Chipping Norton

I USED to constantly worry about visitors coming round and accidentally treading dog muck into my nice clean carpet. So I bought a new carpet that's the exact same shade of brown as most canine foulage, so now, even if someone DOES tread faeces into it, you'd never be able to tell. I also insert a fresh dog turd into the air conditioning unit every morning so the house already smells strongly of shit

whether it's been trodden into the carpet or not. Now I can rest easy whenever visitors come trampling through the house in their mucky shoes. Although, to be honest, I get fewer visitors these days than I used to.

Ethel Shift-Work, Dundee

I UNDERSTAND there's a film called *Pink Flamingos* where you see a fat transvestite eat a dog dirt. Well, I have to admit, that doesn't really sound like my cup of tea. I would always prefer a nice musical like *Seven Brides for Seven Brothers* or *The King and I* to a film where a fat transvestite eats a dog dirt.

Mrs Audrey Frobisher, Froome

IMAGINE IF some primary school, probably in Brighton or somewhere, run by *Guardian*-reading, loony left, 'elf-n-safety' killjoys, decided to BAN a little kiddy from playing with a plastic dog turd. I mean, imagine that. A ruddy plastic dog turd. What would this country be coming to when a traditional, much-loved British joke shop item is suddenly considered 'improper' or 'politically incorrect' by pen-pushing woolly liberal jobsworths? You couldn't make it up, honestly. Even though, admittedly, I just have.

R Littlejohn, Florida

SEVERAL MONTHS ago, I suffered a bang on the head and completely lost my memory. I had no recollection of who I was and couldn't recall anything from my previous life. Following extensive counselling and cognitive therapy, my past slowly started to return. Unfortunately, my first memory was of a day-trip where our pet dog had diarrhoea all over me in the family car on the way to Alton Towers and I had to spend the whole day wearing my dad's cardigan.

Hampton Fiver, Nottingham

I DON'T know why some people complain about occasionally having to clean up dog shit - I spent three years of my life doing it several times a day. That's because my son is notorious west coast gangsta rapper Snoop Dogg, and I used to change his nappy when he was a baby.

Mrs Ada Dogg, Los Angeles

MOST PEOPLE will think I'm mad for saying this, but I've always found stepping in dog shit to be lucky. You see, believe it or not, I trod in canine faeces the day my five-a-side team won the league, the day I met my wife AND the day my son was born. Of course, I also trod in it the day my five-a-side team got relegated, the day my

wife left me for my brother and the day my doctor told me I had septic piles. In fact, come to think of it, I tread in dog dirt most days, as I am employed to muck out the greyhounds at Walthamstow dog track.

Channing Dragnet, Walthamstow

«Ploptips»

PRANK NEIGHBOURS into thinking their dog has got piles and worms by emptying tins of spaghetti in tomato sauce onto their lawn.

A Krunt, Grantham

HOUSETRAIN YOUR dog by telling it to "sit" on the toilet, saying "Busy busy" and giving it a biscuit when it successfully curls one off. It will soon learn to associate the sound of the flush with a treat.

BG Wodehouse, Bracknell

A DANISH pastry stuck onto the back of a dog turd makes it look a bit like a big brown snail.

Gilbert Piles, Clerkenwell

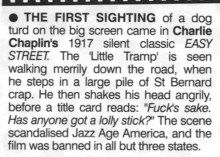

10 Things You Never Knew... About Dog Shit

1 The Ancient Egyptians worshipped dogs as sacred creatures, and as such, their highest form of currency was none other than... the dog turd. Believe it or not, in Cairo circa-3000BC, one barker's egg was equivalent to a £100 note in today's British money. Smaller denominations of currency were represented by items that were similar to dog shit, but not quite as good - such as cat shit or bird shit.

2 The Battle of Bosworth Field in 1485 marked the beginning of more than a century of Tudor reign in England. However, it nearly didn't happen at all... because of dog shit. The notorious battle was originally meant to take place at nearby Osbaston Field, a popular area amongst Plantagenet-time dog walkers. But when the Houses of Lancaster and York arrived there, they found the grass hideously befouled by canine excrement. The battle referee suggested that both armies returned to their castles to get a load of rubber gloves and plastic bags to clear up the messes, but Lancastrian leader Henry Tudor had the bright idea to simply move the battle across the road to dog-free Bosworth Field.

3 The world record for the most dog dirts trodden in within a 24 hour-period is currently held by Herb Geysermeyer of Des Moines, Iowa, USA. Luckless Herb managed to drag his feet through a whopping 309 different turds on his way to and from the local Dunkin' Donuts - which was located just 40 feet from his front door.

4 The smallest ever dog turd was expelled by the world's smallest man's best friend. The miniscule mutt belonged to the planet's shortest human, Calvin Phillips, and it expelled a barker's egg that was barely the size of a cashew nut. Phillips subsequently trod in it and spent the next 25 minutes furiously scraping it out of the sole of his shoe with a lolly stick the size of a pine needle.

5 Despite owning literally dozens of Corgis, Her Majesty the Queen has NEVER stepped in a dog dirt. That's because, when she takes them for their daily walk, she is accompanied by liveried palace flunkie whose job it is to step in them on her behalf.

6 Incredibly, atheist maverick Richard Dawkins does not believe in dog shit. "If you rearrange the letters in 'dog shit' you get 'its god', with an 'h' left over", the blasphemous firebrand told *Autotrader* magazine. "As such, I simply cannot and will not accept its existence."

7 Recently deceased Motörhead rocker Lemmy was well known for his large collection of Nazi memorabilia. And the rarest and most priceless artefact he owned was a dog dirt trodden in by none other than Adolf Hitler himself. The turd - which connected with the Fuhrer's jackboot during the 1923 Munich Beer Hall Putsch - is thought to be worth in the region of £15 million.

8 In years gone by, dog owners weren't required to clean up after their pets. However, since the Dog Fouling Act of 2003, they must pick up any faeces their dogs deposit using a small plastic bag, before tying the top securely and throwing it into somebody's hedge.

9 Just like Christmas for turkeys or Valentine's Day for roses, Halloween is the busiest time of the year for dog shit. Fun-loving trick-or-treaters push more than SIX HUNDRED TONS of canine excrement through letterboxes across the UK every October 31st, and as such, Britain's dogs are fed double portions throughout the month to ensure there's enough faeces to go around.

10 In much the same way that no two snowflakes are ever the same, no two dog turds are ever the same either. "There's always something slightly different about them," said canine foulage specialist Dr Herringbone Cack. "You might see two shits that look identical, but trust me, they're not."

«Ploptips»

DOG WALKERS. In addition to your pooper scooper, carry a flask of liquid nitrogen. If your dog has an attack of diarrhoea, the offending puddle of feculant can be quickly frozen solid and lifted from the pavement using a fish slice before being disposed of in an old pizza box.

Reg Varnish, Oswestry

DOG OWNERS. Avoid having to clean up after your pet while walking it in the park by taking several twelve-inch squares of turf with you and placing them neatly over its turds. Alternatively, if in an urban environment, take a selection of twelve-inch square paving slabs.

Handy Bill, Oldham

CONVINCE FAMILY members that you have trodden in a dog dirt in your bare feet by rubbing chocolate mousse between your toes and dipping your foot in mercaptoethanol.

P Lambton, Worms

CONVINCE NEIGHBOURS you've got a large poodle by painting Cumberland sausages white and leaving piles of them by their gates.

Jim Lewellyn-Bowen, Dartmouth

Miriam's Dog Doo Problem — PHOTO CASEBOOK

Debbie's Dogdirt Dilemma ~ Day 12

Pretty young Debbie Diggory has been going out with boyfriend Tom for 6 months, but lately he's been behaving strangely and she suspects he's trod in a dog dirt.

Prof. Stephen Hawkins's Brief History of TIME TRAVEL

L IKE THE GRAINS OF SAND falling through an hourglass, time is all around us. At the moment, it flows just one way, second by second, hour by hour and day by day from the past towards the future, with us trapped as prisoners of the present. Throughout history, the idea of travelling through time, turning over that hourglass in which we are trapped, has always been the stuff of outlandish fantasy. But now that science fiction dream is set to become a reality. For quantum physics is on the verge of unlocking the secrets of time, and armed with that knowledge we will be able to build machines in which we can travel through time at will, backwards into the distant past and forwards into the far future.

Imagine being able to go back millennia to watch the pyramids being built before zipping forwards countless billions of years to witness the death of the sun. Our lives will be revolutionised once we are freed from the tyranny of living in the present. Let's take a trip into a future where time travel has changed every aspect of our daily lives...

Fast Food

A NYONE who's ever ordered a Filet-O-Fish at their local McDonald's drive-through knows the sinking feeling of being told there's a four minute wait for their food. But once time travel becomes an everyday realit[y] instead of heading off to sit anxiously checking their wing mirrors in the gr[i] order parking bay, fast food customers will be able to stay where they are at the serving window, set the coordinates of their time machine to four minutes in the future and collect their meal straight away.

And it's not only Filet-O-Fish fans who will benefit from time travel. After picking up their Big Mac and fries, burger eaters will be able to go back twenty minutes to when they were warm, before heading two hours into the future, to a time when their apple pie has cooled sufficiently not to take the roof of their fucking mouth off.

Crime and Punishment

A CCORDING to current Home Office figures, the average time between a crime being committed and the perpetrator being brought to justice is currently twelve months; police can easily spend a year making enquiries, sifting through evidence and checking alibis. Time travel will become a valuable tool for the detectives of the future, speeding up the whole process beyond recognition.

As soon as a report of an offence is received at the station, cops will jump into a Police time machine and, with blue lights flashing, speed forward eighteen months to find out who has already been tried, found guilty and is serving time for the crime in question. Armed with this information, they will head back to the present and arrest the culprit the same night.

But it's not all good news for the forces of law and order. Fugitive robbers will be able to simply high-tail it back to the 1960s in a hot-wired getaway time machine. Safely ensconced in the past, their stolen loot will be worth twenty times as much as it was when they stole it, and Scotland Yard won't be looking for them yet as their crime is still fifty years in the future.

Firefighters

A S soon as a 999 call comes in, firefighters race to th[e] scene of a conflagration with lights flashing and siren blaring. But no matter how fast they drive, on average it takes a fire engine eleven minutes to reach a blaze, by which time the inferno can easily be roaring out of control. In contrast, the time tender of the future will be able to set off before the fire has even started, thus arriving at the scene while the flames are still at a more manageable level.

Also, every time they are called out to rescue a cat stuck up a tree, the firemen of the future will be able to leave their ladders back at home. They will simply travel back a couple of hundred years into the past when the tree in question was a young sapling and snap it. That way the future problem of the stuck cat will never arise, the emergency call will never come in and the firemen can stay at the station playing table tennis, eating pasta bake and watching hardcore pornography.

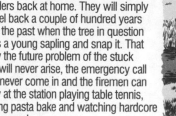

Dry cleaners

HAVING taken a favourite suit to the dry cleaners, there's nothing worse than going back to collect it three days later only to be told that they couldn't get the stain out. But in a future where time travel has become a commonplace reality, such inconveniences of today will be a thing of the past.

Tomorrow's dry cleaning customers will be faced with two options: going back to a time before the garment was stained and being more careful, or travelling forward to the year 2525, by when the technology to actually remove stains will have been developed. The dry cleaners of the future may scoff at the outmoded style of clothes that are 500 years out of fashion, but it is their customer who will have the last laugh as he travels back to the present day with his pristine, now spotless clothes packed in a thin plastic bag and smelling of whatever it is that eventually supersedes carbon tetrachloride.

Gambling

YOU might think that punters of the future would be queuing up to buy time machines. After all, if you're thinking of having a flutter on the 3.30 from Haydock Park, what could be easier than travelling through time to 3.35 and seeing which horse romps home in first place, before popping back to the present and sticking a fiver on it?

But it's not that simple. The bookie will also be able to go forward into the future to see if you're going to win. Then, if it looks like he's going to have to pay out, he may simply refuse to take your bet. Or, alternatively, he might take your bet but then stamp on a butterfly, safe in the knowledge that this will skew the timeline into a dystopian future where your horse comes in second, falls at the first fence or there's a hurricane that causes the meeting to be abandoned.

Adult Entertainment

IT is said that pornographers are always the first people to exploit new technologies and time travel will be no exception. At present, an hour-long blue movie can easily take a whole morning to shoot, because after every "pop-shot" there is significant downtime while the crew sits around waiting for the male star to become ready for action once again. However once time travel is an everyday reality, he will be able to simply jump into a time machine after ejaculating and scoot twenty-five minutes into the future when he will be stonked right up again and raring to go for the next scene. The time it takes to make a video will thus be cut in half, allowing moviemakers to produce twice as many bongo flicks as they presently do.

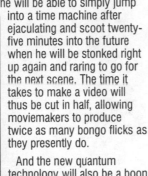

And the new quantum technology will also be a boon for viewers of pornography. Every time a tiresome bit of plot occurs when they are watching a XXX film, they will be able to simply head two minutes into the future to when the hardcore action starts. And if they particularly enjoyed a certain raunchy scene, they will be able to travel back through time five minutes into the past and enjoy it all over again!

Holidays and Leisure

EVERYONE loves going on holiday. A complete change of scenery provides a welcome break from the 9-to-5 drudgery of our everyday lives. But at present, we are limited to just two weeks a year, squeezed in around school holidays and work commitments. But with a caravan hooked up to the back of a time machine, the holiday-making family of the future will be able to make their vacation last as long as they like, setting off and staying away for weeks, months or even years.

And when they've had enough, they can simply set the coordinates for a fortnight after they left. And the kids will even be able to take time off during term time too, heading off after 4 o'clock on a school night for a refreshing two-weeks in the sun and getting home in time for the next day's lessons ... and all without incurring the head teacher's wrath!

What's more, unlike today there's no need for them to fret if their favourite campsite is fully booked, as they can simply travel through time to another week when there are plenty of vacancies. Or, for a change, they could try a different holiday destination, such as a fortnight in medieval Cornwall, seven nights at the Battle of Hastings or a week in Jurassic Mablethorpe.

Next week: THINGS CAN ONLY GET BATTER. Professor Brian Cox looks at the future of Fish & Chips.

Middle Class
ALLOTMENT
HOLDER

October 2019   £149.99

incorporating **Affluent Herb Growing**

BOOTY CALL: Must-have designer wellies that will set you back ten times your annual allotment rent

"I only harvested one okra this year, but it tasted so much better than anything you could buy in Waitrose" ~ One senior advertising executive's tale

CARRY OUT: We look at the best artisan trugs to put your three surviving carrots in

HIRED HELP: We teach you how to say "60p an hour" in 25 Eastern European languages

GLASS ACT: Forget plastic pop bottles cut in half – these hand-blown Murano glass bell jars cost *£250 EACH!*

HENNY PENNY: We reveal this year's *TOP TEN GIRLS' NAMES* for chickens

MASTERCLASS: Le Chameau clogs, bronze trowels, cast iron Victorian cloches and hand-forged hori-hori knives - *we show you how to bring your lettuces in for under £75 A HEAD!*

BUMPER CROPS: "I grew so many spring onions, they lasted me almost *TWO MEALS!"*

PLUS - *Why Kohlrabi is the new Romanesque • The £6000 Husky2000 rotavator reviewed • A* **FREE** *packet of Persimmon seeds that you won't be able to grow, and wouldn't eat if you could*

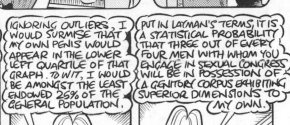

FRUITS AND VEGETABLES... we all eat them every day except in Scotland. They come in all shapes, sizes and colours and can be enjoyed raw or cooked, but how much do we really know about these non-meat things that we buy from the greengrocers? Now, in part 1 of a groundbreaking new educational 25-installment series, we take an in-depth look at the world of fruit and vegetables, starting with the cucurbitaceous fruits. That's right, it's time to make sure you get your 20-a-day as we pick up, squeeze, and then put down again...

20 Things You Never Knew About
MELONS
& other cucurbitaceous fruits

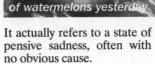

Big and juicy: A large pile of watermelons yesterday.

1 MELONS are members of the *Cucurbitaceae* family, which also includes cucumbers, courgettes, marrows, pumpkins and squashes. Remarkably, many people eat these as vegetables... *but they are wrong!* That's because - believe it or not - cucumbers, courgettes, marrows, pumpkins and squashes are all in fact fruits - specifically botanical organs formed from fertilized flowers.

2 IF YOU happen to hear a builder on some scaffolding shouting *"Phwooar! Look at the melons on that bird,"* do not expect to see a seagull somehow carrying two or more fruits of *Cucumis melo* on its back. The cheeky chap is more likely to be making a good-natured, ribald comment about the size of a passing woman's mammary glands.

3 CELEBRITIES who might find themselves on the receiving end of such a comment, on account of their larger than average mammary glands, include *Scarlett Johansson*, *Kate Upton*, *Kelly Brook* and former Doctor Who assistant *Nicola Bryant*.

4 YOU would probably not hear a builder on some scaffolding shout *"Phwooar! Look at the melons on that bird,"* if you were in Portugal. As a native Portuguese speaker, he would be more likely to shout *"Phwooar! Olhe para os melões no que pássaro,"* instead.

5 AND if you were in Rio de Janeiro, he would shout that as well. That's because not only is Portuguese the national language of Brazil, the women there also have really big tits.

6 IF YOU were in Stockholm, you wouldn't hear a builder shout *"Phwooar! Look at the melons on that bird."* What's more, it's unlikely you'd hear him shout *"Phwooar! Titta på meloner på den fågel,"* either. That's because Swedes have a mature attitude to sexual matters and a healthy respect for women, even though the birds there generally have really big tits.

7 ALTHOUGH cucumbers - also fruits of the *Cucurbitaceae* family - resemble large penises, women builders tend not to shout *"Phwooar! Look at the cucumber on that,"* at well-endowed men who walk past.

Phallic: a cucumber, yesterday

8 IF THEY did, some likely recipients of their good-natured, ribald comments would be former Olympic athlete *Linford Christie*, MP for Ealing North *Stephen Pound* and late pornographic actor *"Big" John Holmes*.

9 THE Bible lists many foods which God forbids believers to eat, including bats, pigs and ossifrages. However, nowhere in the good book are melons mentioned. Devout Christians are therefore left in a quandary ever time they are faced with a slice of melon at a hotel breakfast buffet.

No mention of melons: A man listing what ye shall and shall notteth eat In Bible times.

10 IN FACT the only mention of a cucurbitaceous fruit in the Bible is in Isaiah 1:8, which says: *"And the daughter of Zion is left as a cottage in a vineyard, as a lodge in a garden of cucumbers, as a besieged city."* Theologians believe that this reference to the organised cultivation of cucumbers implies that God is happy for us to eat them, even though they don't taste of much.

11 THE melon is unique in that it is the only fruit whose name is an anagram of another fruit - the lemon.

12 CONTRARY to popular belief, the Queen's second cousin *Lady Helen "Melons" Windsor* didn't get her fruity nickname because of her outsize breasts, but rather as a consequence of her fondness for tucking into canteloupe melons. In between royal engagements, Windsor - daughter of the Duke and Duchess of Kent - regularly polishes off three slices of the handball-sized fruits a day.

13 THE word "melancholy", despite containing the word melon - albeit inaccurately spelled - has nothing to do with melons. It actually refers to a state of pensive sadness, often with no obvious cause.

14 "DESPAIR" is another word for an unhappy state of mind that likewise sounds a bit like it includes an inaccurately spelled fruit.

15 WHEN it comes to fruit and vegetables, the government's chief medical officer recommends that we should all eat "five a day" if we want to stay healthy. However, if you were to eat five melons a day, you'd probably end up with chronic stomach ache and terrible diarrhoea.

16 BOTANICALLY speaking, cucumbers, courgettes, marrows and melons are fruiting structures developed from a single ovary, lacking a stone but containing multiple seeds, and so are classed as berries, along with strawberries and raspberries.

17 DESPITE their name, strawberries and raspberries are not really berries at all. The strawberry is a swollen flower stalk, or receptacle, whilst the raspberry is in fact an aggregation of drupelets. The blackberry is a type of obsolete handheld communication device, and Halle Berry is a type of actress.

18 IN THE film *Carry On Henry*, at Hampton Court Palace, Lady Bettina, (*Barbara Windsor*) tells Henry VIII, (*Sid James*) to close his eyes. She then places two melons in his hands, which the king mistakenly assumes are her breasts. When her trick is revealed, the king gives a dirty laugh and chases a squealing Bettina round the summerhouse. Eventually he catches her and they engage in a clinch, during which the king's leg goes rigid causing his garter to ping off, accompanied by a loud 'boing.' However, Tudor historian *Dr Lucy Worsley* says that there is no documented evidence that such an episode ever actually took place.

19 IN HER book, *The Tudor Kings: Chivalry and Betrayal in the 16th Century Court*, Worsley also casts doubt on another of the film's key plotpoints, where the king's aide, Sir Roger de Lodgerly (*Charles Hawtree*) is stretched on the rack before walking away with his arms and legs about six feet long.

20 IN THE same book, Dr Worsley also says: "If de Lodgerly existed, and there are no records of his birth and death to be found in the archives of Hampton Court, it is most unlikely that, in the event that he was given a drink after being released from a spike-filled Iron Maiden, water would have spouted from dozens of holes all over his torso."

Historically innacurate: Babs and Sid in 1971

ortuguese: Rio de Janeiro, yesterday

Next week: 20 Things You Never Knew About Aubergines and other Solanaceous vegetables

IT HAPPENED ON Christmas Day

1978 A 17-year-old *Jeremy Clarkson* punches his grandmother in the mouth after being offered cold turkey sandwiches for his Christmas Day tea.

2015 Britain is gripped with fear after a series of mysterious sightings of "Killer Clunes." Panic spreads as photographs and videos of creepy figures dressed as the *Doc Martin* actor - complete with baggy suits, comically exaggerated grinning mouths, tiny, expressionless eyes, bright red cheeks, unruly hair and enormous sticky-out ears - are shared on social media by terrified members of the public.

1936 *Edward, Prince of Wales* declares he will travel the whole country in a bid to find a mysterious beauty with whom he danced at a grand Christmas Eve ball, vowing to marry the first person whose foot fits a glass slipper that fell from her foot when she fled down the steps as the palace clock struck midnight. Unfortunately for his highness, the slipper - a size 11G - fits easily onto the foot of the first person who tries it on, a 22-stone divorced American businessman named *Wallace Simpson*, who is visiting London for a meat grinding machinery conference.

1793 The Devon & Cornwall Constabulary launches the UK's very first Christmas drink-driving publicity campaign, as billboard posters and newspaper adverts all over the county urge revellers not to get behind the wheel. Officers posted outside Cornish pubs, however, have to wait eight years before making an arrest, when the inventor *Richard Trevithick* attempts to drive the world's first car - his newly constructed "Puffing Devil" steam carriage - back home from the pub on Christmas Day 1801. However, when they breathalyse Trevithick, he puts a penny under his tongue and the reading comes up clear.

1838 Against the wishes of her husband *Prince Albert*, *Queen Victoria* invites her half brother to spend Christmas Day at Buckingham Palace. Albert becomes increasingly annoyed as *Carl, 3rd Prince of Leiningen* drinks all his claret, talks far too loudly at the dinner table and puts what he wants to listen to on the polyphonic music box. When he finally leaves on Boxing Day, Albert warns that if he comes next year, he will spend Christmas with his brother *Ernst August Karl Johann Leopold Alexander Eduard* in Saxe-Coburg-Saalfeld.

1932 A Christmas day test screening of monster movie *King Kong* gets a poor reaction from the audience at the RKO Movie Theater in New York. Director *Merian C Cooper* is forced to hastily re-shoot the entire second half of the film, adding thrilling scenes of the escaped ape climbing the Empire State Building with a screaming, scantily clad *Fay Wray* gripped in his hand, whilst scrapping over 45 minutes of meticulously animated footage of King Kong sat in a corner drinking 5000 gallons of Ribena.

1888 The hoop and stick becomes the 'must have' toy of the year. In London, supplies run low and there are ugly scenes in toyshops as top hatted gentlemen fight in an undignified manner to secure remaining stock. A black market in the toy is quickly established with urchins being employed to steal hoops and sticks from shops and houses, and some change hands for as much as 7 shillings.

1942 The New York Paramount Theatre hosts the glitzy premiere of *Bing Crosby* and *Fred Astaire*'s latest movie - *Holiday Inn*, a Christmas musical extravaganza set in a budget hotel overlooking a Matalan. *Irving Berlin* has written twelve new songs for the movie, including *My Door Card Don't Work*, *I Can't Get the Fucking Window to Open*, *This Reception Sure Does Smell of Bleach*, *Stealin' All the Little Shampoos*, *I'd Like to Query Something on my Bill*, *Just Press Nine (for an Outside Line)*, *I Think the Guy in the Next Room Just Punched His Honey* and *I'm Dreaming of Some Hot Toast*.

1840 *Prince Albert* introduces to Britain the German tradition of bringing a tree into the house at Christmas. The 6 foot tall Nordman fir is decorated with lights, glass baubles and small sweets. On Twelfth Night, he drags it out and throws into the back lane behind Buckingham Palace, but drags it down a bit so it's not outside his gate. The tradition continues to this day.

0 BC An angel of the Lord appears before a simple shepherd to inform him that it is the very first Christmas Day. The shepherd, *Simon who is called Peter*, immediately runs into a betting shop in Bethlehem and places a bet on it snowing. Unfortunately, the following day, the Nazareth Meteorological Office confirms that not a single flake landed on the roof of Bethlehem Town Hall in the 24 hour period, and Simon who is called Peter loses his 25 Denarii stake.

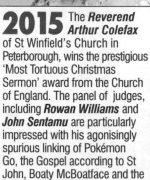

2015 The *Reverend Arthur Colefax* of St Winfield's Church in Peterborough, wins the prestigious 'Most Tortuous Christmas Sermon' award from the Church of England. The panel of judges, including *Rowan Williams* and *John Sentamu* are particularly impressed with his agonisingly spurious linking of Pokémon Go, the Gospel according to St John, Boaty McBoatface and the Trololololol man.

1931 American artist *Haddon Sundblom* is commissioned to provide an illustration of Santa Claus for a Coca-Cola advertisement. The iconic jolly figure he paints, with his bright red suit, thick white beard and ruddy cheeks, is an immediate hit with the public, and sets the pattern for practically all future depictions of Father Christmas. In contrast, rival drinks company Pepsi's Santa is depicted by German expressionist *Otto Dix* as a screaming, scarred, toothless maniac brandishing a bloody hammer. It proves less popular with the public and is dropped from the firm's adverts after a couple of years.

1066 *William I of England* makes the very first Christmas speech to the nation. In it, he says that losing the Battle of Hastings and being conquered by a foreign power must have made it an 'Annus Horribilis' for his subjects. But he goes on to say that he is looking forward to ruling them all in the coming year with a fist of iron, before wishing them all a Merry Christmas and a subservient and plague-free new year.

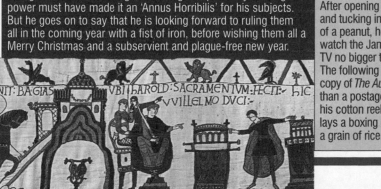

1978 The world's smallest man, *Calvin Philips* celebrates the smallest Christmas on record. After opening tiny little presents and tucking into a turkey the size of a peanut, he settles down to watch the James Bond film on a TV no bigger than a matchbox. The following day, armed with a copy of *The Autotrader* no bigger than a postage stamp, he sits on his cotton reel-sized toilet and lays a boxing day log the size of a grain of rice.

Charlie and the Sportswear Factory

What have you got there, Charlie?

It's a pair of Mickey Wonga trainers, grandad! They were only £1.99.

£1.99? Eeh, how do they do it for the price?

They get them made in the Far East, grandad. The workers are paid a pittance and there's no health and safety.

Aren't they smart? A proper pair of Bobby Dazzlers!

They certainly are, but what's this in the bottom of the box?

Wow! It's a golden ticket! Grandad, we've won a trip round Mickey Wonga's magical sports clothing warehouse!

Well I never! Nobody's ever seen what goes on inside there - not even a Parliamentary Select Committee!

Next morning ...

Gosh grandad! This is going to be the best day ever!

Look, Charlie. Someone's coming.

MICKEY WONGA SPORTS.COM

You the two with the golden ticket?

Yes sir! We're so excited.

Up against the van and spread 'em.

MERCILESS 24 HOUR SECURITY SERVICES

Isn't this magical, Charlie? You'll be the envy of all your schoolchums when you tell them of your adventure.

Once inside the premises, you will not leave the designated route, you will not touch anything, you will not speak to anyone. Do you understand?

Yes, Wow!

They're clean.

Two inward at loading bay D-Delta, repeat D-Delta. Over.

Roger that. Mr Wonga's here to meet them. Over.

Look, grandpa! It's Mickey Wonga!

Goodness me, Charlie! It's him! It's really him!

My honoured guests, winners of the golden ticket! It is time for you to enter my wonderful, magical, stupendous, splendiferous sports clothing warehouse!

♪ Follow me, and we'll be, in a world of worker exploitation... ♪♪

FOOTBALL SHIRTS XXXXL - XXXXXL

♪ Football tops, for my shops, and their price defies all explanation... ♪

See my staff, they never laugh, from clocking on, to fucking off at home time...

CLOCK OFF BEFORE USING THE TOILET. YOU ARE PAID TO WORK, NOT PISS

TOILETS

THESE TOILETS MONITORED BY CCTV TO PREVENT THEFT

An employee, who wants tea, or a wee, can do it in their own time...

Excuse me, Mr Wonga. What's behind this door?

Ah, that's the most secret, magical part of my whole wonderful warehouse, Charlie.

It's the room where, at the end of every shift, my workers are strip-searched before being allowed off the premises.

Wow! Why do you search them?

Well, you see Charlie, these people are thieving scum. They want to steal all my extraordinary, stupendous, fantabulous things from me!

Gosh!

And what are you doing, young fellow me lad? My, that looks fun!

A pair of replica Man United socks has gone missing. If I can't find them, Mr Wonga will take it out of my wages.

Stop shirking! I don't pay you less than the minimum wage to talk! You're fired! Guards!

Shirker! Worker! Doob-a-dee-doo! He's got the push for talking to you!

Shirker! Worker! Dibb-a-tee-dee! It's one strike and out at this factoree!

And get that uniform off the bastard before you throw him out! It's company property!

Go on, fuck off!

Come along! Let me show you where the container-loads of cheap trainers from the Far East are unpacked!

Cor! Can we really see it, Mr Wonga?

Of course you can, Charlie. All things are possible in my wonderful, magnificent, profititious sports warehouse!

Suddenly ...

AROOGA! AROOGA!

What is it?! What's happened?!

It's one of the packers in the dispatch department, Mr Wonga! He's had a heart attack!

Oh no! Has he stopped working?

Yes, Mr Wonga. He's just lying on the floor.

The idle bastard! Get the cattle prods!

Wow! What a magical day this is turning out to be!

53

Next week: James and the Giant Sweatshop

letterbocks

EMAIL: LETTERS@VIZ.CO.UK

GENE Roddenberry is credited as being one of the foremost scientific visionaries of his generation. Whilst *Star Trek* was a groundbreaking series and ideas such as phasers, hyperspace travel and voice-activated computers were way ahead of their time, why was the captain called Jim, the doctor, Len and the nurse Christine? They're hardly space-aged names. Where was Kanye, Brooklin and Shaniqua? Come on Gene, this has made the whole thing rather unbelievable for me.

Donna Kebab, Lands End

FOR all his big talk, how come Professor Brian Cox didn't discover Gravitational Waves? Bit less fannying around on telly and being in pop groups and he might have done. The same goes for that "Dr" Brian May. Tchoh!

Galileo Figaro, Canterbury

GOING to hell sounds bad enough, but evidently going to hell in a handcart is much worse. Logically this means going to heaven in a handcart must be much better than just flying up there.

S Meatfart, Australia

THEY say good things come to those who wait. Well I'm 57 and fuck all good has happened to me so far. Do any readers know what the average waiting time is?

Mark Longden, Manchester

THOSE dogs whose tails stick up vertically showing off their disgusting arseholes all the time, what's that all about? I think the people in charge of breeding or evolution or whatever the fuck should take a long, hard look at themselves.

John The Cheeks, email

I DON'T know why Doctor Jekyll spent all that time in a lab concocting a drink that would turn him into a right nasty bastard who can't remember a fucking thing the following morning. A couple of bottles of White Lightning would have cost him about a fiver and would have had exactly the same result.

Torbjorn O'Malley, Crewe

I'VE listened to Donald Trump quite a lot recently, airing his political views on a wide-ranging list of topics in his bid for the White House. After some consideration, I've concluded that he is a Grade-A twat and should be thrown into a bunch of stinging nettles in his underpants at the earliest opportunity. Come on, USA, throw him in the stingies!

Harriet Kempton-Park, Cheltenham

IN my change, I recently received an Olympic 2012 commemorative 50p coin depicting the women's beach volleyball event. I immediately wondered if there was enough detail on the coin to fuel a successful act of shame. Have your other readers ever considered a more base level of scud material to warrant consideration of 'gloy chucking'?

C Cuntington OBE, email

WHY is the term 'like a broken record' used to describe something that's boring and tedious? I just saw someone break the record for eating the most hard boiled eggs whilst riding a unicycle, and it was one of the most amazing things I've ever seen.

Gustav Fox, Toddington

THEY just said on *Crimewatch* that the suspect referred to only as 'Basil' in the recent multi-million pound Hatton Garden jewellery heist might not actually be called Basil. Is there nothing these people won't stoop to?

Seb Kramer, Nantwich

WHOEVER it was that first said 'Breast is Best' is absolutely spot on. I love a good set of wangers.

Darren Symonds, Watford

MY Gran always used to say "If you need a poo, go use the loo." It always served me well, except for the time I shat my pants in Carlisle. But she fell off a bus and died in 1982, so I had the last laugh.

Sara Titcrease, Hull

DOES anyone know where I can get one of those *Hollyoaks* phones that show text messages floating in mid-air? Only I'm pretty sure the missus is fucking about with that nightclub bouncer again.

Hapag Lloyd, Runcorn

IS it just me or have sleeves got longer recently? Not all sleeves but most of them?

Glen Cooper, Bristol

WHY is it when bands like One Direction finish a song they hug each other in celebration? Me and my mate Dave work in Lidl and we are never seen high-fiving after showing an old woman where the haemorrhoid cream is.

Joe B, Bradford

WHY is it that we are only allowed to have 26 letters in the alphabet, yet numbers can run on to infinity? As usual, its one rule for the Phoenicians of 1050BC and another for ancient Indian mathematicians.

T O'Neil, Glasgow

ABCDEFG HIJKLMN OPQRSTU VWXYZ

IF you're going to wear your wife's knickers when she's not around, it's best to check for skidmarks or follow through. The ear ache I'm getting at the minute is proper getting on my tits.

Keith Queef, Llanllyfni

NOBODY plays baseball in Britain, so why are so many assaults committed with baseball bats? I live in England and if I am to be beaten into bloody pulp, I expect my assailant to use a cricket bat, or if in Scotland, a golf club. Why must we pander to the relentless tide of Americanism with which our nation is awash?

Morris Violence, Truro

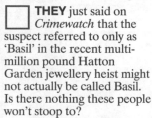

I KNOW it was an outrage that Cecil the lion was shot or whatever, but my late grandfather was a big-game hunter, and I had always admired him. That is until I checked out one of his lion head trophies recently. It was only on closer inspection that I discovered that both eyes were actually made of glass. Shooting an innocent lion is bad enough, but shooting a blind one is beyond the pale if you ask me.

Walter Gordeno Jr, London

I LOVE the new McDonalds adverts in which they show where their eggs and fries come from. I can't wait for the one where they show a cow getting stunned and minced up.

Norris Norwood, Colchester

WIE wäre es ein Bild von diesem Kerl , dass Vogel Arsch küssen?

W Reid, Dortmund

Kein Problem, Herr Reid. Hier ist es.

drug-induced psychotic episode by following them round while playing random tunes on an Alto Saxophone.

T O'Neil, Glasgow

SURE when the school days are? Simply visit the Centre Parcs website and see when prices are three times higher than the rest of the year.

Chris Sleight, Coulsdon

CONVINCE your neighbours that you're an English test match batsman by simply walking out on to your lawn and prodding it with a cricket bat for a few minutes, then

---

ACCORDING to the Bible, bats are birds, yet owls fly around at night like bats. As usual it's one law for Hebrew mythology and another for animals of the order *Strigiformes*. And what does the Archbishop of Canterbury have to say about it? Fuck all as always.

A O'Tool, Isles of Scilly

MAYBE high-risk prisoners would behave better if they had free mini-bars in their cells.

Hapag Lloyd, Runcorn

HAVE you heard about this new government initiative to give new house buyers three grand towards their new home? What I want to know is, where the fuck am I going to get the rest from? I haven't even got a job. The government needs to think things through a little more before making these outrageous statements.

Daniel, Townhill Park

WHY are porn actresses constantly overlooked for the Oscars? If the people who decided on the awards has bothered to watch *One Girl Takes it in Three Holes* they would have seen the leading lady had plenty of genuine acting talent. She made me believe she was a proper maid who happened to stumble across three men who had to fill her with fluid to save her life.

Trevor Trevorson, Trevortown

I WAS quite arsed to have to take my old mum to church last Sunday, but I tell you what, they passed around this plate half way through and it was full of money. I only

simply walking back inside five minutes later.

Iain Devenney, Oxford

MAKE safari park visits more exciting by shooting harmless paintball guns at elephants and rhinos.

Hapag Lloyd, Runcorn

ENVIRONMENTALISTS. Save water by pissing in your cistern. After a shite, flush it away with your accumulated piss.

Alfie Cockburn, Glasgow

---

took £10 as I didn't want to be cheeky on my first time there, but how nice is that?

Mal Alcock, email

IF everyone loved Terry Wogan so much, how come they didn't put his body on a massive wooden Viking ship and set fire to it as it sailed out to sea? The hypocrisy of it all is sickening.

Fat Dan, Piëländ

I'VE watched Major Tim Peake's space adventures with limited interest, and have done some pretty basic arithmetic. The ISS is 250miles above the Earth, and Tim and his mates took off at 11am-ish and it took 7 hrs to get there. Fuck me. That's a little over 35mph. I had a FS1E that would have got there quicker.

Ted Slow-Cooker, Evesham

BACK in the 80s, Bonnie Tyler was "Holding out for a hero," but Tina Turner quite definitely told us "We don't need another hero." I hope these two got together and sorted their differences out.

Amused, Cardiff

I RECENTLY joined a dating website and was astounded by the amount of women looking for 'A Knight in Shining Armour.' Given that the last known knights to wear 'shining armour' were back in the Franco-Prussian war of 1870, I think it highly unlikely that their expectations will be met. Were they to put 'looking for a bald, chinless wanker in a waxed jacket' they would have far more chance of success.

Phyllis Rinseblue, Ringwood

I PAID a hundred fucking quid to take my mum to see *War Horse* on stage in London and you can see how it's fucking done. What a complete rip-off. At least that Derren Blaine uses mirrors and stuff so you can't see the strings. My kid's school play was more professional. Proper legged over. No wonder these theatre bosses are all millionaires.

Spenner, Warrington

I'VE noticed that whenever hooded gunmen raid a bank, they're always shouting things like "Fill the fucking bags now," and "Nobody move - get down." However, in my experience, bank staff can be quite surly and unhelpful if you piss them off even slightly. A please and a thank you costs nothing after all.

M. Hoverboard, Tooting

I SEE on TV that Oxfam is asking for 3 pounds which will provide clean water for a family in Africa for 30 days. I wonder if they could supply my water too, because Thames Water charge me close to £385 a year for the same fucking thing.

A Fudd, Kingston upon Thames

MY wife recently told me that now I am a parent I should make sacrifices. But then she hit the roof when she came home and saw the giant pentagram on the kitchen table and what I had done to the cat. Mixed messages.

Hapag Lloyd, Runcorn

STAINLESS steel? What a load of rubbish. My kitchen sink's absolutely filthy.

Jim Vegas, Sweden

ROBSON'S CHOICE

Geordie actor sets sights on Queen ~ Fear

BUCKINGHAM PALACE insiders have voiced concern that Geordie actor **ROBSON GREEN** may be attempting to woo the Queen, and that as a result, her famously strong seven-decade marriage to the Duke of Edinburgh may be heading for the rocks. Green, 51, who shot to fame after starring in ITV drama *Soldier Soldier*, is said to have turned on the charm after being introduced to her majesty at a recent garden party.

Unchained majesty: Robson makes a right royal impression.

"The pair hit it off immediately," commented Ingrid Ffartsucker, editor of royalwatchers' bible *Majesty*. "The Queen seemed very taken with Robson. The body language was obvious for all to see. They chatted for several minutes and she even gave him her phone number, scribbled on a beermat."

In the following days, the actor is understood to have rung the Queen on several occasions, even sending her a series of flirty Snapchat messages . What's more, according to sources close to the Palace, the 90-year-old monarch has been very flattered by the attention. "She has started talking about Robson Green all the time," a royal household insider told us. "It's Robson Green this and Robson Green that all the time. She can't see that it's making Prince Philip jealous."

duke

The Duke is said to be annoyed that his wife has begun insisting on tuning in to Green's Channel 5 show *Extreme Fishing* whenever it is on. "When it finishes, she

EXCLUSIVE!

immediately turns over to Channel 5 ı 1 to watch it all over again," the source added. "Not to mention all the repeats on Quest. Philip can't stand it, and it's starting to put strains on the marriage."

earl

Matters are understood to have come to a head last week when the Queen bailed out of an official engagement at the Chinese Embassy complaining of a "stomach upset", leaving the Duke of Edinburgh to attend the function on his own. The source told us: "When he got back to the Palace, instead of finding his wife poorly in bed, he found her sat binge-watching a DVD boxset of Green's forensic psychology drama *Wire in the Blood*."

"To say Philip hit the roof would be an understatement," said the insider. "There was an almighty row during which the Duke accused her majesty of fancying Robson Green, calling him a "shortarse little working class pipsqueak", to which the Queen screamed that he was twice the man he would ever be."

baron

The next day, the royal couple were seen attending the Trooping of the Colour. They smiled for tourist cameras, but onlookers said that relations were clearly strained.

Meanwhile Green's agent, Andrea Aguecheek, refused to comment. "I can neither confirm or deny that Robson and Her Majesty are in an extra-marital relationship," she told reporters gathered outside the randy star's £1million Northumberland mansion. "Their private lives are nobody else's business," she added.

Queen and Prince Philip: Could marriage be under threat?

70 Year Itch

THE QUEEN married Prince Philip in 1947. Their famously strong marriage has endured through seven turbulent decades. But now, with her majesty falling for Robson Green's glib garden party patter, cracks are beginning to show in their seven-decade relationship. We asked constitutional expert *Dr David Starkey*: What would be the consequences of a reigning monarch throwing her marriage away to shack up with a randy Geordie jobbing actor?

❝The monarchy is an extraordinary resilient institution. The case of Henry VIII shows that the sovereign state can easily survive the breakup of a ruler's marriage. Divorcing two Queens and beheading two more proved no barrier to Henry becoming one of the longest-serving Kings in British history. But never before has a ruling Queen been the one to break up a royal marriage.

So as we face the very real possibility of Elizabeth II upping sticks and running off with Robson Green out of *Soldier Soldier*, we are entering uncharted constitutional waters. The only thing that is certain is that Robson would not become King. How he would be addressed is less certain; at the very least he would find himself elevated to the peerage, perhaps becoming Lord Robson, Baron Green or even the Duke of Northumberland.

Like his predecessor Prince Philip and Queen Victoria's husband Prince Albert, his formal role would be one of Queen's Consort, accompanying the monarch on formal and ceremonial occasions. And it is while acting in this capacity that a conflict of interest could easily arise. Were Robson and Jerome to be invited to sing their hit *Unchained Melody* at a Royal Variety Performance, there would be a problem. Robson would be simultaneously required to stand alongside his partner on the stage of the London Paladium, whilst royal etiquette demanded that as consort he should not leave the side of the Queen in the Royal Box. The song would have to be performed twice, and it's bad enough having to listen to it once.

Even worse, after the show when the cast are lined up backstage to be presented to the Royal party, Green would be forced to shake hands and make fatuous smalltalk with himself whilst simultaneously sneering and doing a cringing smile, and this could well lead to a constitutional crisis from which the monarchy could take years to recover."❞

Upturn for Essex Town

Chelmsford's status upgraded from 'fucking crap' to 'crap'

THE ESSEX town of Chelmsford was given a boost yesterday when it was announced that its status was to be upgraded to 'crap' from 'fucking crap.' And the news was greeted with delight by members of the local council.

"This is terrific news," Alderman Simon Brakeshaft told the *Chelmsford Clarinet and Advertiser*. "Being fucking crap has long been a handicap to Chelmsford when trying to attract new businesses and tourism to the area."

"Now that we're officially crap, we're looking forward to a boost in visitors, particularly those who come here with staggeringly low expectations," he added.

The upgrade was achieved following last month's announcement that the town was to see the opening of a Wagamamas. This, coupled with a recently built craft ale pub, was enough to allow Chelmsford to shake off its 'fucking crap' label and step firmly into the 'crap' band.

Residents were predictably thrilled. "No longer fucking crap? Really?" said a man walking his dog near the town centre's High Chelmer Shopping Mall. "This will be a real boost for the town."

"I'm stunned by the news, to be honest," said a Chelmsford woman outside the Riverside Ice and Leisure Centre. "I've always wanted to live in a town that's just crap."

"This must be what it feels like to live in Reading," she added.

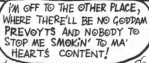

58

"I gave myself the bum's rush" ~Gallagher

FORMER Beady Eye members Liam Gallagher, Andy Bell, Gem Archer and Ken have finally revealed the sensational truth behind the band's decision to split up... *vocalist LIAM was sacked by himself!*

Gallagher and bile: Beady Eye frontman Liam had angry spat with himself during recording sessions.

Beady Eye reveal truth behind split

Gallagher, 43, said: "We were in the studio listening to a playback of some tracks from our new album when I realised the vocals simply weren't up to standard. I decided it was time for the singer to do one."

mixing

According to guitarist Gem Archer, Liam burst into the mixing room and told himself he was out. He told us: "Liam wasn't going to take the news lying down. As far as he was concerned, Beady Eye was his band and it was right out of order to treat himself like that."

Hollywood

Liam said: "There was no fucking way I was leaving, and to be told I was being sacked in front of all the other guys merely made me even madder." Tempers flared and an argument broke out, with Gallagher reportedly attempting to throw a punch at himself.

"It was ugly," said bassist Andy Bell. "There was an almighty commotion as Liam tried to remove himself by force from the studio." According to Bell, after five minutes of scuffling Gallagher eventually manhandled himself out of the fire escape and onto the street.

The ex-Oasis frontman told us: "I was gutted. I've given everything to this band, you know what I mean. To be thrown out on my arse in the middle of a recording session was right out of fucking order."

Beady Eye fans, if any, will be pleased to know that the band may have already lined up a replacement singer to replace Gallagher. Archer explained he had received a phone call just minutes after the altercation.

Camilla Parker

"It was ex-Oasis singer Liam Gallagher," he told us. "He said he had heard we were short of a singer and that he was mad for it. He'd got the looks, the voice and the attitude, so we offered him the gig there and then."

This follows news last week that Liam's brother had received a written warning from himself after turning up late for several Noel Gallagher's High Flying Birds rehearsals.

All sex acts will be electronic by end of decade, says boffin ROBOT PHWOOARS!

AS WE APPROACH 2020 - the year of the future - our lives are becoming ever more dominated by computers. Whether we're using contactless payment to buy a cup of coffee, checking our bank balance via a smartphone 'app' or threatening to hunt down and skin someone who's made a mild error of judgement on Twitter, we're now dependent on modern technology in all aspects of our lives 24-7.

Tartificial intelligence: Lifelike computerised lovebots similar to the one played by Kristanna Loken in the movie Terminator 3: Rise of the Machines (right) are coming to Britain's bedrooms, says Cheshire-based inventor Gladstone Bagg (below).

And nowhere is this more true than in the bedroom, because experts believe that traditional SEX between two living, breathing human beings will soon be a thing of the past, consigned to the dustbin of history along with Betamax video recorders, the Sinclair C5 scooter and Stonehenges. Boffins around the world are already hard at work developing the first generation of computerised android "lovebots," artificial humanoids programmed with just one thing in mind - to provide us with the ultimate erotic experience.

And, according to a Cheshire scientist who is at the forefront of the race to perfect the new breed of synthetic robo-babes, men of the future have a treat in store.

better

"I've had my fair share of traditional fanny in my time, and the latest prototype in my laboratory is ten times better than the real thing, I can tell you," Professor Gladstone Bagg, lead researcher at the Crewe Year 3000 SexBot Project, told us. "Once you've had a shot on the electronic version, you'll never go back to a flesh and blood woman, and that's a promise."

"In fact, I bet real birds are shitting themselves," Professor Bagg continued. "Because my lovebots are going to put them out of a job. They are programmed to never say no, never have a headache and never go to the police if you put your hand up their skirt on the number three bus to Stoke."

"Not only that, they're really dirty," he told us. "Androids aren't prudes like real women, where they won't let you try certain things that you've seen on the internet."

"Oh no, my bots are right up for it. In fact, they're insatiable. On many occasions I've had to pull the plug out because they've been going at it too hard for me to keep up," he added.

thing

Professor Bagg's interest in the science of robo-dildonics arose following a series of failed relationships in the seventies, eighties and nineties. He told us: "It eventually dawned on me that every time a wife or bird left me, it was because of problems we'd had in the bedroom. There was always a mismatch between what I wanted and what she would let me do, and that led to friction, conflict and then her fucking off back to her mum in Thailand or Russia or wherever I'd got her from."

away

"I realised that if I wanted to meet a soulmate who was 100% compatible with my needs and desires, I was going to have to build her myself," he said.

Professor Bagg used skills gained working on the production line at a Nantwich vacuum cleaner factory to begin developing his first sexbot prototype in his spare time. He told us: "The mark one version took me a couple of weeks to construct. It was a pretty crude affair, consisting of a small cylinder hoover housed in a dressmaker's dummy I found in a skip."

"It worked, but it certainly had its limitations. It was very loud, and the fuse kept blowing every time stuff went in the motor."

me

But like any good scientist, Bagg refined and improved his original design in an attempt to iron out the bugs.

"For version 2.0, I added the windscreen wiper mechanism of a Hillman Imp, two doorbells and one of those novelty hand buzzers from a joke shop. When I plugged it in and gave it one, the difference was immediately obvious. This was the future of sexual intercourse and I had just fired the opening salvo in the battle of the sexes."

THE modern lovebots being developed by scientists are now so realistic that they are practically indistinguishable from flesh and blood women. In fact, believe it or not, you may even be married to one without realising it! Take our 5-minute test to discover...

...is YOUR missus a SEX ROBOT?

Over the following decade, Bagg has worked round the clock, tirelessly fine-tuning his invention in the modest 6'x8' larch lap laboratory at the end of his garden. And only now, after exhaustive testing, is his Year 3000 SexBot ready to be launched onto the market.

love

"My Mark 15 SexBot is the most perfect artificial woman ever created," he told us. "She is always ready, always willing and always up for it, even round the back, in the cab or in her hair. She has been custom designed from the ground up to please her man." But tragically, a lack of funding may yet see Bagg's dream of a cyber-sex revolution fall at the final hurdle.

"Cutting edge scientific research and development is notoriously expensive," he told us. "By my own estimate I must have sunk nearly £00 of my own money into this project. But I can't begin full scale production and turn out 1500 of these fuckers an hour from my back garden. It's just not practical."

"I need a purpose-built factory, and for that I need £10 million. Once we're up and running, every man in Britain is going to want one of these by the end of his charlie. That's fifteen million sales in the first year, guaranteed."

world

Bagg applied to go on *Dragons' Den* in a bid to secure funding capital. He told us: "I knew that as soon as Theo Paphitis, Peter Jones or Duncan Bannatyne had had a shot on my final prototype they'd be spunking money at me. It's that good." But sadly, the professor never heard back from the show's production office.

"I dare say that her with the face like a slapped arse or her off the Addams Family with the shoulder pads got scared and put the kybosh on it, the frigid cows," he told us.

1. IT is your wedding anniversary and you fancy a spot of oral sex like in the good old days before you were married. You broach the subject with your wife in bed. How does she react?

a. She says: "Yes master" in an electronic monotone before immediately diving under the duvet to give you the most mind-blowing nosh you have ever had until you are forced to beg her to stop.

b. She curls up her nose and tells you she's never heard of anything so ridiculous at your age, before buttoning up her 2" thick quilted nightgown, turning over, farting and going to sleep.

2. IT is your wife's birthday, so you summon up all your courage and go into Ann Summers to buy her a sexy basque and a pair of crotchless leather-look knickers. What does she do after opening her present?

a. She immediately strips off and puts them on before having sex with you there and then for hours until you both lie exhausted and spent across the kitchen table.

b. She asks if you've kept the receipt before taking them back to the shop for a refund, which she then spends at Matalan on a stout pair of velcro-fastening slippers.

3. YOU are out for a walk in the country with your wife. You realise that there is nobody around for miles, and decide to suggest a spot of al fresco nookie. What happens next?

a. She doesn't say a word, but drags you into a haystack, tears off your clothes and starts making wild, passionate love to you until smoke starts to come out of her ears and her nipples light up like LEDs.

b. She laughs hollowly and informs you that if you think she's going to lie down on that ruddy wet grass you've got another think coming.

4. WHEN going to the fridge, you spill some jam on the kitchen floor. Inspired by the movie *9½ Weeks*, you suggest to your wife that you'd like to smear jam on her naked body and then lick it off. What is her response?

a. She grins lasciviously before emptying the rest of the jar onto her breasts and between her thighs, encouraging you to get on with it.

b. She looks at you with an expression like there's a dog turd under her nose, before handing you the dustpan and brush and telling you to get on with it.

5. AFTER being excited by some saucy amateur snaps you see in a magazine, you sneak into the bathroom while your wife is having a shower and suggest an X-rated photoshoot to send into the *Readers' Wives* section. What happens next?

a. She readily agrees and starts striking a series of imaginative, gymnastic and explicit poses, using shampoo bottles, loofahs and aerosol cans as hardcore erotic props while you snap away.

b. Before you manage to get all the words out, she slaps you round the face and you drop the camera down the toilet. Then she bundles you out of the room and you have to sleep on the couch for a fortnight.

HOW DID YOU DO?...

Mainly As: *Oh dear. Without you realising it, it appears that you are married to an auton - a flawless, pert-breasted robot whose only purpose in life is to satisfy you sexually. Any love or warmth that you feel in the brief pauses between bouts of frenzied, poly-orgasmic intercourse is entirely illusory, merely a binary series of ones and zeros hard-wired by boffins into your mechanical wife's emotionless computer brain.*

Mainly Bs: *Congratulations. Your wife is a 100% bona fide woman. Rest assured her feelings for you are not just a computer program running on her hard drive, all the frosty glances, tuts, folded arms and bollockings she gives you are real and straight from her real, live human heart.*

No *SEX ROBOTS*, Please, We're British Landladies!

Guest house owners vote for Bot ban in UK B&Bs

THE DIRTY WEEKEND has always been a Great British tradition, celebrated in bawdy music hall songs, saucy seaside postcards and *Carry On* films alike. Guesthouse proprietors have always turned a blind eye to unmarried couples booking into their establishments for two stolen nights of illicit slap and tickle.

But new developments in sex robotics have finally proved to be the final straw for the members of the British Landladies Association. And yesterday, at their annual conference, they put their slippered feet down and passed a motion banning ALL space age love androids from Britain's B&Bs.

"Like all seaside landladies, I consider myself very broad-minded," said Mavis Narrowmind, owner of the Excelsior Guesthouse in Sutton-on-Sea, Lincolnshire, addressing the delegates. "But I draw the line at sex robots."

"It's bad enough when a man books in with a real woman and they leave all their messes behind on the sheets, without adding engine oil

ROBOSEXCLUSIVE!

and hydraulic fluids to the mix," she continued. And other speakers echoed Mrs Narrowmind's sentiments.

"I'm no prude, but there'll be none of that sort of thing going on under my roof," said Mrs Edna Prude of Cromer, to loud applause from other landladies.

"The Mulberry Tree B&B is a respectable establishment, and I will not tolerate men bringing mechanical women in to cavort and carry on in the double rooms, no matter how lifelike they are," she said.

members

The conference also voted to purchase 10,000 hand held metal detectors to be distribute amongst its members.

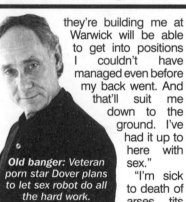
Beside themselves: Seaside landladies are up in arms at the prospect of robotic dirty weekends under their roofs, and have voted to impose a Britain-wide ban.

"When a couple books in for a weekend, we'll sweep it across the lady's wotnots to make sure they're not made of metal," said BLA chairwoman Edith Frigid. "If the

bleeper goes off, it means she's a sex robot and they'll have to book two single rooms, it's as simple as that. Them's are the rules."

"And we'll put them on separate floors, too. We know their little game," added Mrs Frigid.

SEX MACHINE!

Robo Dover to hit screens this year!

BRITISH pornographic impresario *Ben Dover* has commissioned boffins at Warwick University to build the world's first robotic porn star... an electronic version of himself. And when his computerised body double appears in its first blue movie later this year, it will be so lifelike that masturbating viewers will be unable to tell it from the real thing.

"My 'doppelbanger' is going to revolutionise the way I work," said Dover, real name Linseed Honeybunch. "Viewers have no idea what hard work it is having to knob dozens of young women, day in and day out. Getting a mechanical man in to do all the repetitive rubbing, fingering and thrusting in my movies will take a lot of the pressure off."

sick

"They say that robots will eventually take all our jobs," said Dover, 78. "Well, if it's BLOW jobs, they're welcome to them. I've had twenty a day for the past forty years, and I'm sick of the ruddy things."

"Honestly, if I have one more bird put her mouth round my poor old chopper, I think I'll go mad," he added.

ford

Dover, who suffered a severe back injury on set in 1994, whilst attempting to pleasure six women simultaneously, says that he is looking forward to farming out his more demanding physical roles to his cybernetic understudy.

"I'll still appear on screen in the plot-related scenes, knocking on the door with a pizza, fiddling about under the sink with a wrench, that kind of thing," he told us.

"But as soon the undercrackers start dropping, I'll hand over to my computerised cunt double and pop backstage to put my feet up with a nice cup of tea and a slice of fruit cake," he continued. "This robot

Old banger: Veteran porn star Dover plans to let sex robot do all the hard work.

they're building me at Warwick will be able to get into positions I couldn't have managed even before my back went. And that'll suit me down to the ground. I've had it up to here with sex."

"I'm sick to death of arses, tits and fannies," he confided.

But the legendary bongo star legions of fans are far from happy the prospect of seeing their priap hero being replaced with a robot. pay to see a real willy going in," sa Wakefield porn fan Onan Palmer.

settled in

"If I know it's just an electrica operated, hard, titanium endo-sha covered in lifelike pink plastic sk going in, it just won't be the same

"Although I'll probably still go o he added.

Have Your Say

COULD MAKING LOVE with a cold, emotionless electronic machine ever compare to a warm, intimate, physical relationship with another human being? However lifelike it was, would there always be a certain indefinable something lacking from the experience? We went out on the street to see if the Great British public would be prepared to fuck a robot...

"...ALL the robots I've seen in films have got spinning radar aerials on the tops of their heads and banks of flashing lights instead of teeth. If I had to look at that whilst getting my leg over I reckon I'd quickly be on the flop."

Randall O'Hopkirk, paint stripper

"...I'M into soapy titwanks, and all the robots I've seen in films have got reel-to-reel tape spools on their chests. I'd be too scared of cutting the underside of my banjo string on the tape as it whizzed backwards and forwards."

Morecambe McWise, paint stripper's mate

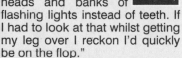

"...I THINK I've already had sex with a robot. I paid a woman in Wakefield £10 to pull me off behind a skip last night and she was completely emotionless and had cold hands."

Liddell Enlarge, tea caddy

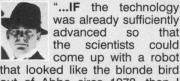

"...IF the technology was already sufficiently advanced so that the scientists could come up with a robot that looked like the blonde bird out of Abba circa 1978, then I would definitely have sex with it. However, if they could only manage to build the dark haired one, then I wouldn't bother."

Mitchell Handweb, washing lineman

"...ON balance I don't think I would, because I'm on an electric meter that takes fifty pences, and the anxiety that the power would go off halfway through a bout of love-making would cause me to lose turgidity."

Cannon Handball, search engineer

"...I THINK I'd be reluctant to have sex with an android, in case it suddenly became self-aware while we were at it and try to destroy me, like in *I, Robot*. However, on second thoughts, if it had really big tits I'd probably be prepared to take the risk."

Alias Smithandjones, pools panelist

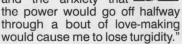

"...I WOULD definitely not have sex with a robot, because I'd love it and give it thirty years of my life, even though after we got married it would go off sex completely. I'd be very understanding but then I'd come home from work early and find it in bed with my best mate Stan and it would confess that this had been going on for ten years. The lying robot bitch."

Tuoron Knees, coconut milkman

"...MUCH as I'd like to, I don't think I'd ever have sex with a robot, as I'd have to keep it hidden from my wife. I've got a couple of DVDs and a few Scan mags hidden behind my shoes in the wardrobe, but I don't think there's enough room in there for a 6 foot tall electronic blonde Amazon with 48DD jugs."

Anton Deck, rabbit tailor

"...I'D HAPPILY have sex with a robot as long as it was realistic. But not so realistic that it wouldn't let me on the nest until I'd put some shelves up."

Rowan N Martin, class 2 betty driver

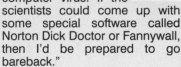

"...I WOULD definitely wear a blob in case it was a promiscuous robot and gave me a computer virus. If the scientists could come up with some special software called Norton Dick Doctor or Fannywall, then I'd be prepared to go bareback."

Mel Andsew, laughing gasman

"...I would certainly not have sex with a robot, as it is against the teachings of the Bible. God made Adam and Eve, not Adam and SexBot ZX3.2B."

Terry N June, gravel driver

"...I ONCE got a nasty burn whilst trying to poke a slice of toast out of a toaster. I vowed from that day on that I would never put my cock into a machine again."

Arm Stronghand, pepper miller

"...I DARE say when they develop a sex robot, the boffins will follow this ridiculous pornographic film trend and not give it any pubes. Why do these scientists and porn stars have to mess around with nature? I'll only have sex with a robot if it has pubes made out of a brillo pad or a handful of industrial swarf."

Donny Handmarie, salt seller

Living Doll!

Shads set to test World's first Lovebot

CLIFF RICHARDS'S backing band *The Shadows* have been lined up by boffins to try out the UK's first sex robot. The Nuffield Institute of Sexatronics says that a prototype female sex android will be ready for testing next week and the fifties chart-toppers have agreed to put the new invention through its paces.

"To say me and the lads are excited is putting it mildly," said bespectacled lead guitarist **Hank Marvin**, 74. "Apparently this electric bird they've built for us will do anything you tell it, and no backchat."

train

And bandmate **Bruce Welch**, 75, was equally enthusiastic. "We're going to plug it in in our dressing room and do all sorts," he told *Disc* magazine. "We'll probably end up pulling a train on it."

sadness

But the backstage gang bang will be tinged with sadness for the instrumental four-piece, as long time bandmate **Jet Harris** won't be there to share the fun, having died in 2011.

fours-up

"Jet always said how he'd love to have a fours-up with a robot woman," said drummer **Tony Meehan**, 73. "But sadly he didn't live long enough to see his fondest dream become a reality."

~Reuters

Star Wars Boost for British Firm

SALES OF A British-made pocket fanny are sky high following the success of the new *Star Wars* film *The Force Awakens*. Fans of the sci-fi blockbuster have been clamouring to get their hands on the £10 device ever since one of the movie's stars *Harrison Ford* praised it online.

"Never without my Shipton's when I'm filming. Better than the real thing! #MayTheFannyBeWithYou," the 74-year-old actor tweeted to his 8 million followers. He accompanied the message with a photo of himself on the bridge of the Millennium Falcon, holding a Shipton's Slick Lips Pleauremax and giving it the thumbs up.

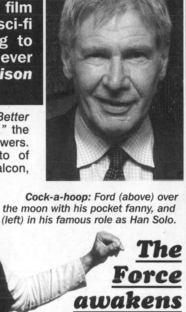

Star Wars fans immediately began re-tweeting the post and within minutes, sales of our pocket fannies had gone through the roof," said Ada Shipton, who runs the small family business that makes the anatomically accurate masturbatory aids in a tiny factory just outside Stoke on Trent.

"Orders were coming in so thick and fast that our small production line just couldn't keep up. In the end we had to make twelve new fanny moulds and order a load of new pallet of rubber just to meet the demand."

surprise

Mrs Shipton, 66, said that it had come as a great surprise that the Han Solo actor was a fan of her company's products. "We've had a few famous customers over the years,

Cock-a-hoop: Ford (above) over the moon with his pocket fanny, and (left) in his famous role as Han Solo.

The Force awakens sales success for family-run business

such as *Ross Kemp*, *Benedict Cumberbatch* and *Philip Davies*, the MP for Shipley," she told reporters.

"But getting such a glowing endorsement from a Hollywood A-lister like Mr Ford is beyond our wildest dreams."

garden

"Hopefully this sudden celebrity boost for our pocket fannies will lead to increased sales of our other products, such as vibrating

Pocket fanny magnate: Mrs Ada Shipton, yesterday.

butt plugs, Vietnamese love eggs and strap-on cocks," added Mrs Shipton.

All Change for Minister

HEALTH Secretary *Jeremy Hunt* yesterday announced that he has changed his name by deed poll to *JEREMY CUNT*.

The government minister said he was taking the legal step to formally alter his surname after a spate of newsreaders had inadvertently mispronounced it when referring to him in reports.

paperwork

Solicitor Dixon Curry, who drew up the official documentation, told us: "Changing one's name by deed poll is a straightforward legal process for which I charge £25 plus disbursements. I have all the paperwork prepared already, and as soon as he signs it, Mr Cunt, sorry, Hunt will officially become Mr Hunt, sorry, Cunt."

flush

The minister, who is MP for South West Surrey, says he hopes the name change will finally put a stop to years of embarrassing four-letter mix-ups.

"It all started in 2010 when Jim Naughtie got my name wrong on Radio 4's Today programme," he told the *Daily Telegraph*'s Barclay Sark.

Health Secretary announces surname re-shuffle

"About an hour later, Andrew Marr did the same thing on Start the Week, and since then practically every time my name is mentioned on a television or radio news report, my surname is mispronounced as the C-word."

"It occurred to me that if I just called myself Jeremy Cunt and had done with it, they might start accidentally calling me Jeremy Hunt for a change instead," added Mr Cunt, sorry, Hunt.

SLIGHTLY OUT OF DATE LASAGNA

LASAGNA

BEST BEFORE 29 JULY 2016

LADS! LADS!! I'VE GOT A GREAT TV SHOW FOR YOU! YOU HAVE GOT TO WATCH BREAKING BAD!

WHISPER!

SMIRK!

SIGH... REALLY?!

WHAT NEXT? THE SOPRANOS?

TONY PARSEHOLE

JANUARY 17th 1942 was a momentous day in the history of boxing. For January 17th 1942 was the day that Muhammad Ali was born, to a humble sign-painter and his humble wife, in a humble clapboard house in the humble town of Louisville in the humble state of Kentucky. (can't find thesaurus - subs drop in different words for humble).

But even from those humble beginnings, Muhammad Ali rose to become the greatest boxer the world has ever seen.

But Muhammad Ali wasn't merely the greatest boxer the world has ever seen.

He was also the greatest poet the world has ever seen.

For Ali could write sonnets that would have made Shakespeare weep. Iambic pentameters that would of shamed Keats, Shelley and Byron.

And his limericks would of beat Pam Ayres on Opportunity Knocks.

And he could dance. Oh, he could dance! When he was in the ring with Henry Cooper, Sonny Liston or George Formby, his lightning fast feet would of put Fred Astaire to shame. He was a true artist in every sense of the world.

For Muhammad Ali took boxing -

the most savage and brutal of sports - and turned it into ballet.

In his hands, those big hands, a fight became a beautiful work of art. It was a joy to behold him punch somebody in the face really hard till they went unconscious.

But he didn't just stand up against people in the boxing ring. He also stood up against them in real life.

He stood up for what he believed. And he was prepared to go to jail to stood up for what he believed.

For above all Ali was a man of principle. And unlike other, lesser boxers, he never demeaned himself by inventing grilling machines, advertising cheap aftershave or biting somebody's ear off.

And I should know.

For I was there, a wide-eyed cub reporter still wet behind the ears, sat at the side of the ring on that steaming hot night in Zaire, when he fought George Formby in the Rumble in the Jungle.

I watched the blows rain down on his hapless opponent until he finally claimed victory in the xxxth round (subs check he won).

And I was also there a year later, a wide-eared cub reporter still wet behind the eyes, sat at the side of the ring on that steaming hot night in the Philippines, when he fought Joe Frazier in the Thrilla in Manilla.

But his greatest battle was one he could never win, against the cruel disease that ravaged him for decades.

But it is as he was in his prime that we should remember him. He was the Greatest - the man who floated

When I heard that day that Ali was dead, I cried like a butterfly and wept like a bee

like a butterfly and stang like a bee.

Muhammad Ali (1942-2016) RIP. Fuck it, I'm still 50 words short.

January 17th 1942 was a momentous day in the history of boxing. For January 17th 1942 was the day that Muhammad Ali was born, to a humble sign-painter and his humble wife, in a humble clapboard house in the humble town of Louisville in the humble state of there that's 600 inv enc.

PIERCE DORGAN
The Day Ali met Me

DECEMBER 4th 1992 was a momentous day in the life of Muhammad Ali. For that was the day that the greatest boxer the world has ever seen, met me, Pierce Dorgan.

I was born to a humble stockbroking family in a modest, 8-bedroom detached shack on the lower east side of Kingston-upon-Thames. But even from these lowly beginnings, I was from an early age destined for greatness.

As a young child I showed remarkable prowess. I was a precocious talent. I had charm, good looks, charisma. And above all that, I had a determination to succeed in spite of all the odds.

So it was that in December 1992, I found myself at the pinnacle of my powers, the youngest editor the *Sun*'s Bizarre column had ever known. And it was in this capacity that Muhammad Ali met me.

He had heard of me and wanted to meet me, so I deigned to grant him an audience at a press conference he was giving to

promote his own range of soft drinks. Hundreds of other reporters had also turned up to see me, and - modest to a tee - I sat at the back behind a pillar.

I was a little tired that morning as I had been out the night before with my close friends **Richard Gere**, **Liza Minelli** and **Dr Christian Barnard**. We had been to a restaurant, where we had sat late into the evening talking about me, my life, my loves, my hopes for the future.

After coffee, we had been joined by **David Niven**, **Peter Ustinov**, **Ginger Rogers**, **Marlo Brando**, **Nelson Mandela**, **Mother Teresa of Calcutta**, **Bear Grylls**, **Henry Kissinger**, **Sammy Davis Junior**, **The Beatles**, **Harry Styles** out of One Direction and **Adele**. Once again, the conversation turned to me, as I held them in my thrall with my witty repartee.

And everyone was very excited when they heard who was going to meet me the next day. "Ali's going to love you," they all gushed. But with my typical modesty, I brushed off their comments. But their words came back to me as I sat in the conference room at Heathrow Airport, where a nervous Ali was waiting to be introduced to me.

When he finally came out onto the podium, he was so in awe of me that he was unable to speak to me or meet my gaze. Instead, he answered six or seven questions from other reporters who were sat nearer the front, before getting up and leaving.

When the news of Ali's death came through, I was having supper with **Robert Downey Jnr.**, **Arnold Schwarzenegger**, **Carol Kirkwood**, **Bernie Ecclestone**, **Chris Packham**, **Emerson**, **Lake** & **Palmer**, and **Jonathan Ross**.

I was devastated to think that he would never again get the chance to meet me.

A nervous Ali meets me in 1992

But I was cheered when they pointed out that Ali had been lucky to have met me once. "His final thoughts will have been of you," they all said.

And they were right. But what a tragedy it is that he will never see my greatness again.

Take a Shit...  Take a Shit...

WINNER!
MAGAZINE of the YEAR
~Take a Shit Magazine of the
Year Awards

"I've fathered more stars than you've had hot dinners," says Britain's most prolific sperm donor

Meet King Spunk

As told to
Fanny Gaslight

Bernie the Jizzbolt: *75-year-old Fleetwood sperm donor Bernard Pluckacre is convinced that he is the father of the Prime Minister.*

A FLEETWOOD MAN who has been making regular deposits at a sperm bank for the last fifty years says he is finally hanging up his wanking spanners. "It's time to retire," says **Bernie Pluckacre**, 75. "I've been pulling myself off for profit for half a century and it's time to take it easy and enjoy a bit of me-time."

"From now on, when I pull myself off it will be for pleasure only."

During his career, Pluckacre reckons his seed has resulted in more than 100,000 births, earning him his nickname of King Spunk. "That's what they call me down at the sperm bank," Bernie says. And even more amazingly, out of that Wembley Stadium-filling brood of offspring, many have gone on to become household names.

"The rollcall of stars that have issued from my fertile loins reads like a Who's Who of A-listers," he chuckles. "I couldn't be more proud of my kids and what they've achieved."

Bernie opened his wank account at the Lytham St Annes Sperm Bank in 1965. "I was unemployed at the time and I'd run up quite a tab at the

bookies," he remembers. "A mate of mine at the pub told me you could get two and six a pop at the local fertility centre, so I went down there straight away. It seemed a good way to turn my hobby into a living."

"I had to fill in a few forms at the reception desk, but I soon found myself in a booth with a small pot and a copy of Health and Efficiency. It was really soft stuff. There wasn't even any pubes in it because the Lord Chamberlain's office used to airbrush them out.

But I'd worked with worse. I flicked through the pages and carried on regardless. Two minutes later the job was done and I was heading off down the street with the missing fish in my pants and a shiny half crown in my pocket. As I walked into Ladbrokes I reflected that it was the easiest money I'd ever earned.

I'd had a hot tip about a horse that was running in the 4.15 at Kempton Park. According to my source, whose brother-in-law's mate was a stable boy at Towcester, all the other horses in the race had been nobbled and it couldn't lose.

> **"...I soon found myself in a booth with a small pot and a copy of Health and Efficiency. It was really soft stuff. There wasn't even any pubes in it..."**

Unfortunately, it went down at the first fence, broke a leg and had to be shot. I was gutted. I'd lost my money even quicker than I'd earned it.

But here's the thing, exactly nine months later to the day, a baby called David Cameron was born in Marylebone Hospital, London. Now I'm not saying that his mother used a turkey baster full of my jitler. But just consider the evidence: we both have green eyes and we both have hair loss problems - Cameron a slightly receding hairline and myself

completely bald except for some tufts over my ears.

And the name of the nag that I blew my wad on that day in 1965? It was Downing Street Lad. Coincidence? Perhaps. Or then again perhaps not. I'll leave it up to others to decide."

Over the next few years, Bernie's betting tab at the bookmakers continued to grow, and he found himself visiting the clinic four or five times a week in an attempt to keep the bailiffs from his front door.

"By the early seventies, the jazzmags in the booth had improved quite a bit. They were in colour for a start, and printed on glossy paper, although there were still crude black stars censoring all the good bits. Nevertheless, it all made the job a bit easier to complete, and I got my time down to an impressive minute and a half. Of course, prices continued to rise, and the sperm bank's rate of pay went up accordingly. I was now getting ten bob a shot, or fifty pence in the new money.

I remember this one time, I put in a ninety second shift on a Wednesday afternoon, collected my wages of sin and headed straight for my local greyhound track. I'd met a bloke at the pawnbrokers who owned a share in one of the dogs. He'd told me, in strictest confidence, that the

Take a Shit...

WINNER! MAGAZINE of the YEAR
~Take a Shit Magazine of the Year Awards

...rainer had been feeding it nothing but strong laxatives and liquorice allsorts for a week. He explained that nothing runs faster than a lean, hungry dog with no shit in it, and this one - called Dr Who - was just a bag of bones. There was no way it could lose.

I put my spunk money on it at 20-1 and retired to the stands to watch my dog romp home a mile ahead. Unfortunately, I think the trainer must have overdone it on the starving. As the hare whizzed past, Dr Who stumbled out of the trap, weak as a kitten, and collapsed on the ground. The greyhound attempted to stand up on its shaking legs, but collapsed back to the ground too weak to even support its own weight and I wept at the thought of my hard-on-earned cash that I had just thrown away on my reckless wager.

Long shot: Pluckacre wagered ejaculation bonus at 20-1.

Ex-sperm-inate: Dr Who actor Tennant could be long lost son.

I thought no more about it until 2005, when a little-known actor called David Tennant took over the role of Dr Who. Of course, all the transactions at the fertility clinic are confidential, and nobody ever knows whose fanny their tadpoles eventually end up up.

But when I checked Tennant's birthdate and discovered it was exactly nine months after that day at the dog track, I couldn't help harbouring a suspicion that the Timelord's mum might have popped into Lytham and been given a bottle of my spangle. After the David Cameron affair, I wondered now if there weren't mysterious forces at work. Were the fates giving me cryptic hints about the famous children I had anonymously fathered?"

As his gambling debts spiralled, the frequency of Pluckacre's visits to the clinic increased. And so did the clues to the identities of the celebrities he believed himself to have anonymously sired.

"In the eighties, the quality of the mags in the clinic went through the roof. Many of them were imported and you could see everything ... spam butterflies, hamburger shots, close up pink, the lot. As a consequence, I was never in my booth for more than a minute before I made a deposit.

And the icing on the cake? I was now getting proper money - two pound fifty a whack. You don't need to be a mathematician to work out that, with me making ten visits a week to the sperm bank, financially I was doing pretty well. Not to put too fine a point on it, I should have been living high on the hog.

Unfortunately, I'd had some terrible luck on the gee-gees. My losing spell had now lasted the best part of twenty years. As a result I owed a lot of money and most of the bookies in Fleetwood were looking for me. I could never have hoped to tug myself out of debt. That would have been a physical impossibility, even if I had a hundred cocks. No, I had to be realistic, I was going to have to put all my jizz money on a long odds bet and hope that the Gods were smiling on me.

A mate of mine was a copper, and he told me that all the big money was in dog fighting. I'd heard there was a fight planned one night for an outbuilding behind the Old King Cole pub up near Bispham. On my way I popped into the clinic to pick up a bit of stake money. They'd had these new fangled things called videos fitted in the booths, which were showing mucky films. They were pretty hardcore - I'd never seen anything like it. My eyes were out on stalks. I barely even had to rub it and I was out of there in thirty seconds with a smile on my face and a pocket full of cash.

At the dog fight, I knew it was all or nothing. The dogs were barking and snarling at one another, desperate

> "...In the eighties, the quality of the mags in the clinic went through the roof... you could see everything ... spam butterflies, close up pink, the lot...."

to get on with it. One of the bookies realised I was a rookie and kindly explained to me that in dog fighting, just like boxing, winning is more about what you can take without going down than what you can dish out. You should always bet on the dog with the most scars because they are the ones who can clearly take the punishment, he told me.

Needless to say, I heeded his expert advice and slapped my two pounds fifty on a battered-looking old dog with no ears, no tail and one eye. I got good odds too, 100-1, enough to pay off at least part of the tabs I'd run up with one of the bookies. I wasn't given a betting slip; this was an unlicensed meeting and everything was done on trust. In the end it didn't make any difference, because my dog got its throat ripped out thirty seconds after it went in the ring.

Twenty-odd years later, I was watching television and a brand new girl group came on to sing their latest single. They were called Girls Aloud and one of the singers reminded me of myself. I couldn't put my finger on exactly what it was, just something about the way she moved, the way she held herself.

Somehow, I wasn't surprised to learn that she was called Cheryl Cole, and she had been born exactly nine months after that fateful evening at the dog fight behind the Old King Cole pub."

Bernie was now absolutely convinced that he had unknowingly fathered hundreds of celebrities. Looking back at his diaries and his copies of the Racing Post, he has been able to identify a glittering array of famous progeny. He believes the evidence is overwhelming and he

Wank outsiders: Pluckacre had run of bad luck on the horses.

provides several examples to back up his claims, including...

● 1-Direction singer **Harry Styles**, born in 1994, exactly nine months after Bernie lost his £5 sperm money betting on a horse called **Go Harry Go**, which was disqualified for excessive use of the whip.

● Football star **David Beckham**, born in 1975, exactly nine months after Bernie lost his 50p sperm money in a Manchester United-branded fruit machine.

● **Prince William**, born in 1982, exactly nine months after Bernie lost his £2.50 sperm money after wagering it on a badger that was torn to pieces by six border terriers on some wasteground near the Billy Prince trading estate, just outside Lytham.

Pluckacre says he has enjoyed every moment of his his long career, but now retirement has been forced on him. "My tadpoles are still as swimmy as ever. The doctors at the sperm bank told me that if there was a jism Olympics, mine would be Mark Spitz. But I'm afraid age has finally caught up with me and my wrists are going," he says.

"I'm just happy that thanks to my tireless efforts in that booth over the last half century, I have given the gift of life to some of this country's best loved and wealthiest celebrities. I know I wasn't there for them when they were growing up, and I've never met any of them, but surely the least they could do is all chip in to pay off some of their old dad's gambling debts."

"I remember in 1965, losing seven bob on a whippet called Wizard Prang, nine months before JK Rowling was born. Surely she can spare a little bit from all her Harry Potter millions so I can clear the slate and start again. Just £600 would do it."

Take a Shit

CRACKER-TOA!

Post-EU crackers to be louder than ever, says May

THERESA May last night told Britain's cracker makers that they would soon be free to put as much explosives as they liked in their products. At the moment, Brussels red tape limits the amount of volatile chemicals in a cracker to just 3mg – enough to produce a pathetically feeble snap when pulled. But, said the Prime Minister, following the UK's planned hard Brexit in 2019, manufacturers would be free to pack their crackers with as much punch as they liked.

"Post Brexit Christmasses are really going to go with a bang," the weary-looking Premier told delegates at the UK Christmas Novelty Industry dinner at the Mansion House, London. And manufacturers at the event confirmed they were already working on hugely more powerful cracker bang-strips.

crackers

"If you think crackers are fun now, just wait till you try one of our post-Article 50 models," said industry spokesman George Motto. "They're going to be ten times louder, ten times more dangerous and ten times more fun than the ones the EU allows us to sell."

EXCLUSIVE!

"Come Christmas 2019, there's every chance your Christmas cracker will catch fire when you pull it," he continued. "People are going to get perforated eardrums off these things. That's how good they are."

Wrestler-faced Brexit minister David Davis welcomed the Prime Minister's announcement. "The Bremoaners who are solely responsible for talking our economy into its present terrible state will have to eat humble pie when we start selling our crackers around the globe, unfettered by the European Single Market and its petty rules and regulations," he said.

"Be in no doubt that Britain is poised to take a lead when it comes to powerful crackers. The world will be beating a path to our door, desperate to sign hugely lucrative trade deals with us just so they can pull big British crackers after their Christmas dinner."

club

8 people were killed yesterday and 12 were taken to hospital with life-threatening injuries, following a loud explosion at a Beaconsfield Christmas cracker factory. A spokesman for Thompson's Crackers told local news: "An incident occurred in our research and development facility and we are looking into it."

"The public should be reassured that this company is constantly striving to produce a cracker that maximises fun whilst minimising as much as possible the risk of serious injuries," the spokesman added.

Bang to rights: May plans to lift limit on novelty yuletide dinner explosives.

The Xmas Cracker of the FUTURE...

SNAP — **THE SHAPE** of 2020's cracker may look reassuringly familiar, but from the moment you pull it, the differences become clear – starting with the initial 'snap!'. Thanks to strict health & safety regulations, the explosive cardboard splint has been replaced with a tiny electronic microchip. When the cracker is pulled, this sends a signal via Bluetooth to your mobile phone, activating an 'app' which makes a snapping sound. To accurately recreate the effect of a real cracker, the chip has been programmed to not go off in about a quarter of the crackers in the box.

MOTTO — **EVERYONE'S** favourite part of the cracker is the corny joke inside, and rest assured in the year 2020 these quips – albeit updated to reflect the scientific and technological advances of life in the future – are just as corny as ever. Such bons mots as "If your wife wants to learn to drive a hover-car, don't stand in her way" and "Why doesn't Santa smoke E-cigarettes? They're bad for his elf," will still have your fellow diners groaning over their sprouts just like they always have. But the big difference is, they're no longer printed on paper. Instead, they come in the form of tiny silver psycho-active pills which, once eaten, put the joke directly into your mind.

HAT — **THE SHORTCOMINGS** of the gaily coloured hats found in the crackers of 2016 were well known to anyone who ever put one on. They were too small, they tore easily, and they stuck to your forehead with sweat, because they were made from tissue paper. In contrast, the hats in 2020's crackers are made from a high-tech graphene polymer – a microscopic lattice designed at a sub-atomic level to look and feel exactly like tissue paper. In addition, these hats are also too small, tear easily and stick to your forehead with sweat.

NOVELTY — **AS TECHNOLOGY** advances, everything becomes smaller, more advanced and cheaper with each passing year. In 2020, the unwieldy cutting edge gadgets of 2016 have shrunk so much in size and price that they are small enough and cheap enough to fit inside a Christmas cracker. Instead of thimbles, combs and plastic puzzles, crackers of the future spill out postage-stamp-sized widescreen televisions, 4K HD video cameras the size of a sugar cube and iPhone 500s the size of a broad bean, all destined to be thrown away without a second thought in the post-Christmas dinner clear-up.

Think this sounds like science fiction? *Then think again.* The first of this new generation of Christmas crackers are already on the drawing board and waiting to go into production. The future of crackers is just around the corner, and it's going to arrive with a bang.

NEXT CHRISTMAS: We take a look at Egg-Nog in the year 2021

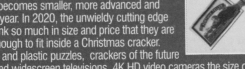

It's Crackers!

Crackers magnate Tom completely bewildered by New Year sales slump

THE MANAGING director of the UK's biggest cracker company is once again bracing himself for a disastrous January, as sales of his product are once again set to slump. "I just don't understand it," says Sir Tom Merry of Merry's Christmas Crackers of Church Stretton. "This happens every single year. We have a fantastic December, with business booming and our Christmas crackers flying off the shelves as quick as we can make them."

"Then in the new year our order books are suddenly completely empty. It's very perplexing," he told us. "Between the start of January and the end of November, every single cracker that comes off our production line ends up going in a skip because we simply can't sell it."

fluctuations

Sir Tom is at a loss to explain the yearly dramatic fluctuations in his business. "No matter how much we spend on promotion and advertising throughout the rest of the year, nothing seems to work and trade completely flatlines until the start of December," he said.

"Then, just when I'm just about to pack it all in, lay all my workers off and close the factory, wouldn't you know it, business suddenly picks up for some reason that I simply can't fathom and once again we're working double shifts round the clock to try to keep up with demand."

Merry has even brought in business troubleshooters Duncan Bannatyne

Gone with a bang: Merry's post-Christmas sales slump is a mystery.

and Deborah Meaden to look at the pattern of his company's Christmas cracker sales. Sir Tom told us: "Quite frankly, they were as bewildered as me. They think it's probably got something to do with global exchange rates and the world markets, but they said it's so complicated even they don't understand it properly."

The Traffic Warden of 2020

OUR ROADS are fast becoming a warzone. Contemptuous of the Highway Code, motorists routinely ride roughshod over UK parking rules, flouting resident-only permit regulations, ignoring yellow lines and overstaying their meter times by minutes at a time with impunity. Indeed, if things continue the way they are, we are fast heading for a *Mad Max*-style dystopia, with the country's army of hard-working traffic wardens as our last desperate line of defence against out-and-out car parking anarchy.

As the stakes in this battle against motorised mob rule are ratcheted ever higher, technology is at last coming to the traffic warden's aid. And the meter men and meter maids of the not-too-distant future will be unrecognisable from the bitter police rejects familiar to us today. Here we take a sneak peek at how the high-tech traffic wardens of the year 2020 will enforce order on our streets.

● The **Automatic Infra-Red Numberplate Recognition Unit** (1) is a computerised podule incorporated into the traffic warden's helmet which can spot a car where the ticket has fallen off the windscreen from a distance of over 200 miles. The registration number is then checked against a database held at the all-powerful Confederation of Vehicle Information to identify the vehicle's owner and debit £60 from his bank account within nanoseconds. If the motorist doesn't have sufficient funds, a squad of CVI Enforcement Agents will be despatched to his home, from where his wife and/or children will be forcibly removed and detained until the fine is paid.

● Many motorists today park with some part of their car very slightly overhanging the official lines painted on the road; but without objective proof of infringement, traffic wardens are often obliged to give offenders the benefit of the doubt. But in 2020, using a sophisticated laser array and 3-D holographic imaging software, the **Micro-Infringement Detector** (2) will enable them to measure such encroachments down to a resolution of less than 0.25 microns - that's twenty times thinner than a human hair! It's just like the Hawkeye system used at Wimbledon, only instead of a point being at stake, it's a £60 fine for being "Out." Game, set and match to the traffic warden.

● After buying a ticket entitling them to park for 30 minutes, many of today's arrogant motorists think it's perfectly okay to saunter back 5, 10 or even 15 seconds after their ticket has elapsed, safe in the knowledge that the warden can't prove the exact time they parked up. But 2020's highway enforcers will each be equipped with a **Gauntlet-mounted Atomic Chronometer** (3), telling the time to an accuracy of 1×10^{-15} seconds. That's equivalent to one second in every hundred million years, or to put it another way, a billion times more accurate than Big Ben! So look out, car owners of the future. If you're 1 femtasecond late getting back to your motor with your shopping, you're going to get a ticket. No ifs. No buts. End of.

● Today's traffic wardens rely on nothing more sophisticated than a pair of well-worn Dr Martens to get them round their beat, dejectedly tramping the streets for hours each day while brooding on how different their lives would have been had they passed the army medical or the police intelligence test. But all that will change in the future, where our meter man of 2020 is sitting astride a **1000 HP Hybrid Turbo Bike** (4), capable of racing to parking infringements at twice the speed of sound, easily thwarting any motorist who is standing by his car, patting his pockets and looking for his keys as his meter ticks over into the red.

They Are The Law - Traffic wardens of the future equipped to impose justice on errant motorists

● Meanwhile, our 2020 meter maid is equipped with a **Vertical Take-Off Jet Pack** (5). Using its 16,000lbs of thrust, our traffic warden can hover 2 miles above the city, using her bird's eye vantage point to spot minor Highway Code violations. If she spots a car that has put one two wheels into a bus lane in order to let an ambulance get past, she can engage full power and swoop down like an angel of vengeance to slap a ticket in a plastic bag under the driver's windscreen wiper before he knows what's hit him.

Next week: Queen Elizabeth the 14th — How the Monarchy will look in 2116.

72

Boffins Develop First Robo-Twat

ROBOTICISTS from the Massachusetts Institute of Technology showcased a breakthrough in artificial intelligence last week after unveiling the first robotic twat.

Guests at London's annual Information Technology conference were treated to an ultra-believable display of twattishness from the android, including a Michael McIntyre stand-up routine and a rendition of *Gangnam Style*.

annoying

"It was amazing," said one attendee. "The android even looked like a twat. I wanted to kick its annoying, metal face in."

Robo tops: Some leading boffins yesterday

However, MIT roboticist Dirk Diggler insisted it was still in the early stages of development.

"So far the robotic twat has the ability talk through films and then give away the ending, but our aim is to have people all over the world calling it a twat," he said. "Programming it to present TV shows about cars will be the natural step forward."

1D TO DO SHIT

MILLIONS of fans have been left devastated after One Direction revealed they'll be taking a twenty-minute hiatus to "squeeze one out" this evening.

Band member **Niall Horan** told reporters that it might even take him five minutes longer. "I've eaten a three bananas today, so your guess is as good as mine," he said.

wiping

"Also, I'm about two-thirds into a good book, so I'll probably reach the end of the chapter before I start wiping, even after my log's been pinched off."

inconsolable

The band's legions of followers were inconsolable at the news, storming social media to express their concern.

One posted: *"25 mins!?! :(Can't they just wear nappies?!?!"* Another wrote: *"If only 1D ate more prunes I cud stop crying. Does the drama neva end???"*

However, others managed to take a more philosophical point of view. *"1D r th Rolling Stones of this era,"* wrote one, *"they need to turd like ANY OTHER ARTISTS."*

The group assured fans they'll be getting back together as soon as they've washed their hands. *~Reuters*

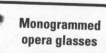

HELL BELOW ZERO

LettERbOCKS

email: letters@viz.co.uk

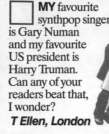

MY favourite synthpop singer is Gary Numan and my favourite US president is Harry Truman. Can any of your readers beat that, I wonder?

T Ellen, London

I AM infuriated by these automated cash machines that blight our streets. Every time I insert my card, the infernal contraptions ask me for my PIN. I can't tell you how many times I have used these machines yet still they are unable to remember a simple 4-digit number. Come on banks, get a bigger hard drive so you don't have to keep asking for my number.

Percy Fawcett, Durham

I DECIDED to act out the phrase "When the shit hits the fan" the other day, and believe me the results weren't as magnificent as you would expect. And it shorted out the electricity in the dental practice where my mate works.

Tim Buktu, Timbuktu

WHY does everyone always go on about being able to see the Great Wall of China from space? I can see my garden wall on Google Earth easily and it's fucking tiny.

James Leighton, Portsmouth

AS I left for work the other morning, the weather forecast was on breakfast TV. Moments later there was another weather forecast on the radio in the car. What's the point of putting it on the wireless when I've already seen it on the telly? I reckon the Met Office must be creaming it in.

Dave Gibbs, Nether on the Blob

"WHY do birds suddenly appear, every time you are near?" sang Karen Carpenter in 1970. As a seagull stole my battered sausage in St Ives in 2004, I can entirely sympathise. I was thinking of writing a song about the event too, possibly called 'That fucker stole my saveloy.'

Huntley Palmer, Bude

ON *Star Trek*, how come the USS Enterprise can 'beam' people from a planet to the ship, but can't 'beam' people from room to room, or deck to deck? It would certainly save the crew a lot of time and energy and it would also save having to carpet the corridors.

Ma Shun, Mons Olympus.

LAST night I dreamed I was on the toilet in the middle of the reptile house at a zoo, and I couldn't get my bum clean no matter how much loo roll I used. I'd like to see the so-called dream experts interpret that one.

Phil Atio, Devon

STAR LETTER

WHY don't the FA insist that a large sheet of glass is placed inside each goal, a football's width behind the line. This will put an end to the eternal "did the ball cross the line" argument, since any shot that smashes the glass clearly crossed the line completely. After each goal, the two teams could help clear up the broken glass whilst the linesmen and referee install a new pane before getting the game restarted.

Tom Crabpaste, Acton

WHEN I lived in Nottingham, I was stang off a wasp once too many times, so I moved to Australia. However, last Friday I got bit off a snake! How unlucky is that?

Sidney Sydney, Sydney

I USE newspapers to light the fire at night, which I know a lot of people do. Would it not make sense for the newspaper companies to save money on writers, photographers and ink, and just sell blank newspapers instead? This would also make them much cheaper.

S Cat, email

MY girlfriend won't stop banging on about this affair I had once. When will women let things go? It's been nearly half an hour now since she caught me at it with her best friend, and yet she's still shouting and being a mardy arse.

Keith Queef, Llanllyfni

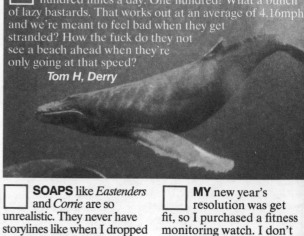

I JUST read that a whale can swim up to one hundred miles a day. One hundred! What a bunch of lazy bastards. That works out at an average of 4.16mph and we're meant to feel bad when they get stranded? How the fuck do they not see a beach ahead when they're only going at that speed?

Tom H, Derry

SOAPS like *Eastenders* and *Corrie* are so unrealistic. They never have storylines like when I dropped so many farts the people in the flat upstairs thought there was a gas leak and tried to evacuate the entire block. You never see Rita Sullivan doing that, do you?

T Barlow, The Lakes

PEOPLE say that owls are wise, but I just saw one sick up a half digested mouse and then fly into the side of a bus. It seems these so called 'nature experts' don't always know what they're talking about.

Gus Haydock, Tunbridge Wells

MY missus asked me the other day to explain the concept of parallel universes to her. I explained it means that all possibilities are played out, so that in one universe I would be married to breakfast telly sexpot Susanna Reid, and in another I would be married to telly news sexpot Natasha Kaplinsky. Furthermore, in a third universe bigamy would be allowed and I would be married to them both and also to the Cheeky Girls. For some reason she threw a hissy fit and stormed off. I guess science isn't her thing.

Tony Baloney, Westcliff

I RECENTLY found my childhood pogo stick in the shed and I managed almost 5 bounces on it before I fell off and shattered my elbow in 3 places. Can any of your readers beat that?

B. Arscott, email

MY new year's resolution was get fit, so I purchased a fitness monitoring watch. I don't actually exercise, but now I masturbate for 4 miles before breakfast.

Sandy Soil, Truro

I DON'T understand what all these gravitational waves are. In my day, we just had plain old gravity that kept you stuck to the floor. Now I suppose we'll have kids 'surfing' gravity on their fancy new hover boards, leaving a trail of destruction and moon boot footprints for the hard working British taxpayer to clean up. We are all going to hell in a handcart.

R. Littlejohn, Florida

FOOTBALL these days seems to be a chaotic parody of the former beautiful game; what with 3-points, 1-point or no-points, 6-pointer games, new-fangled cup games, away draws and re-matches, it's difficult to keep up. What's wrong with the old system where the team who scores the most goals wins? I blame Sky TV and that old bloke Fish Batter.

Jonny Johnson, Wigan

DAVID Attenborough says we shouldn't visit the Galapagos Islands as tourism is destroying the fragile ecosystem. Yet he has the temerity to say this on camera whilst filming his own holiday there and broadcasting it to the nation. As usual, it's simply one rule for the greatest TV naturalist of our times and another for everyone else.

George, Weston-super-Nightmare

WANK SPENCER

MATERNITY UNIT

PUFF PUFF!

YOU'RE DOING REALLY WELL! A FEW MORE PUSHES SHOULD DO IT!

OOPS! MY GOWN SEEMS TO HAVE COME UNDONE!

SPROING!

MR. SPENCER! WHERE ARE YOU GOING?!

BACK IN A JIFFY!

CLEANING CUPBOARD

WHAT ARE YOU DOING IN THERE? YOU'VE MISSED THE BIRTH OF YOUR DAUGHTER!

RATTLE!

OOOH, BETTY!

—Tayler—

WHY is it that when I use my missus's really expensive shampoo on my pubes, the whole area still looks like Bob Dylan when he's just got out of bed? If it made my bush look a bit more like Prince Charles's well-groomed hair, then perhaps I'd be worth the money.

Shenkin Arsecandle, Fishguard

WHAT is the point of driverless cars? There's already enough cars on the roads with people in them.

Tarmac Adam, Birmingham

WHO do these so called 'emergency services' think they are? With their blaring sirens and flashing lights, they seem to think they own the road. We're all in a hurry to get where we're going. Why can't they be patient like the rest of us? No wonder people get road rage with these bullies driving about.

Friarton Bridge, Perth

OUR gloomy newspapers are quick to report the death of a much-loved celebrity, but there's rarely a mention when a new one is born. Bring us some good news for a change!

Limahl, Nantwich

I SAW this piss stain on the floor of the toilet of a pub called The Old Cock Inn. Coincidence?

Tom, Manchester

I THINK this compulsory microchipping of dogs is a crazy EU idea that will lead to chaos. With the advancement of technology, what's to say our microchipped pets won't become super-intelligent cyborg-animal hybrids, rising up against us? You might think I'm being hyperbolic, but you mark my words, by 2020 we'll be the ones forced to eat Pedigree Chum.

Pete Prodge, Wellingborough

WHAT'S the point of donkeys when we've already got horses? It's a complete waste of time if you ask me.

Greg Alam, Hanham

IF I live to be 100 years old, I want more than just a telegram off the Queen. I'd want Kate Middleton doing a striptease and getting me to lick whipped cream off her tits. However, I'm only 30 at the moment, so, thinking about it, by the time I'm 100, she'll be 104, and I wouldn't want to be licking cream off Queen Kate's saggy old bangers. I'll just take any royal princess who's over 18 and under 30, and who looks like she'd be up for getting her kit off.

Bill Marney, Warsaw

I JUST shat the bed after 8 pints of lager, yet I know the wife's had a long day, so I'm not going to wake her. I'll just go and sleep in the spare room and she can wash the sheets in the morning. It's important to be thoughtful to make a marriage work.

P. Robinson, Erinsborough

I THINK that North Korean fat lad Kim Jong-Un would be a lot more likeable if he took a leaf out of the late Bernie Winters's book and did a few daft, toothy grins whilst going "Eeeeee!" It certainly couldn't do any harm.

Bobby Bowels, Merthyr Tydfil

TOP CHILDREN

CHILDREN. Confuse elderly relatives by pinching their cheek and offering them a hard boiled sweet from your coat pocket.

Will Mylchreest, Leamington Spa

TRICK people into thinking that you live in a museum by simply roping off most of the rooms in your house and having a gift shop near the front door.

David Craik, Hull

MANUFACTURERS of in-ear headphones. Learn a lesson from testicles and make one lead slightly longer than the other so they don't clack together.

Luis Felipe, Colchagua

DO your bit to prevent global warming by attaching a bin-liner to your car's exhaust pipe to catch the harmful emissions. Then leave the bags out for your council refuse department to dispose of responsibly.

Mark Gubb, Cardiff

CONVINCE your friends that you have a problem with excess earwax by crunching up a Wotsit and smearing the orange crumbs over the insides of your ears.

B. Crumblebitch, Leeds

FOOL people into thinking you're a fugitive from justice/T Mobile customer by throwing your phone in a litter bin after every time you use it.

Adolf Noutros Ghali, Leeds

FOOTY fans. Add a degree of decency to your sport, by chanting "You DO know what you're doing" when a referee makes a good decision.

Tim Buktu, Timbuktu

FOOL your friends into thinking that you are in the FBI by taking binoculars to a funeral.

James Bradbury, London

INTERVIEWEES. Prove to your potential new employers that you're capable of delegating responsibility by sending someone else to the interview for you.

Scruffy Brenda, Scarborough

ISLAMIC State. Get one over the infidel Western media by officially changing your name to The So-Called Islamic State.

Big Gay Algernon, London

MEN. Take an onion with you when you go to see an emotional film at the cinema. If you feel yourself filling up as the music builds to a crescendo, whip out the onion and start chopping it on your knee. Everyone will blame the onion for your tears and your reputation as a hardcase will remain intact.

Raul Duke, Harrow

RECREATE that airport holiday feeling by wheeling a suitcase around the perfume department in Debenhams.

Neil, Llandudno

JINX pickpockets by placing a small open sachet of salt in your wallet. If they spill the salt while taking your money they will have some bad luck.

Robert Marshall, Kildare

TiPs

Where Are They NOW?

WHATEVER happened to *Pippa Middleton's arse?* It was all over the papers a few years ago, but you very really see it these days.

Bobby Bowels, Merthyr Tydfil

＊ Although not so much in the news, Pippa's arse is still very busy. In 2013, it became the sole director and shareholder in PMX Enterprises, Ltd, and has contributed articles to The Spectator, the Sunday Telegraph and Vanity Fair. In addition, in 2014 it took part in a 3,000 mile cycle race across America and a 6.5km swim in Istanbul to raise money for the British Heart Foundation.

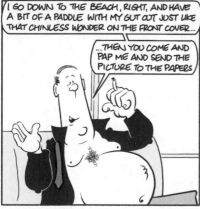

SHORTLY...

HAVE YOU GOT YOUR SHOTS YET, TOM?.. ONLY I'M FREEZING MY FUCKING KNACKERS OFF, HERE...

THIS WATER'S COLDER THAN A WITCH'S TIT

JUST A COUPLE MORE, ROGER

THERE! ALL DONE!

OKAY, ROGER!

RIGHT! SEND THEM TO THE SUN, STAR, MIRROR, EXPRESS AND MAIL, OKAY?

OH, AND YOU MIGHT AS WELL SEND THEM TO THE GUARDIAN AS WELL... THEY'LL USE THEM IN A SPLASH ABOUT INVASION OF PRIVACY

NEXT MORNING...

WELL... IT LOOKS LIKE YOU MADE IT ONTO THE FRONT OF EVERY SINGLE TABLOID, ROGER...

...AND THE GUARDIAN WENT WITH 'PAPARAZZI MUST BE STOPPED!'

YES! AND I'M ON THE SIDEBAR OF SHAME ON THE MAIL'S WEBSITE, TOO... 'ROGER FIVE-BELLIES

SO FAR, SO GOOD, TOM

WHAT HAPPENS NEXT, ROGER?

WELL, I'M JUST GOING TO SCRATCH MY ARSE FOR A MONTH, TOM, WHILE YOU SORT OUT THE PUBLISHING DEAL... THEN I'LL REAPPEAR AND WE CAN START THE BOOK SIGNING TOUR

AND DON'T WORRY, TOM... I'LL NOT FORGET YOUR PART IN THIS... THERE'LL BE A DRINK IN IT FOR YOU.

RIGHT!

ER... THANKS!

FOUR WEEKS LATER...

MORNING, TOM

AFTERNOON, ROGER

I CAN'T WAIT TO SEE THIS DIET BOOK I'VE WRITTEN... WHICH PUBLISHER DID I GO WITH IN THE END, TOM... SOMEBODY BIG?

ERM...

I HOPE YOU GOT A GOOD DEAL, TOM. NONE OF THIS SALE OR RETURN BOLLOCKS... THEY BUY IT, THEY'VE BOUGHT IT!

AND A NICE ADVANCE, TOO... A PROPER ONE... FOLDING MONEY!

WE'LL DO AN EXERCISE VIDEO TO GO WITH IT AS WELL, TOM... EXTRA, OF COURSE... NOT INCLUDED...

BUST THAT BELLY WITH ROGER MELLIE!

ROGER... I'M...

I'LL NOT BE IN IT, THOUGH... I'LL JUST DO THE VOICE OVERS. WE'LL GET SOME REALLY FIT BIRDS TO DO ALL THE BENDING OVER.

I CAN SEE IT NOW, TOM! LEG WARMERS... LEOTARDS... CAMELS' TOES, THE LOT

I'M GOING TO STOP YOU THERE, ROGER. ...THERE'S NO BOOK

NO BOOK!?...

WHAT DO YOU MEAN, NO FUCKING BOOK?

I MEAN, ROGER, THAT NONE OF THE PUBLISHERS WERE INTERESTED. THEY SAID THE MARKET FOR CELEBRITY DIET BOOKS IS ALREADY FLOODED.

WHAT!? YOU'RE PULLING MY COCK, TOM!

NO I'M NOT, ROGER. THERE WAS ONLY ONE PUBLISHER WHO SHOWED ANY INTEREST, BUT THEY EVENTUALLY WENT WITH THIS ONE INSTEAD

THE FOUR SALADS & A FRUITBOWL DIET

LOSE 2 STONE IN 4 WEEKS WITH HUGH GRANT

IF HUGH CAN, YOU CAN!

THE MERCENARY BASTARD!

SHORTLY...

...AND WHAT'S MORE, PAUL, IT'S SO EASY TO PUT ON... AND BELIEVE ME, IT'S SO COMFORTABLE, YOU'LL FORGET YOU'RE WEARING THE FU...

...SO THAT'S THE ABDO 3000 GENTLEMEN'S UNDETECTABLE SLIMMING GIRDLE...

QVC

NEW TODAY

THE ABDO 3000 GENTLEMANS SLIMMING GIRDLE WITH ROGER MELLIE

Retail Price £40.00

ONE TIME ONLY VALUE £39.99

30 DAY MONEY BACK GUARANTEE
01 811 8055 - ABDO 3000
CALL NOW AND PLACE YOUR ORDER

QVC

OKAY... ONWARDS AND UPWARDS. TIME FOR PLAN B

PLAN B!?

HELLO!?... IS THAT THE ABDO 3000 GIRDLE COMPANY?...

...ROGER MELLIE, HERE... LISTEN, I'VE GOT A PROPOSITION TO PUT TO YOU

...JUST £39.99... BUT MY PRODUCER HAS JUST TOLD ME THAT THEY HAVE GONE LIMITED STOCK, SO IF YOU WANT TO GET ONE, PLACE YOUR ORDER QUICKLY BY CALLING THE NUMBER AT THE BOTTOM OF YOUR SCREEN, OR VIA OUR WEBSITE...

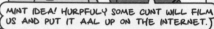

80

Ear we go again!

HE FOUND HIMSELF in hot water back in 2007 after allegedly biting a homeless man on the ear. And *QI* funnyman *ALAN DAVIES* is in similar trouble this morning for doing the same thing... *to a fully-grown African elephant!*

The shocking incident occurred yesterday afternoon as the corkscrew-haired jester was leaving London Zoo after a day out.

enclosure

Onlooker Ferris Zarathustra claimed: "Mr Davies was heading towards the main exit, when he suddenly turned and did a sort of double take at the elephant enclosure. He was staring angrily at the animals through the fence, and he kept shouting, 'What the fuck are you lot looking at?'"

CCTV footage then shows Davies, 50, furiously scaling the 40ft wall of the elephant house and striding menacingly towards the gaggle of bewildered pachyderms.

TV Alan under fire for chomping elephant's lug

"The Jonathan Creek star began frantically waving his arms at the creatures while making insulting gestures," said Zarathustra. "It drew quite a crowd."

patriot

When the perplexed beasts failed to respond to Davies' threatening taunts, the curly-locked quipster leapt wildly at the nearest elephant and sank his teeth into its gigantic leathery ear.

Trunk and disorderly: Funnyman Davies lost temper and shocked bystanders with his actions.

"He must have hung there by his gnashers for a good fifteen seconds", Zarathustra claimed. "I think everyone was too shocked to move, so we all just stood there filming it on our phones instead."

The quick-witted telly fave was eventually dragged off the terrified six-ton mammal by members of zoo staff, and strong-armed towards the exit. He has been given a lifetime ban from the facility.

London Zoo CEO Kelvin Taciturnus assured reporters that the elephant in question was fine. "He was badly shaken by the incident, but he's recovering nicely," said Taciturnus. "We have learned our lesson and will henceforth keep celebrities with a track record of biting, nibbling or chewing ears well away from the elephant house."

sister

The horrific event mirrors another which took place earlier this month, when *Reservoir Dogs* actor Michael Madsen breached the large mammal enclosure at Los Angeles Zoo and proceeded to saw an elephant's ear off whilst dancing to Seventies rock.

Eat up your pinna: Comic chowed down on elephant's ear.

God Help Us!

CHANCELLOR of the Exchequer Phillip Hammond last night urged the country to start praying for Britain's beleaguered currency, whose value has plummeted on world markets following June's shock Brexit vote.

The pound, which recently hit a thirty year low, has failed to rally despite a series of reassuring statements from the Treasury and a £250 billion cash injection from Bank of England chief Mark Carney.

Addressing a press conference, Hammond pleaded with believers to beseech their chosen deity to intercede and arrest the pound's sharp decline. "Turning to God to boost the pound may sound like a desperate act of last resort, but it is in fact part of a well thought out fiscal plan to stabilise the British economy," he said. "Unlike more traditional means of propping up the national currency, such as quantitative easing or lowering interest rates, divine intercession will guarantee long term stability for our post-European economy."

Hammond begs: Chancellor urges Brits to beseech the Lord

service

Archbishop of Canterbury Dr Justin Welby was quick to welcome the plan, and immediately conducted a Service for Sterling in St Paul's Cathedral, where worshippers sang hymns and prayed for an upturn on international currency markets. "Asking the Lord to intervene is a very effective mechanism for managing sterling's value as He doesn't have to wait to see what's happening on the Dow Jones or Hang Seng before making His move on the exchange rate," said Welby.

"Because He's omniscient, He already knows what the long term future trends are going to be, and can adjust the value of the pound accordingly."

express

And Dr Welby said that his prayers were already beginning to have an effect. "After I held a Mass for the pound, it momentarily rallied, rising 0.3 cents against the dollar," he said. "It was a striking demonstration of God's power, mercy and munificence in these troubled times."

lottery

Although the pound's value immediately plummeted again, this time to a new low level not seen since the Depression, Dr Welby was confident that a concerted national effort could pull the embattled economy back from the brink of ruin.

"Pray for the pound," says Hammond

"If everyone prays really hard, then I believe we can boost the value of the pound to around $1.70," he said. "This would put sterling back on an even keel and bring confidence back to the markets."

portrait gallery

And he called upon followers of all Britain's faiths to join in the effort. "It would be great if they could pray to their Gods too, just in case us Christians have been barking up the wrong tree for the last two thousand years," he added.

Sterling effort: Chancellor called for national prayer campaign to save pound.

Let Us Pray

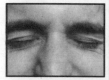

THESE DAYS most of us pray very rarely if at all, saving our occasional religious invocations for funerals, penalty shoot-outs and during severe turbulence in an aeroplane. Some of us haven't prayed since we were last in a school assembly. So if you're a bit rusty about the basics of praying, here's the Archbishop of Canterbury's step-by-step guide to getting the most from your Heavenly Host.

1. Hands. Palms should be pressed flat together and pointing upwards, so that the prayers go straight up to Heaven out the ends of your fingertips. None of this hands-clasped nonsense. Whoever saw a ball-shaped aerial on a walkie-talkie?

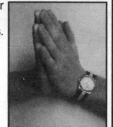

2. Eyes. Keeps your eyes very tightly closed while you are praying. If it helps, think of your eyes like an oven door and your prayer like a cheese soufflé. If you open your eyes for just a second, your cheese soufflé prayer will fall flat and you'll have to start again.

3. Posture. For some reason God prefers prayers that are made whilst in a kneeling position. Obviously, if you are unable to kneel due to arthritis or rheumatism then don't worry. God will forgive you, as it was Him that gave you the dodgy knees in the first place. But if you can smile through the pain and suffer your infirmities with love in your heart, then it's highly likely that God will look more favourably upon your prayer. For, as Mother Teresa said, suffering is beautiful, especially to the Lord.

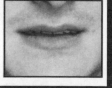

4. Words. God receives upwards of 6 billion prayers a day, so keep yours short, snappy and to the point. Start with a couple of sentences about how unworthy you are and how great He is. Then get to the meat of your prayer and beseech Him for what it is that you want and tell Him how great He is again. Don't forget to finish with the word "Amen" so that God knows you've finished and can start acting on your prayer. Or not, as the case may be.

85

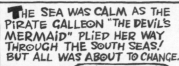

captain MORGAN AND HIS Hammond Organ

THE SEA WAS CALM AS THE PIRATE GALLEON "THE DEVIL'S MERMAID" PLIED HER WAY THROUGH THE SOUTH SEAS! BUT ALL WAS ABOUT TO CHANGE...

OMINOUS CLOUD AHOY, CAP'N!

WHAT D'YE WANT ME TO DO, CAP'N? TURN HER ATHWART, OR PULL HER AFT TO PORT?

AARR-THERE BE PLENTY O'TIME FOR STEERIN' THE SHIP AFTER WE'VE ENJOYED—

—A MEDLEY OF TUNES FROM THE TELLY ADS!

OH WE'RE HERE ON A PICNIC- YOU CAN JOIN US IF YOU'LL BE QUICK! WE'VE GOT LOTS OF TASTY GOODIES AND OF COURSE COUNTRY LIFE!

BUT CAP'N THE STORM IS GETTING CLOSER...

IT'S FRESH AND IT'S ENGLISH, AND IT'S CREAMY AS YOU COULD WISH OH YOU'LL NEVER PUT A BETTER BIT OF BUTTER ON YOUR KNIFE!

THE WIND IS GETTING UP, CAP'N! YOU MUST TAKE IN SAIL!

COME ON - ALTOGETHER NOW! YOU CAN JAM IT, MEAT PASTE IT, ON FRESH BREAD YOU REALLY TASTE IT, AND IT'S LOVELY WITH CRUMPET BUT DON'T TELL THE WIFE!

HA-HARRR!

AND WHO REMEMBERS THIS ONE? IT'S ALL YOU HAVE TO DO...DO THE SHAKE AND VAC, AND PUT THE FRESHNESS BACK... DO THE SHAKE AND VAC AND PUT THE FRESHNESS BACK...

...WHEN YOUR CARPET SMELLS FRESH YOUR ROOM DOES TOO-OO-OO - EVERY TIME YOU VACUUM, REMEMBER WHAT TO DO...

'ERE'S ANOTHER GOOD ONE, ME HEARTIES...

C'MON YOU SCURVY DOGS! I'M DOING ALL THE WORK HERE!

A FINGER OF FUDGE IS JUST ENOUGH, TO GIVE YOUR KIDS A TREAT! A FINGER OF FUDGE IS JUST ENOUGH - UNTIL IT'S TIME TO EAT!

IT'S FULL OF CADBURY GOODNESS, AND VERY SMALL AND NEAT— A FINGER OF FUDGE IS JUST ENOUGH TO GIVE YOUR KIDS A TREAT HA-HARR!

IF YOU LIKE A LOT OF CHOCOLATE ON YOUR BISCUIT, JOIN OUR CLUB!

SHE BE GOING DOWN, CAP'N!

AND WHO REMEMBERS THIS ONE? 'TWAS ON ALL THE TIME! CREAM MAKES SIMPLE THINGS SUPER! POUR SOME OVER YOUR PUD! CREAM WILL ALWAYS BE A NECESSITY- NOTHING TASTES QUITE AS GOOD!

ABANDON SHIP! SAVE YERSELVES! IT BE EVERY MAN FOR HIMSELF!

MWOO-AAH! BODYFORM! BODYFORM FOR YOOOU! GLUB-GLUB...

SWIM FOR YOUR LIVES, LADS!

NEXT MORNING...

NUTS!

WHA...?

WHO-OLE HAZEL NUTS... HURGH! CADBURY'S TAKE 'EM AND THEY COVER 'EM IN CHOCOLATE...

COME ON, LADS! YOU ALL KNOW THIS ONE- ALL TOGETHER NOW... SHOW 'EM—YOU'RE A SLIMCEA GIRL...!

NO, CAP'N- WE'RE OFF.

WE'VE HAD ENOUGH!

WE WANT THE LIFE OF A PROPER PIRATE... PILLAGIN' AND A' PLUNDERIN'!

DRINKIN' RUM!

AAAR! MAKIN' LILY-LIVERED LANDLUBBERS WALK THE PLANK.

DRINKIN' RUM!

AR!

AYE! NOT LISTENIN' TO THE CAPTAIN SINGIN' STUPID SONGS ALL THE TIME...

AND RUM!

LOOK! A PIRATE SHIP!

COME ON, MY LADS- LET'S JOIN THEIR CREW INSTEAD!

SHORTLY...

WELCOME ABOARD! WE CAN ALWAYS USE A FEW MORE CUT-THROATS ON "THE BLUE CORSAIR"! HA- HAARRR...

COME ON, MEN- I'LL TAKE 'EE TO MEET THE SKIPPER!

SOME NEW RECRUITS, CAPTAIN BLUESBEARD!

WELL I WOKE UP THIS MORNIN'- I HAD THEM SPANISH MAIN BLUES...

LAWD HAVE MERCY, AIN'T IT TH' TRUTH?

HE

WALKIN' DAWKINS

AT OXFORD UNIVERSITY

HELLO DEAR. **PHEWF!** WHAT A MORNING I'VE HAD!

HEAD MASTER'S HOUSE

IT'S A BUSY LIFE BEING HEADMASTER OF OXFORD UNIVERSITY!

I'M JUST GOING TO RELAX WITH A NICE CUP OF TEA AND READ THE LATEST ISSUE OF THE CHURCH 'TIMES'...

OH NO! THAT DRATTED PROFESSOR RICHARD DAWKINS HAS GOT HOLD OF MY COPY OF THE CHURCH TIMES!

HE'S RIPPED ITS ARTICLES ON CONTEMPORARY ANGLICANISM INTO SHREDS!

WELL IT'S YOUR OWN FAULT FOR NOT TAKING PROFESSOR DAWKINS OUT FOR HIS WALKIES THIS MORNING!

YOU KNOW HOW FRUSTRATED HE GETS IF HE DOESN'T EXERCISE HIS INTELLECT EVERY DAY!

GO AND TAKE HIM FOR A RUN ROUND THE NATURAL HISTORY MUSEUM, SO THAT HE CAN STRETCH HIS RATIONAL FACULTIES!

(GRUMBLE GRUMBLE)

I CAN'T BE BOTHERED TO TAKE DAWKINS ALL THE WAY TO THE MUSEUM...

GOD

I'LL JUST TIE THIS STUFFED MODEL OF AN ALL-POWERFUL AND BENEVOLENT GOD TO THE ROTATING WASHING LINE...

HO HO!

GOD

ARF! ARF! ARF! ARF!

ARF! ARF! ARF! ARF!

PROFESSOR DAWKINS WILL CHASE THAT IRRATIONAL CONCEPT ROUND AND ROUND IN CIRCLES FOR HOURS!

WOW! DAWKINS'S LEAD HAS SNAPPED — WHERE'S HE OFF TO?

ARF! ARF! ARF!

YIKES! HE'S SPOTTED THAT LITTLE GIRL WRITING A LETTER TO THE TOOTH FAIRY!

GROWL! SNARL! SLAVER!

Deer Toof Fairy

HE'LL GIVE HER A RIGHT SAVAGING FOR BELIEVING IN SUCH NONSENSE!

PHWEEEP! DAWKINS! HERE, BOY! LOOK WHAT I'VE GOT...

SCREEEECH!

IT'S A HOLY COMMUNION WAFER WHICH, THE CHURCH TELLS US, LITERALLY BECOMES THE BODY OF CHRIST THROUGH THE PROCESS OF TRANSUBSTANTIATION.

HO HO! C'MON BOY!

ARF! ARF!

PROFESSOR DAWKINS JUST CAN'T RESIST SINKING HIS TEETH INTO A BIT OF THEOLOGICAL CODSWALLOP!

YOW! HE'S GONE STRAIGHT PAST ME!

WHAT'S HE AFTER NOW?

OO-ER! IT'S A BUNCH OF KIDS ON A 'HARRY POTTER' THEMED FLOAT!

GRAND SCHOOLS PARADE TODAY

HOGWARTS

ROWF! ROWF!

HOORAY! WE CAN DO MAGIC!

AND THEY'RE PRETENDING TO HAVE SUPERNATURAL POWERS, IN A GAME OF MAKE-BELIEVE'!

HEY, LOOK AT ME — I'M INVISIBLE!

NO YOU'RE NOT! NO YOU'RE NOT!

WHEEE! AND I CAN FLY!

NO YOU CAN'T

DAWKINS! (GASP!) COME BACK HERE!

HOURS LATER

(PANT, WHEEZE)

TOWN

THE PESKY PROF CHASED THAT FLOAT FOR MILES!

BACK AT HOME

I'M TAKING NO MORE CHANCES!

I'LL CHAIN HIM UP TO HIS KENNEL IN THE GARDEN.

SHORTLY

PROF

I'LL JUST TAKE DAWKINS HIS SUPPER, DEAR.

OH NO! PROFESSOR DAWKINS HAS DISAPPEARED!

HE'S BEEN STOLEN!

MEANWHILE, IN A BARN

OK GENTLEMEN, PLACE YOUR BETS!

GURR! SNARL! SNAP GROWL! SLAVER!

FRANKEN CARSON

THE QUIET Lancashire town of Fleetwood was in the grip of terror last night after *FRANK CARSON* was briefly brought back to life during a thunder storm. A bolt of lightning struck a crypt in which the late comedian was interred and it is thought that this powerful electrical pulse somehow re-animated his corpse. The revivified funnyman then staggered out of the graveyard wearing extremely heavy boots and went on a joke-telling rampage in a nearby housing estate.

Horror comic: Carson's long dead corpse was galvanised by bolt of lightning.

"It's a Cracker" comic re-animated by electrical storm

Locals were alarmed to see the Irish funnyman, who died in 2012, lumbering around with his arms outstretched near a parade of shops.

"He was uttering strange guttural noises, whilst trying to tell a joke about three Irishmen on a building site," said onlooker Edna Woodplumpton. "But there was a pitiful look of confusion and fear in his eyes, as if he didn't know why he had been brought back to life."

mob

Frightened residents eventually formed a mob outside the post office on Hesketh Road. "Everyone loved Frank when he was alive and cracking jokes ten to the dozen on *The Comedians*,"

said mob spokesperson Ada Bilsborrow. "But seeing him as a re-vivified cadaver lurching round near the shops by the light of the moon was certainly no laughing matter. He had to be destroyed."

dance

Brandishing pitchforks and flaming torches, the vociferous rabble drove the "It's the way I tell 'em" gagster's blasphemous monstrosity up Beechey

Avenue, along Garstang Road and eventually back into the cemetery.

Here, Carson retreated back into his mausoleum which was then set on fire and burnt to the ground. "You could see the shape of him writhing around in the flames," said local innkeeper and mob member Elswick Inskip.

The Lord Mayor of Fleetwood told local TV

news that measures would be put in place to prevent other deceased comics buried in the town being similarly re-animated.

gordon

"Locals can be reassured that we are bringing forward plans to fit lightning conductors to all graves containing late comedians

as a matter of urgency," said Councillor Barton Nateby.

"We will also be fitting a glass box near the cemetery gates containing an emergency wooden stake and a mallet, and a gun loaded with a silver bullet, in case any of them come back as a Dracula or a werewolf," Councillor Nateby added.

Forward to the Future *with Professor Frank Forwardtothefuture*

THE YEAR IS 2020, and the global population has exploded to 50 trillion. The human race has outgrown the Earth and must now find a fresh new world to colonise. 20 dauntless pioneers have been selected - probably on some sort of Saturday evening television game show - to colonise our nearest neighbour in the Solar System... Mars. These 21st century Pilgrim Fathers and Mothers - 10 men and 10 women - must make the 8-month journey to the Red Planet aboard a new kind of spaceship, one equipped for long term deep space travel. Whilst nobody can imagine what perils they will face when they reach their destination, the difficulties they will encounter during their long voyage have already been well thought through by scientists. Let's take a look at some of the incredible technical challenges that will have to be surmounted before man can finally blast off on a...

Mission to MARS!

ONE OF THE biggest problems astronauts flying to Mars will face is one of boredom; with nothing to do, the 250-day voyage could feel like 250 years. To combat the humdrum routine of spaceship life, the craft will be equipped with an Entertainments Podule *(1)*, containing a state-of-the-art 52" plasma screen TV with Netflix, Amazon Prime, Sky Atlantic and BT Sport. To keep the lady astronauts up to date with all their favourite soaps, a weekly digest of all the goings-on in Albert Square, Weatherfield and the Woolpack will be beamed up to the ship from Jodrell Bank every Sunday afternoon for them to watch after they've cleared away the dinner pots. Each night, the men astronauts will be able to tune into a selection of programmes that they are interested in too, on adult subscription channels including Red Hot TV, Television X and XXX Mums. Also provided to help them while away the endless hours of intergalactic travel will be a selection of traditional boardgames, such as Ker-Plunk, Cluedo and Hungry Hippos, all magnetized to enable them to be played in the weightless vacuum of space. But there won't be a set of Mousetrap; in parabolic flight tests aboard NASA's zero-gravity aircraft, it was found that when the big ball landed on the seesaw, the diver simply shot up in the air and floated about instead of landing in the wooden tub, meaning that the trap never went off.

EVERYONE likes to kick back with a drink in the evening, and the crew of MTM2020 will be encouraged to socialise in their very own On-Board Bar *(2)*. But as you can imagine, taking enough booze to keep twenty astronauts topped-up for eight months would mean the craft would be too heavy to leave the launchpad. The mariners will therefore make beer on board, re-cycling their urine with special genetically engineered space yeast to create their own gravity-free "home brew". You might think such a beer would be unpalatable, but in tasting tests at the NASA Jet Propulsion Laboratory, it was rated top against six leading brands of Spanish lager. The untreated urine came second. There will also be a selection of soft drinks available for whoever is driving the spaceship that night.

IN THE PRESSURISED, oxygen-rich atmosphere of the space capsule, the slightest spark could lead to a catastrophic explosion, so smoking will be strictly prohibited for the duration of the flight; anyone wishing to light up will have to go outside the Main Airlock *(3)*. And cigarettes aren't merely a safety risk; they also pose a logistical nightmare for interplanetary flight scientists, for a light-smoking astronaut on 20 a day will require a whopping 250 packs to get them through the 8-month trip, whilst a heavy smoker could easily puff their way through 1000 or more. As a result, cigarettes will be at a premium on any interplanetary mission and all dog-ends will have to be recycled, even ones with a duck's arse on the end. And it might not be good news for health-conscious vapers either, as NASA bosses have not yet decided whether they will be permitted to spark up their e-cigs inside the spaceship or whether they'll have to join their tobacco-addicted pals out on the inter-stellar cancer verandah.

WITH 20 ASTRONAUTS aboard for 8 months, NASA statisticians have calculated that between them, the crew will celebrate 13.333333 birthdays during the flight to Mars. For this reason, 14 long life birthday cakes will have to be included in the Ship's Stores *(4)*. But statistics are not an exact science, and it could be that no crew member - or indeed every crew member - has a birthday during the 40 million mile journey. For this reason, 20 cakes will actually be packed, just to be on the safe side. What's more, if the rocket blasts off on any day of the year after April 25th, the festive season is bound to occur at some point during the flight, so an artificial Christmas tree and a cardboard box of decorations will also be packed. A real tree is out of the question as a single dropped needle could easily short out a delicate navigation computer circuit, sending the spacecraft spiralling out of control into the Sun, or alternatively get stuck in an astronaut's sock.

THE PROVISION of home comforts will play an important part in keeping up crew morale during the mammoth voyage to the Red Planet. Everyone loves biscuits, and astronauts are no exception. A tasty nibble, "dunked" into their afternoon cuppa via a tea-tight airlock in the side of the cup, will provide a welcome and cheering reminder of the lives they have left behind and to which they can never return. However, with space at a premium in the Galley Stowage Compartments *(5)*, the only biscuits that will be taken on the mission will be square or rectangular ones that can be packed efficiently to maximise the limited storage capacity available and which do not waste valuable space like their round counterparts. So Malted Milk, Nice and Custard Creams will be blasting off to Mars, whilst Hob-Nobs, Ginger Nuts and Jammy Dodgers will be left languishing on the launchpad. But there is a crumb of comfort for sweet-toothed astronauts who crave the occasional choccy treat. Food technologists at Cape Canaveral are working on a revolutionary prototype that they hope will be ready in time for the 2020 mission - a fully tessellatable hexagonal chocolate digestive.

WE ALL LOVE a delicious curry, but sadly most Indian takeaways impose a limit on deliveries of around 5 miles or so. With its 4 Scramjet Plasma Engines *(6)* generating a thrust of more than 50 million Newtons apiece, the spaceship will experience a vertical acceleration force of 6G, meaning it will be out of free delivery range just 6 seconds into its one-way 8-month flight to the farside of the galaxy. But that doesn't mean that the astronauts aboard will never again be able to enjoy their favourite spicy curry on a Friday night. Stowed on board MTM2020 will be an array of scientifically formulated three-part freeze-dried curry kits: 1. A tiny pill that accurately recreates the flavour of any Indian food from a gentle Biryani to a hot Murg Phaal. 2. A small ampule of liquid which is designed to give the astronaut stomach cramps and an uncomfortable night of gastric reflux. 3. The following morning a small tube of caustic gel is rubbed onto the anus to give an authentic burnt arsehole sensation.

Next Week in Forward to the Future - We look at Leeds in the year 2020

20 THINGS YOU NEVER KNEW ABOUT THE GREAT BRITISH BAKE OFF

1 *The Great British Bake Off* almost didn't make it onto our screens. Luckily, in 1922 John Reith became general manager of a new national broadcasting company funded by a licence fee levied upon users. Initially concentrating on radio, the company eventually expanded its services to encompass television, initially via a 405 lines black and white system. Just under 80 years later, an independent production company approached the BBC with a proposal for a weekly baking competition, to be broadcast in full colour at an increased resolution of 625 lines (interlaced) and the commissioning team felt the show had a good chance of gaining a wide audience in a key target demographic. *The Great British Bake Off* was born and the rest is history!

2 Mel and Sue weren't the first choice as hosts for *Bake Off*. In 2010, producers approached another well-loved British double act – Mike and Bernie Winters – to front the new show. However, their agent declined the offer because Bernie Winters had by that point been dead for 19 years, and Mike was already booked in to die in 2013.

3 The smallest cake ever baked was made in the third series by the world's smallest man Calvin Phillips. His microscopic recipe called for one atom of flour, an electron of butter and an up quark of butter. The mixture was baked at 180° in a Large Hadron Collider for 2 nanoseconds. However, he had got his calculations wrong and the cake came out of the cyclotron badly undercooked. It was only Phillips's showstopper – 24 Eccles Cakes on the head of a pin – that saved him from elimination that week.

4 The show has been credited with introducing the term "soggy bottom" into the English lexicon. Indeed, so popular has the expression become that "Soggy Bottom" was fourth in a list of 2016's most popular girls' names, after Amelia, Olivia and Brexit.

5 Presenter Sue Perkins's name is uncannily similar to that of a famous brand of cigarettes - Superkings - even though, amazingly, Sue doesn't smoke! Even more amazingly, if she did smoke, she wouldn't spark up her namesake cigarettes, preferring instead the milder Park Drive brand or even ladies' favourites, Dunhill Consulate.

6 The *GBBO* format has been one of the BBC's most successful exports, with countless countries around the world producing their own versions of the show. In America millions tune into *The Great American Cookie Cookout*, whilst German fans never miss *Der Endgültige Sieg des Stärkeren Bäcker*. Meanwhile, in the Netherlands, viewers gather round their TVs to watch fully nude contestants take part in *The Super XXX Randy Cake Sex Show*.

7 If someone offers you a slice of yellow cake, think twice before tucking in. That's because yellow cake – also called *urania* – is a radioactive substance used in the nuclear fuel enrichment process with a half-life of 4 billion years. To put that into some kind of perspective, each slice of a yellow cake would itself have a half life of 500 million years, meaning that if you scoffed a slice now, it wouldn't be until November 500,002,016 until you had finally burnt off all the calories.

8 Another type of yellow cakes you probably wouldn't want to eat are the ones that sit in pub urinals to make your piss smell like lemony piss and snare pubes before they go down the plug.

9 *GBBO* judge Mary Berry is extremely old. Her actual age is unknown, but BBC insiders say she is still as sprightly as a woman half her age, whatever it is.

10 Mel and Sue's ages, if added together, probably come to about the same as Mary Berry's age. Although, since Mary Berry's age is unknown, it's difficult to say with any certainty.

11 According to mathematicians, if you multiply Paul Hollywood's age by that of Mel Giedroyc, and divide the result by Sue Perkins's age, you will always get a prime number.

12 If the ages of all the *Great British Bake Off* presenters are added together, and the sum of those ages is divided by the product of multiplying them all together, the log of the square root of that number could be found using the formula... where A1 is the age of Mary Berry (if known), A2 is the age of Paul Hollywood, A3 is the age of Sue Perkins and A4 is the age of Mel Giedroyc.

$$x = \text{Log} \sqrt{\frac{\sum A1 \ldots A4}{A1 \cdot A2 \cdot A3 \cdot A4}}$$

13 If a circle is drawn with a diameter equal to Mel Giedroyc's age, then the circumference of that circle would be $\pi \times$ her age and the area of that circle would be $\pi \times$ half her age squared.

14 And the volume of a sphere would be $\frac{4}{3}\pi \times$ half her age cubed.

15 Sue Perkins is the only *GBBO* presenter to wear glasses, and as a result is regularly teased by her co-stars. On her first day of filming for the series, Paul Hollywood stole her glasses and threw them to Mary Berry, who stamped on them. A laughing Mel Giedroyc then handed her back her shattered specs, telling her: "Here, give these to your mum, four-eyes."

16 Laser-eyed silver fox Paul Hollywood refuses to use the Elsan chemical toilets provided in the *Bake Off* tent. Each time the housewives' favourite requires a tinkle or a plop, he gets in his car and drives the 260 miles to his luxury home in Cheshire, before doing his business, running his hands under the tap and then driving all the way back.

17 In a typical series of *GBBO*, the contestants bake their way through an amazing 4,000kg of flour. That's the same weight as 8,000 500g bags of sugar. They also get through 4,000kg of sugar. That's the same weight as 16,000 250g bags of flour.

18 In series 2, whilst making a batch of scones one of the contestants was killed after being dragged into a Kitchenaid mixer. Luckily, he had an identical twin brother who was also a keen baker, and he was persuaded to take over his place in the competition.

19 Famous *Bake Off* fans include Bank of England governor Mark Carney, former Monkee Mickey Dolenz, Icelandic weirdo Bjork, former TV magician Ali Bongo, former TV magician the Great Soprendo and that woman who put a cat in a wheelie bin.

20 Other celebrity fans of the show include that man who chased his dog whilst shouting "Fenton!", Techno Viking, the Trololololol man and one of the girls out of *2 Girls 1 Cup*.

● **EVERYBODY** loves their granny, don't they? Well count me out. I *hate* my granny. And I hate *your* granny too.

In fact, I hate *all* grannies, every single last one of them. With their twinkly smiles, pensions and bags of Werther's Originals, they make my blood boil. Call me unfeeling if you like, but the sooner every last granny in Britain is dead and buried, the better.

And I'll be the first one to dance on their graves.

COUNTRY IS AN EYESORE

● **SO BRITAIN** boasts some of the most beautiful countryside in the world, does it? *Well no, frankly, it doesn't. I hate it.* I hate and despise Britain's landscape from the bottom of my heart.

I'd rather go blind than have to look at this green and pleasant land for another single second.

It should be carpet-bombed until it's nothing more than a scorched wasteland. *And the sooner the better, as far as I'm concerned.*

Puppies and kittens? Pass the sick bag!

● **KITTENS** and puppies. Aren't they cute? Well *no*, as it happens, *they're not.* I hate them. With their big eyes, little wet noses and waggy tails, they make me sick to the very pit of my stomach.

And what's more, I hate anyone who owns a kitten or a puppy too.

If I had my way, all kittens and puppies would be be tied up in a sack with a few bricks, and then thrown in the nearest canal.

And then their owners after them.

NOT NICE TO SEE YOU

● **I'LL TELL** you who I hate. *Nice people*, that's who. With their smiling faces, their good deeds and their cheerily helpful demeanour, I simply *can't stand them*. Pardon me while I stick my fingers down my throat.

Hanging's too good for nice people. They deserve worse. *Much worse.*

The sooner we make niceness a capital offence the better.

And I'll pull the lever.

● **WANT** to know a secret? *I hate everything*. Lock, stock and barrel, if it is in the world I have nothing but total and utter contempt for it. Spoons? *I hate them*. Trees? *They are repugnant*. Newts? *Don't get me started on newts*. Love? *Hate it*, pure and simple.

And the same goes for anything else that exists, has ever existed or will ever exist.

I say roll on the end of the world, when this universe falls into a black hole. *And good riddance to it too.*

FRU T. BUNN the MASTER BAKER & HIS GINGERBREAD SEX DOLLS

RIGHT, WELL I'M TAKING CHELSEA TO THE HOSPITAL FOR HER TEST RESULTS, THEN FRUBERT.

WHA.? OH, RIGHT YOU ARE, DEAR.

ARE YOU SURE YOU DON'T WANT TO COME? THE SPECIALIST SAID...

QUITE SURE, THANK-YOU. I THINK I WOULD FIND IT ALL TOO UPSETTING, YOU KNOW.

SEE YOU LATER, THEN. WE'LL BE GONE ABOUT AN HOUR.

ABOUT AN HOUR, OKAY.

OOPS! NEARLY FORGOT MY GLOVES!

SPOLT BASTARD

IN THE SCHOOLYARD...

TIMMY, MY LOVE... HOW I'VE MISSED YOU! HOW WAS YOUR FIRST DAY AT BIG SCHOOL?

IT WAS GREAT! I WAS THE BEST AT EVERYTHING! BEST AT P.E. BEST AT SPELLING, BEST AT MATHS, BEST AT ART...

OF COURSE YOU WERE!

OF COURSE YOU DID...

...I HAD THE BEST TRAINERS, THE BEST PENCIL CASE, THE BEST SATCHEL, THE BEST LUNCHBOX, THE BEST MOBILE PHONE...

...AND THE WORST MOTHER!

OF COURSE YOU...

...WHAT!?... BUT, TIMMY... WHAT DO YOU MEAN?

WHAT DO YOU MEAN, WHAT DO I MEAN?...

JUST LOOK AROUND YOU, WOMAN...

...EVERYBODY ELSE HAS GOT A YUMMY MUMMY TO PICK THEM UP. THEY'RE ALL ATTRACTIVE THIRTYSOMETHINGS!

...AND LOOK AT YOU, YOU DOWDY OLD FRUMP!.. YOU'RE LIKE A BALLOON WITH THE AIR LET OUT

ALL THE OTHER CHILDREN DIDN'T KNOW YOU WERE MY MUM!... THEY THOUGHT YOU WERE MY GREAT GREAT GREAT GREAT GREAT GREAT GREAT GREAT GREAT GRANDMOTHER!

OH, NO TIMMY, NO!

YES THEY DID!...I DIDN'T KNOW WHERE TO PUT MY FACE... I WAS SO ASHAMED!

OH, MY POPPET... I'M SO SORRY!

UTTERLY HUMILIATED!

TOMORROW WHEN YOU PICK ME UP, YOU'D BETTER BE LOOKING YOUNG AND ATTRACTIVE AND YUMMY. OR I'M GOING TO RUDDY WELL KICK OFF, DO YOU HEAR ME, WOMAN?

YES!, YES, OF COURSE! I'LL SORT MYSELF OUT TONIGHT, I PROMISE

SEE THAT YOU BLIMMING WELL DO

PUT SOME MAKE-UP ON... AND SOME GLOSSY LIPSTICK FOR GOD'S SAKE

YES, MY LOVE!

AND PUT SOME TRENDIER CLOTHES ON INSTEAD OF THOSE POTATO SACKS YOU USUALLY WEAR

YES, MY LOVE

AND TAKE THOSE STUPID GLASSES OFF

OF COURSE, MY ANGEL

THEY MAKE YOU LOOK IDIOTIC...

...LIKE BRAINS OUT OF THUNDERBIRDS

AND DON'T YOU DARE END UP LOOKING LIKE MUTTON DRESSED AS LAMB...

NO, MY POPPET

...I'LL NOT HAVE YOU EMBARRASS ME IN THE PLAYGROUND AGAIN...

IT'S BAD FOR MY SELF ESTEEM!

SHORTLY...

A LA MODE
BOUTIQUE DE FASHION

NEXT DAY...

BYE BYE, CHILDREN! SEE YOU TOMORROW

TIMMY, MY DARLING... HOW I'VE MISSED YOU!

WELL, TIMMY... DO I LOOK OKAY?

...ERM...YOU KNOW... ERM... YOUNG AND... ER...YUMMY?

HE GETS PICKED UP FROM SCHOOL BY HIS BIG SISTER WHO'S A MODEL...

...A MODEL FOR FLIP'S SAKE!

...AND SHE GETS PICKED UP BY THE FAMILY AU PAIR WHO IS SWEDISH AND EIGHTEEN AND DROP DEAD RUDDY GORGEOUS!

LOOK AT HER!...

...AND LOOK AT YOURSELF!

NEXT DAY...

LETTERBOCKS

..........email: letters@viz.co.uk...........

ST★R LETTER

MOTOR racing chiefs say that the current F1 rules are designed to make the sport more aligned with the everyday motorist. If that were the case, following his crash at the Australian Grand Prix, Fernando Alonso should have scarpered into the nearest housing estate and hid in a wheelie bin for a few hours, while a helicopter hovered overhead to try and find him. Come on Bernie, pull your finger out.

Steve Bates, Danbury

I PAID 9p today, for a single red onion. That price presumably includes overheads, transport costs, and profit margins for everybody involved in getting it out of the ground and onto the supermarket shelf. There can't have been much in it for them. If I were an onion farmer, I'd make big expensive tellys instead.

Andrew Hussey, Gainsborough

THE other day by my 4-year-old boy challenged me to count to 1 million. Can you imagine both his and my disappointment when, at 175,654, I coughed and followed through?

Tim Buktu, Timbuktu

"I AM a satellite I'm out of control" sings Freddie Mercury on the Queen hit *Don't Stop Me Now*. Surely "I am a satellite I'm fucking out of control" is a stronger statement and emphasises how out of control he is. An opportunity missed, in my opinion.

Gary Smith, Dalkeith

WHEN you send food back to the kitchen, you're basically saying "Can I have the chef rub his genitals over this please?" And I should know, as I was head chef at a countryside pub for two-and-a-half years until they installed CCTV.

Peter Crompton, Sunderland

WHEN adjusting our clocks for British Summer Time and Greenwich Mean Time, we are always reminded by the saying "Spring forward, fall back." However, my mate Alberto is an acrobat in a circus and during his performance he sometimes springs back, sometimes forward and sometimes falls forward, sometimes back. Over the years the clocks in his caravan have got so out of sync that he has a roaring fire in July and wears shorts and flip flops in February.

Horlicks the clown, Somewhere-on-the-road

I DON'T know why they call it Good Friday. On that day this year I fell off my bike and broke my collarbone. Yet another example of religious propaganda spouted to the masses.

Timmy Tibbs, Higher Walton

WHY does Theresa May have someone to open her fucking car door for her, the lazy twat? And her pal who fucked up the budget also has a door opener, the just-as-lazy twat. It drives me fucking bonkers thinking about it. If they can't open car doors, they shouldn't be running the fucking country.

Damian Birnie, email

IMAGINE my disgust the other day when my wife came home early while I was giving her best friend a munch. If she'd come home when she said she would, we'd have been finished. I can't believe she lied about what time she'd be home. To be honest it makes it hard for me to trust her again.

Keith Queef, Ilanllyfni

IN accordance with government instructions, I put my clock forward at 1:00 am on Sunday March 27th. All that happened was it fell off the mantelpiece and broke. Thanks for nothing.

Tim Buktu, Timbuktu

IT'S a little known fact that cheese can actually be harmful to a mouse's digestive system. That's why I always load my mouse traps with a nice healthy homemade blend of fats and seeds.

Warren Rabbit, Nuneaton

MY 23-year-old son phoned me the other day to ask "Is this bacon cooked yet?" This came a week after his 19-year-old brother had called from university to say "My shoe lace has broken. What shall I do?" Have any other readers raised such a couple of fuckwitts?

Hector Plywood, Harpendon

RIGHT Said Fred's Richard Fairbrass famously complained that he was too sexy for his shirt. Well I work at the refunds and returns counter at my local M&S, and I would politely tell him to go fuck himself if he tried to pull that kind of shit on my watch.

Ada Brainstorm, Newcastle

ONE of my pubes formed a perfect ampersand. Have any other readers' hair from their frontal genital area formed logograms?

Ben Green, email

"SMOKE alarms save lives," it says on the side of the fire service response vehicle. What a load of old nonsense. My wife recently choked on a golf ball and even as her face turned purple our smoke alarm didn't go off.

Scott Chegg, Felchester

WHAT a con this so-called Irvine Welsh is. Irvine Scottish, more like. And to make matters worse, he lives in Ireland. You couldn't make it up.

Mike Rampton, London

FOR years we have been told that good manners cost nothing. Yet when I replied to a text thanking my roofer for his quote, the telephone compan[y] charged me 10p.

Steven Martin, Pee[...]

I WAS disgusted the other day when the obituary column of my local newspaper printed that I ha[d] died. Not only that, they got my date of birth, place of residence and family details all wrong. As a result I had to storm into the funeral to tell everyone I was still alive[.] They told me that there was another John Smith living locally, and after speaking t[o] his relatives and opening hi[s] coffin I saw that it was true. We all had a good laugh about it after.

John Smith, Lowe[...] Llandwro[...]

WHILE out driving the other day I was astounded to see the car in front of me had my bank card's PIN number on its number plate for all the world to see. Have any of your readers come across suc[h] a flagrant banking security breach?

Mojo King, Doublin[...]

ANY Christian will tell you that Easter is far more important than Christmas. But I find this har[d] to believe, because you get loads of presents at Christma[s] whereas at Easter you only g[et] a crappy chocolate egg and a bun with an X on it.

Mr Cordwainer, N'hampto[n]

AFTER pondering on the government and NHS guidelines about everyone having two alcohol-free days a week, I have decided to have four alcohol-free half-days a wee[k] instead. I think this would b[e] much better, as it meets the guidelines whilst spreading the boring days out across the week a lot better.

Dave, E[...]

WANK SPENCER

Panel 1: HOW ARE YOU ENJOYING YOUR NEW TELESCOPE, DARLING? — I'VE JUST FINISHED SETTING IT UP, LOVE!

Panel 2: NOW, LET'S SEE WHAT THE MOON HAS TO OFFER TONIGHT... — GUMPH!

Panel 3: SO... I'VE BROUGHT YOU A NICE HOT CHOCOLATE, DEAR... — SPROING!

Panel 4: ERM... WHAT ARE YOU DOING BEHIND THAT BUSH?! — OOOH BETTY!

WHAT'S YOUR FAVOURITE PRINCE SONG?

THE UNTIMELY DEATH of the *Artist Formerly Known as Prince* at the tragically young age of 57 has left a pint-sized purple hole in all our hearts. We went out on the streets to ask members of the great British public to name their favourite Prince song, and tell us what memories it evokes of the late Paisley Park popster...

"...I was a milkman for forty years, and my favourite Prince track would have to be *Cream* from his 1991 album *Diamonds and Pearls*. I used to sing it to myself when I was making my rounds, and the line "Cream, get on top" always used to make me laugh, because the cream does indeed rise to the top as its higher fat content means that it is less dense than the other milk in the bottle."

Ernest Price, retired milkman

"...I'm a dairy farmer, so my favourite Prince track has always been *Cream*. I sing it to my cows every morning while I'm milking them, and do you know, I think it actually increases their yield. One day I sang his other song *Sexy Mother Fucker* to them as an experiment and when I'd finished there was 4 gallons less than usual in the tank."

Arthur Hosier, farmer

"...As chairman of the Milk Marketing Board, with a long-standing professional interest in all aspects of dairy produce, my favourite Prince record has always been *Cream*, which reached number 15 in the hit parade back in the early nineties. The lyrics remind me of happier times in the milk business, when delicious, full-cream gold-top was one of our best-selling lines. These days it's all this semi-skimmed bollocks."

Sir Richard Trehane, Chairman of the Milk Marketing Board

I WONDER if any of your readers are submarine commanders. If so, could you keep an eye out for my Auntie Susan's referee's whistle? It fell out of her handbag and went overboard when she was rummaging about for her fags on the Newcastle to Bergen ferry in 1954. It was an Acme Thunderer and it had great sentimental value as it was given to her by her husband Arthur as a keepsake. I don't have any specific grid references, she just knows it was somewhere in the North Sea between England and Norway.

Danny Volume, Liverpool

Let's see if we can get Danny's Auntie Susan's whistle back. Could all Viz-reading submariners keep an eye out for a 1950s vintage Acme Thunderer referee's whistle when they're between England and Norway, and if they spot it, write and let us know.

I THINK it's marvellous that the Queen keeps being voted back in as monarch, year in, year out, and at her age too. She must hold some kind of record by now. Well done Ma'am, you're a testament to our successful and sensible democratic system. May you have a long and happy retirement when you finally decide to hang up your sparkly hat.

Sir Geraint LT, London

WHEN I was a little boy my grandad used to pull coins out of my ear on every visit to his house. I grew up thinking there was something wrong with me. The worst thing was, he died without telling anybody how he did it. I guess I'll never know.

Dannyboy, Midunbury

DO any of your readers know who the patron saint of televisions is? It's just that mine's on the blink and I've been quoted £300 to have it fixed, so I thought I'd try having a pray. It doesn't seem to work for most people who try it, I know, but it's worth a go before I shell out.

Teddy Flamingou, email

THE TV show *Songs of Praise* was broadcast from our local church recently and as we left the church, Diane Louise-Jordan asked us: "What would you change about your partner?" to which I replied: "She's not that keen on anal." To my astonishment they never broadcast it. But when they asked the old couple behind us the same question and they said something about the Bible, they were on BBC1.

Iwan Carr, Upper Llandwrog

THE kids of today have it easy. Teenagers of my generation had to interact face to face with classmates they fancied. These days they just email photos of their private parts and wait for a response. It seems lazy to me, but I suppose it's progress of sorts.

Mr L Buzzard, Bedfordshire

THESE modern so-called celebrities infuriate me. They all whinge about how stressful life is while they ponce about doing ballroom dancing or baking cakes. In the 70s they were all eating a Mars Bar out of a groupie's fanny, shoving gerbils up their arse or having a pint of spunk pumped out of their stomach. They were real celebrities.

Marjorie Testicles-Brown, St Agnes

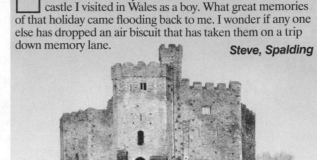

I JUST did a really loud fart that had the smell of a castle I visited in Wales as a boy. What great memories of that holiday came flooding back to me. I wonder if any one else has dropped an air biscuit that has taken them on a trip down memory lane.

Steve, Spalding

HOW come you never see any of them Riverdancers on the telly nowadays? They used to be on all the time, jumping about all over the shop like fucking lunatics, but not any more. Come on, the Irish, pull your fingers out and get leaping.

Bobby Bowels, Merthyr Tydfil

I BELIEVE the government has acted prematurely in trialling driverless vehicles on our streets. I encountered my first one last week as it slowly reversed down a hill on the wrong side of the road before swerving sharply across the other carriageway, mounting a kerb and demolishing a garden wall. The man chasing it, presumably its owner, seemed similarly unimpressed with the new technology.

Richard Cranberry, Idle

WHY do people only want to eat tuna if it's been friends with a dolphin? If anything I think that it makes eating it even more heartbreaking.

Gustav Fox, Shoreditch

THESE activity trackers are not as smart as people make out. My fitness watch just congratulated me for getting up off my fat arse and moving about. What it didn't realise was that I was on my way to the kitchen to make a sandwich and help myself to a large bag of crisps.

Matthew Jones, Ramsbottom

TOP TIPS

CREATE the Primark experience at home by scattering all your clothes on the floor and running your wife over with a pushchair.

Will Mylchreest, Leamington Spa

CANT find a torch and need to see in the attic? Simply put an extension lead onto your fridge, then manoeuvre it into the attic and open the door.

Chris Heel, Newbridge

MANCHESTER bands. Ask the venue staff to turn up the heating so you don't have to wear your coats on stage.

Bret, Stalybridge

FEEL like a heavyweight boxing champion by taking off your belt and wearing it over your shoulder.

Richard Woolford, email

FOOL people into thinking you're a professional boxer by running everywhere with a towel over your shoulders while your friend cycles alongside you.

Damian McCleave, email

PRETEND you're a Formula One driver by remaining in your car while you're at Kwik-Fit.

Will Mylchreest, Leamington Spa

SAVE money on expensive Teasmade machines by setting your wife or girlfriend's alarm 5 minutes before yours.

Mark Graham, Middlesbrough

MOTORISTS. Always keep four muscular hamsters in your car boot. In the event of a breakdown, place one in each tyre and you will at least make it to the nearest garage for an honest assessment of the problem.

Martin Gullible, Southampton

PRETEND you are on a Center Parcs holiday by cycling to your local Leisure Centre with your family while all politely waving at strangers and paying £40 to hire Badminton racquets.

Will Mylchreest, Leamington Spa

AUCTION SETS NEW RECORDS

A HALIFAX Brewery dipstick previously used by *It's A Knockout* judge Arthur Ellis has sold at Sothebys in New York for $19.2 million.

The three-foot piece of half-inch square softwood, marked off in abitrary increments, was bought by an anonymous bidder from Japan. In the same sale, the bright red codpiece worn by Cameo frontman *Larry Blackmon* saw the hammer fall at $15 million, whilst a pair of fawn-coloured Farah slacks worn by Tomorrow's World presenter *William Woollard* failed to meet their somewhat optimistic reserve of $8 million.

Bid-up: Hammer went down on Cameo frontman Blackmon's groinwear (above), but dungaree button (inset) aroused suspicion.

button

Meanwhile, controversy erupted at the auction rooms as the authenticity of one of the sale items was questioned. Lot 238, listed as "a brass button from the dungarees of Benny out of Crossroads", was expected to fetch more than $10 million after the Guggenhein Museum and Getty Foundation both expressed an interest in bidding for it.

intercepter

However, moments before the auction was set to start, the lot was sensa-

tionally withdrawn when *Paul Henry* - the actor who played Benny in the 1970s ATV teatime soap - contacted Sothebys to say that he had the original dungarees from the show at his home in Wednesbury and there were no buttons missing.

The seller, described as a "private Crossroads collector from Manhattan" was last night being questioned by police.

AFTER THE FESTIVE over-indulgences of December, and January's failed New Year's Resolutions, February is the time of year when we finally get serious about our health and join our local gym. And whilst health clubs used to be the preserve of an elite few, with exclusive establishments like Champneys catering to a well-heeled clientelle keen to get in shape, nowadays they are springing up everywhere and anyone can join. Tagged onto budget hotels, hastily installed in former gas showrooms or squeezed into disused call centre offices, it is estimated that there are now more than ten million health clubs in Britain. But what exactly goes on behind the doors of these temples to bodily perfection? Let's take a peek and ask...

Can YOU spot...

○ **A 40-stone man** on his first and last visit, having CPR after collapsing whilst trying to do up the laces on his trainers.

○ **A man drying his knackers** and barse with one of the communal hairdryers.

○ **Some selfish twat** taking the locker key home, thus redering it his own personal locker.

○ **A bloke** who's just popped a massive hernia after overloading a weight machine whilst trying to impress a woman.

○ **Two women** gossiping on adjacent rowing machines who, after two hours, have clocked up a hundred metres of light sculling between them.

○ **A 50-year-old man** who ran a half-marathon in his twenties, trying to match his personal best after spending the intervening three decades eating pies and smoking Capstan full strength.

○ **A woman** anxiously checking the calorie counter on her treadmill until it's clocked up enough to justify a Mars Bar out the vending machine in the foyer.

○ **An attractive middle-aged woman** who never breaks a sweat, but comes to the gym to model her new exercising outfit, which changes with every visit.

○ **A man** waiting for a woman to finish her strenuous workout on the exercise bike, who will then put his face a little too close to the saddle when adjusting the height.

○ **A couple of sexy women** who only go in once a month but nevertheless appear in all the gym's publicity photographs.

○ **The owner of the gym**, whose portfolio also includes six pubs and a chain of chip shops.

○ **An 85-year-old man** desperately hoping to postpone death by bench pressing 2 kilogrammes.

○ **A staff member** who is very hands-on when demonstrating how to use the equipment to female members.

○ **An 80-year-old woman** who swims for half an hour every night at continental drift speed, without getting her hair wet.

○ **A young man** with goggles who makes a habit of tailgating young women doing the breaststroke.

○ **A businessman** who only goes to the pool to demonstrate to young women how waterproof his £5,000 Rolex is.

○ **A 40-stone man** with circus tent swimming trunks, who stands for twenty minutes at the end of the pool splashing water over his shoulders before hauling himself out and going to sit in the steam room.

○ **An aquarobics class**, with a super-fit 20-year-old instructor playing techno music whilst half a dozen deaf, incontinent octagenarian women bob up and down in the water.

○ **Someone** using an exercise machine incorrectly, who consequently thinks he's a lot fitter than he is.

○ **A man** who has eaten nothing but a health bar all day, watching *Man vs Food* whilst doing 10k on the cross trainer.

○ **A bloke** who has accidentally set a suicidal pace on his treadmill, but has opted for potential death rather than the embarrassment of slowing it down to a more survivable speed.

○ **A couple** paying their yearly subscriptions who, the same as every year, will never come back.

○ **A 6-stone man** who spends all night every night in the sauna in the vain hope that a gorgeous woman might walk in, they'd get chatting and one thing would lead to another, like in an *Electric Blue* video his brother once lent him.

○ **A member of staff** with a degree in Physiology, an MBA in Business Management and a PhD in Sports Psychology unblocking one of the lavatories.

HEALTH ON EARTH
SPA & GYM

can
ot... at the **Health Club?**

Next Week:
What can YOU spot at the
Potato Marketing Board?

HANG UP the bunting, unfurl your Union Jack, and prepare to use the word 'medal' as a verb - the Olympic Games are here again. Yes, as sport-lovers across the globe all turn their eyes to sunny Rio de Janeiro, the world is preparing to go absolutely Olympics bonkers. Over the years, the iconic Games have provided us Brits with some of our most treasured sporting memories - from *Chariots of Fire* star Eric Liddell's famous 400m victory to Mo Farah's legendary double gold, via Paula Radcliffe nipping off for a shit in the middle of the marathon. And the 2016 Brazilian games are already shaping up to be the best ever!

But how much do we REALLY know about this momentous 4-yearly athletic competition? When did it start? Why did it start? And who was the smallest person who's ever competed in it? On your marks ... get set ... GO! and check out...

20 THINGS YOU NEVER KNEW ABOUT THE OLYMPICS

1 THE first ever Olympic Games was held in Ancient Greece in 776 BC as part of a religious festival to honour *Phanatos* - the God of cross-platform merchandising - and *Themeses* - the God of performance-enhancing drugs.

2 THERE were no official Olympic Gameses during the First and Second World Wars, but that didn't stop sport-lovers both at home and in the trenches from hosting their own makeshift versions. In 1916, English and German troops briefly laid down their guns to stage an elaborate four-week Olympiad in the middle of no-man's land, whilst plucky Home Guard members organised a UK-based Games in 1941, using powdered javelins, hammers and relay batons, awarding each other powdered medals on a powdered podium.

3 BELIEVE it or not, the Olympics take place just ONCE every four years. This puts them in a very unique club alongside other four-yearly happenings, such as the World Cup, the leap year and Sting achieving orgasm.

4 OLYMPIC runners are famed for their outlandish celebrations, such as *Usain Bolt*'s iconic 'Lightning Bolt' and *Mo Farah*'s infamous 'Mobot'. Believe it or not, this modern tradition

of Olympians pulling a triumphant pose tenuously linked to a weak pun on their name dates as far back as the 1952 Games, when Britain's *Roger Bannister* finished fourth in the 1500m, and celebrated by stretching himself down a steep flight of stairs and allowing unruly children to slide down him.

5 THE smallest ever Olympic competitor was the world's smallest man, *Calvin Phillips*. In the 1996 Atlanta Games, Phillips tried his minuscule hand at the javelin, managing to throw a spear the size of a cocktail stick a not-so-whopping distance of 26.1cm. This went down as the worst ever throw in Olympic history, but Phillips was soon stripped of even this record when officials forced him to urinate into a beaker the size of a sweetcorn kernel, and discovered microscopic performance-enhancing drugs in his system.

6 BETWEEN 1945 and 1989, the German Olympic Committee cheated in every competition... by entering TWO TEAMS - Germany and West Germany. Nobody watching noticed their 'double entry' scam and the unscrupulous nation swept the board in 10 consecutive games.

7 ALTHOUGH shameful, the German scheme was so successful that it inspired copycat cheating from other countries. Since 1953, Korea has been pulling the same low stunt.

8 IN MUCH the same way that no two snowflakes are exactly the same, no two Olympic Gameses are ever exactly the same either. There's always something slightly different about each one - be it the year they occur, the city where they're held, or the shit cartoon mascot that adorns all their overpriced merchandise.

9 THE 1984 Games in Los Angeles are probably best remembered for the inclusion of *Cluedo* in the official Olympic programme. The Gold medal in the event was eventually claimed by Norway's

Pietr Larssensen, who correctly accused Miss Scarlet in the billiard room with the revolver, in front of 80,000 jubilant fans.

10 WOMEN'S Beach Volleyball currently holds the title of the most wanked over Olympic discipline. Scientists estimate that more than 400 PINTS of ejaculate have been released onto sofas during the event since its Olympic debut in 1992.

11 THOSE same scientists also estimate that if all the tissues used to clean that spunk up were put together, they would make a gloopy tissue the size of a giant football pitch the size of Wales.

12 BELIEVE it or not, the iconic, three-tiered Olympic podium we all know and love was originally meant to be the same height all the way across. Officials at the 732 BC Games in Athens ordered a completely flat, 2ft-high stone platform on which the top three competitors could be awarded their medals. However, the building firm they employed - Xerxes & Son - got the measurements wrong and constructed a block of three slightly different heights. Xerxes Sr told the organisers his spirit level must be knackered, and assured them he was just nipping out to buy a new one. Six months later he had still failed to return, claiming his mother-in-law was very ill, and the frantic officials were left with no choice but to go ahead and use his uneven creation. And the tradition still exists to this day!

13 THE first Olympic velodrome was opened in Paris, France, in 1746. However, the magnificent state-of-the-art facility remained unused right up until 1839, when the bicycle was invented.

14 BELIEVE it or not, an Australian competitor has NEVER medalled at an Olympic running event. That's because, in countries below the equator, runners actually run BACKWARDS around the track - a phenomenon which still baffles scientists today.

15 ALTHOUGH they held the summer games in 2000, Australia has never hosted the Winter games. That's because Australia, as well as near neighbours New Zealand, hold their Winter in the Summer when there is no snow.

16 AS EVERYONE knows, American swimming star *Michael Phelps* is currently the most decorated Olympian of all time, having won a whopping 22 gold medals in three separate Olympiads. What most people don't know, however, is that Phelps can't actually swim. "I just never quite got the hang of it," he told the *Wisconsin Prepuce* last year. "Truth be told, I'm terrified of water, so whenever I'm forced to jump into some, I just thrash my arms and legs about as quickly and wildly as I can until I reach land. It seems to be working so far."

17 IN 2012, cyclist *Bradley Wiggins* became the first ever mod to win an Olympic medal. Prior to this, the closest a sideburn-sporting parka fan had ever come to Olympic glory was at the 1964 Games, when Brighton's *Marvin 'Ace Face' Robinson* won the triple jump, only to be later disqualified for slashing a competitor's cheek with a razor when he found out they preferred Eddie Cochran to The Yardbirds.

18 DURING the 1928 Amsterdam games, host country the Netherlands thought they had a gold medal in the bag when they entered *Simba*, a 4-year-old cheetah from Den Haag Zoological Gardens, in the 100m sprint. Sneaky Dutch lawyers had waded through the IOC rulebook, and found that nowhere did it specify that Olympic competitors had to be human. In an attempt to exploit the loophole, the hapless big cat was taken out onto the track by its keeper and lined up for the first qualifying heat. However, spooked by the cheers from the 40,000 strong crowd, Simba could not keep still and was disqualified after registering two false starts.

19 **BOTH** the Summer and Winter Olympics have seen their share of hapless-yet-lovable underdog competitors - the most famous being Britain's ski jumper *Eddie the Eagle* and Equatorial Guinea's swimmer *Eric the Eel*. Less well remembered, though, is Colombia's Esteban Gonzales who recorded the longest ever time to complete an Olympic marathon. Despite massive efforts, the IOC failed to come up with a loveable nickname for Gonzales, as nobody could think of an animal beginning with 'e' capable of covering 26 miles 385 yards quickly and with little difficulty with which to compare him.

20 **DESPITE** loudly and aggressively not believing in God, blasphemous boffin Professor *Richard Dawkins* DOES believe in the Olympics. "There is definite, scientific proof for the existence of the Olympics," Dawkins told *Grazia* magazine. "I've seen them on telly for a start."

Fanny Batter's OLYMPIC gossip

ALL THE BUZZ FROM THE RACE TRACK TO THE VELODROME... *AND BACK AGAIN!*

MEGA-LOL! Believe it or not, Olympic veteran **LORD SEBASTIAN COE** is set to miss out on the 2016 Opening Ceremony in Rio... because he's grown a SHELL!! That's right, my spies tell me that the Gold medal-winning former athlete, 59, has developed a tough, shiny, calcareous exoskeleton - not unlike a turtle's - which stretches all the way from his shoulders to his lower back. Sources close to Lord Coe say the Tory-supporting Olympic legend is "saddened and appalled" by the bizarre development, and will avoid being seen in public until the shell has been safely removed and disposed of. *Canyablamehim?!!*

FORGET TEAM GB... This year it's all about Team BEE GEE! That's right: word in the Olympic Village is that *Stayin' Alive* singer **BARRY GIBB** has formed his own sovereign state, and will be entering a team into this year's Games! The bearded disco icon was reportedly sick to his giant white back teeth of seeing Team GB constantly trumped in the medal stakes by the USA and Chi-

na, so he went about constructing a brand new, man-made island principality, three miles off the Northumbrian coast! This freshly-formed micronation - which has been tentatively christened 'Barrygibbia' - will start recruiting athletes from all Olympic disciplines straight away, with a view to thumping the Chinese and the Yanks in every category this August!! *Let 'em 'ave it, Bazza!!!!*

OMFG! There were red faces on the Rio Olympic committee yesterday after the official 2016 mascot **VINICIUS** failed a doping test! *Who'dathunkit?!!* The cheeky yellow sort-of cat thing tested POSITIVE for the banned substance 'Bellendetil' - a controversial new drug specifically designed to enhance mascots' performance by making them 16% more fucking irritating than they naturally are. The jovial, vaguely feline

talisman was given its marching orders straight away, with Olympic bigwigs DESPERATELY seeking another weird, shit, slightly unsettling anthropomorphic creature to step into Vinicius' shoes at short notice. *Good luck with that one, guys?!!*

Seeya in four years time, Olympic goss fans!

Fanny x

...DO THEY KNOW IT'S THE OLYMPICS?

They may know it's Christmas, but...

IF THERE'S one thing you can say about the iconic megastars of the 1984 Band Aid single, it's that they definitely know when it is, or isn't, Christmas. However, do they have any idea when it's **THE OLYMPICS**? We called a few of them to ask one simple question: Do you know it's the Olympic Games at all?

BONO, U2

"I'm well aware it's the Olympics, yes. That's largely because we stage our very own 'U2 Olympics' every four years, to coincide with the real thing. It's a great laugh, it really is - me, The Edge, Adam Clayton and the other one all compete against each other in the usual Olympic disciplines, plus a few specially selected additional ones, such as Tax Avoidance, Meaningless Environmental Posturing and Flying A Hat Around The World In First Class. I usually win Gold medals in everything, except for the high jump, as I am famously short-arsed and can barely even reach the crash mat, even with my big heels on."

SIMON LE BON, Duran Duran

"I only just found out it's the Olympics, truth be told. You see, I've got one of them Google alert thingies set up on my computer, and it beeps every time it recognises a keyword related to me, such as 'Hungry' or 'Wolf' or 'Rio' or 'Duran' or 'Duran'. Lately it's been going mental because of all the people blathering on about the Rio Olympics. So I'll probably remove 'Rio' from my keywords for the time being, and replace it with another regularly used word that might relate to me, such as 'Save' or 'Prayer' or 'Bell-end'.

FRANCIS ROSSI, Status Quo

"Yes, of course I know it's the Olympics. The whole reason I called my band *Status Quo* is because I'm fascinated by the current or existing state of affairs, and since the Olympics are happening now, they very much fall into that category. However, come August 21st when they stop happening, they will no longer represent the current or existing state of affairs, and I will thus delete all memory of them in order to make space in my brain for something new, that's actually happening at that particular moment."

BOB GELDOF, The Boomtown Rats

"The Olympics? Is that now, is it? No, I had no idea. I've spent most of the last thirty years concentrating on knowing it's Christmas, so I simply don't have the time or energy to focus on knowing it's anything else. But now that you've told me, I'll probably watch a bit of it on the telly. The one where they make the horses dance is always good for a laugh."

IMPATIENCE OF A SAINT!

EXCLUSIVE!

FOR most of us, the Olympic Games are a great chance to sit back, relax and watch some of the world's top athletes in action. However, for one 3rd Century Gaulish martyr, they represent the busiest time of the year.

SAINT SEBASTIAN - the Catholic Church's patron saint of athletes - is likely to receive upwards of 15 MILLION individual prayers over the course of the 2016 Rio Olympiad, and the Vatican has today expressed concern over his ability to attend to each of them single-handedly.

Speaking to reporters outside St Peter's Basilica this morning, Patron Saint Line Manager Gianluca Battachura said: "Saint Sebastian is an absolutely blinding Saint - one of our best, in fact - but even he is simply not able to deal with the vast influx of prayers that each new Olympic Games brings."

"As soon as that Olympic cauldron is lit at the end of the opening ceremony, the athletic-themed spiritual requests start flooding in thick and fast, and by the time Sebastian's answered one, another fifty have piled up in his ethereal inbox. It's simply not fair on the guy."

Overworked Catholic hallow demands Olympic prayer back-up

Battachura continued: "Last night, the Pope received a personal message from Sebastian, asking politely, but firmly, if we would mind outsourcing some of his prayers to other saints. His Holiness gave the green-light for this request, and we are now implementing this replacement prayer service with immediate effect."

saints

Battachura went on to outline the various new Saints to whom sport-loving Catholics should now address their Olympic-themed prayers:

● All prayers regarding aquatic events - such as rowing, water polo, swimming or diving - should be directed to **ST NICHOLAS OF TOLENTINO**, patron saint of mariners and those travelling by sea.

● Prayers on the subject of equestrian disciplines - including dressage, jumping and eventing - should be propelled towards **ST WALSTAN OF BAWBURGH**, patron saint of farming and animal husbandry.

● Catholics praying about any track event - be it the 100m sprint, hurdles or relay - are advised to contact **ST CRISPIN OF SOISSONS**, patron saint of cobblers and shoemakers.

● Spiritual requests regarding women's beach volleyball should be sent directly to **ST BERNARD OF ESSEX**, patron saint of erotic reverie and masturbation.

Battachura continued: "Saint Sebastian is currently holding a three-day athletic-prayer-answering crash course for all saints involved, and prayer-senders can rest assured that

Saints alive!: Sebastian set for record number of prayers.

he will be available at all hours to offer advice and guidance should their new prayer recipient encounter difficulty with any Olympic-based entreaty."

day breakfast

"The full list of Olympic disciplines and their subsequent replacement Saints can be found at catholic-church.biz/replacementolympic-saints," he added.

The XXX Games!

Your favourite Olympic discipline says a fair bit about what sort of sex you like, claims TV shrink Dr Raj Persaud

WE ALL love the Olympics. From aquatics to cycling and gymnastics to archery, each of us has a favourite discipline. And with modern technology, it's becoming easier and easier to catch whichever event takes our fancy by simply pressing the BBC's infamous red button. However, did you know that YOUR Olympic sport of choice says a lot about what presses YOUR 'red button' in the bedroom? "It's true, you know, it does," says undisgraced-at-time-of-writing TV shrink DR RAJ PERSAUD. Here, Dr Raj writes exclusively for Viz on what your best-loved Olympic event might reveal about your secret sexual peccadilloes.

High jump

This high-flying event is a must-watch for fans of airborne action, as competitors attempt to outdo each other by leaping to superhumanly lofty levels. The discipline is perhaps best known for its signature move - Dick Fosbury's 'Fosbury Flop' - which was made famous at the 1968 Summer Games in Mexico City. Unfortunately, however, fans of this sport are also bona fide 'Fosbury Flops' in the bedroom. Unable to achieve full turgidity in their penii, high jump enthusiasts suffer from chronic impotence and regularly leave their sexual partners feeling angry and unsatisfied, forced to take matters into their own hands to achieve orgasm.

Celebrity high jump fans: Russell Brand, Michael Gove, Sting

100m sprint

Blink and you'll miss this exciting event in which the world's fastest men and women tear across the track at lightning speed. And sadly it's the same story between the sheets, as sprint fans are renowned for their premature ejaculation. Get one of these hapless two-push charlies into bed, and you'll usually find that they've shot their wad in less time than it takes Usain Bolt to cross the finish line.

Celebrity 100m sprint fans: Nick Clegg, Professor Brian Cox, P Diddy

Water polo

This hugely popular discipline made its Olympic debut all the way back in 1900. It's an aquatic team sport, and essentially that means that its admirers are intrigued by two things: water and large groups of people. In the bedroom, this translates into a deep love of being urinated on during a gang-bang. Yes, water polo fans are absolutely piss-bukkake bonkers, often requiring three or more different streams of micturate to be running down their body before they can successfully climax.

Celebrity water polo fans: Paul Burrell, Henry Kissinger, Ena Sharples

Fencing

This ancient and iconic sport requires all manner of strange and exotic equipment: fabulous face masks, dangerous swords, bizarre protective outfits. And it's the same story in the bedroom, as fencing fans get their carnal kicks from a variety of hardcore sex paraphernalia including gimp masks, anal beads and arseless leather chaps. These tooled-up erotic adventurers know no bounds when it comes to pleasure-seeking, and are quite willing to flirt with intense physical pain to reach dizzying new heights of sexual ecstasy.

Celebrity fencing fans: Huw Edwards, James May, Abu Hamza

BREXIT SPELLS DISASTER FOR TEAM GB

Misery for Mo & Co. as mile slumps to 31-year low

TEAM GB's heroic distance runners were up in arms this morning, as the mile plummeted 12% against the kilometre.

Prior to Britain's vote to leave the European Union on June 23rd, the mile was holding steady at a healthy and stable 1.609km. However, the ongoing international turmoil in the weeks following Brexit has seen it tumble over 200 yards to a paltry **1.416km** at close of play yesterday - an unprecedented THREE DECADE low for the beloved imperial unit of measurement.

disaster

This shocking slump could spell disaster for 'Mighty' **MO FARAH** and his fellow Team GB Olympic

EXCLUSIVE!

runners, who record their performances exclusively in miles, and consequently awoke this morning to find themselves 12% slower in overseas territories.

distressed

Speaking at the national squad's training facility in Rio this morning, a visibly distressed Farah told reporters: "It's a shambles, is what it is. I've spent the past four years training like crazy for these Olympic Games, specifically using the imperial mile unit. Now, post-Brexit, I suddenly find that every one of my kilometre-utilising international competitors is three twenty fifths quicker than me."

Farah went on to outline the severe dent in morale and self-belief that the mile's plunge had caused in the camp.

Miles from Mo-where: Farah's miles may be longer abroad.

"I was properly pumped heading into these Games, because last year I ran two miles in 8 minutes 3 seconds

- a new world record," the GB icon claimed. "But now, thanks to Brexit, it turns out I didn't actually run two miles at all - I only ran 1.759. So that's my record shafted and my confidence in tatters to boot."

"To be honest," Farah added, "I'm considering only competing in UK-based events from now on, as the mile should at least remain the same length here. Unless of course Scotland votes to leave Great Britain and rejoin Europe, in which case I'll have to forget Scotland too."

tremors

Post-Brexit tremors will also undoubtedly take their toll on tennis ace Andy Murray, who will arrive on court in Rio to find that his side of the net has risen from 3 feet to 3.24 feet, following news that the foot has slumped 9% against the metre.

CAN THEY KICKBACK? YES THEY CAN!

YOUR cut-out-n-keep guide to the most outlandish bribes ever received by the International Olympic Committee

BEING a member of the International Olympic Committee can be a thankless task. The humble, hard-working individuals of the IOC are charged with the superhumanly stressful job of deciding the destination of each new Olympiad. Their choice is based on a number of different factors including geographical accessibility, media exposure and potential for economic development - but ultimately it comes down to which city is offering the IOC the biggest bribe. Here, we take a look at the most wild and wonderful backhanders in Olympic history...

★ The rich and colourful tradition of Olympic bribery dates all the way back to 550 BC, when newly elected Greek general **ARISTIDES** presented the Ancient IOC with a brown envelope full of mink togas in the hope of staging the next Games in his home town of Olympia. The committee accepted the lavish backhander, but a red-faced Aristedes later discovered that EVERY Ancient Olympic Games was staged in Olympia, so there was absolutely no need for the bribe at all!

★ In 1920, the Mayor of Antwerp, Belgium, secured the Olympics for his city by signing over the complete royalties to **TINTIN**! To this day, every single penny earned from the plucky boy detective's books, films and merchandise goes straight into the Olympic Committee's coffers.

★ London famously won the 1948 Games after presenting the IOC's bibliophile chairman **FEDERICO LIBRARE** with a £15 MILLION book token! To date, the novel-loving Olympic bigwig still has £14.4 million remaining on the token, which can be used at any Waterstones, Foyles or WH Smith.

★ Russia was given the 1980 Olympics for Moscow after presenting each member of the IOC board with a fully functioning sex robot... *made of GOLD!* Each 24-carat carnal automaton had been hand-built by the Soviet Union's top scientists, and programmed to perform more than TEN THOUSAND different sexual acts, including rim jobs, titwanks and felching.

BREAD WINNER

"CALM DOWN dears, it's **MICHAEL WINNER** here! You'll know me from a variety of different things: if you happen to be a film buff, you'll have seen one of my movies, if you're a telly addict, you'll recall my hilarious insurance ads, and if you work in a restaurant, you'll have wanked into something I once ate. However, I don't do much film-making, slogan-spouting or semen-eating these days, because I popped my clogs back in 2013. That's right, I'm currently brown bread - a happy coincidence, as that's also my favourite foodstuff! I absolutely adore baked flour-and-water-based loaves of all shapes, sizes and colours, and judging by this week's *Bread Winner* postbag, so do all you *Viz* readers! So without further a-dough, let's take a look at the best letters I've received so far. Bready, set... go!**"** *Mike xx*

☐ **I FIND** it utterly, utterly sickening that so many of our traditional, green and pleasant bread-related words have somehow gained sordid double meanings. 'Buns' now means buttocks, 'baps' means breasts, and 'crumpet' means an attractive young lady. I for one see absolutely nothing sexual at all about any bread-based product, and I think anyone using bread-related terms in an erotic context should be castrated, forced to do up to 30 hours' community service and put on the sex offenders' register.
Oliver Reaction, Chipping Norton

☐ **OH** dear. Mr Reaction *(above)* claims that he finds "nothing sexual at all" about any bread-based product, but he's clearly failed to take into account bagels. A sturdy, well-baked bagel can be used either as a cheap and effective pocket fanny or a gaudy, outsized cock ring. Perhaps Mr Reaction should think a little more carefully before he puts pen to paper in future.
Randolph Bagelfucker, Herts

☐ **AS** the Poet Laureate I was planning to do a bread-based poem for this letters page. However, I've just given it a go and I genuinely don't think it's possible. There are so many words that rhyme with 'bread' that you literally don't know where to start. It sounds mental but it would actually be easier to do a poem about hummus or cabbage or something, because at least then there are only one or two roads open to you. I'll have another stab at it later, but in all honesty I'm not sure a bread-based poem is do-able.
CA Duffy, Manchester

☐ **I FANCIED** making a sandwich the other day, so I sent my husband out to get bread. Imagine my surprise when he returned six weeks later, accompanied by David Gates, Jimmy Griffiths, Mike Botts, Robb Royer and Larry Knechtel, collectively known as the 1970s US soft rock outfit, Bread. How we all laughed when my hubby realised his mistake. The band were very understanding about the mix-up, and they even did us the honour of staying for lunch: a slap-up round of ham sandwiches, made with - you've guessed it - bread!
Doris Basilisk, Chesterfield

☐ **I HATE** to rain on the above parade, but Mrs Basilisk *(above)* is talking out her goddam asshole. I am the lead singer of the 1970s US soft rock outfit Bread, and I can confirm that a) I have never been to Chesterfield in my life, and b) last time I checked, Jimmy Griffiths, Mike Botts and Larry Knechtel were all dead. There's nothing big nor clever about fabricating a far-fetched, wordplay-based anecdote just to see your name printed on a niche letters forum. I like a light-hearted chuckle as much as the next guy, but Mrs Basilisk has gone too far.
D Gates, Los Angeles

☐ **SORRY,** yes, Mr Gates *(previous letter)* is absolutely right. You'll have to excuse me, I'm a lady of a certain age, and sometimes I get my wires crossed. It wasn't *bread* I sent my husband out for - it was *cream.* And he returned six weeks later with Jack Bruce, Ginger Baker and Eric Clapton. My mistake.
Doris Basilisk, Chesterfield

☐ **HANG** on, scrap what I said above *(above)*. I think I've figured out a way to do it. What about this:

B is for bake it, that's what you do

R is for ready in one hour or two

E is for eat it, it tastes really good

A is for 'ave it for brekkie or pud

D is for dinner is never complete, without a nice slice of some bread for to eat!

The end didn't quite work but I think the first four lines were pretty solid.

CA Duffy, Manchester

I WORKED for several years in a local bakery, making all manner of bread-based products. I have, however, recently chucked that gig in for a new one at a kitchenware factory, where my job is to examine each circular, open-topped container as it comes off the belt. So I suppose you could say that I used to *bake rolls* and now I *rake bowls* (I'm using 'rake' in this sense to mean 'glance over rapidly')!

Dennis Inexplicable, Salisbury

. Please do print this letter, as the only reason I switched jobs in the first place was so I could tell this joke, but I'm now starting to have serious doubts about whether it's funny. In truth, I really miss the bakery; it was such a great place to work, and I had loads of mates there. It's different here at the kitchenware factory. I don't really know anyone, and they tend to keep themselves to themselves. I usually end up eating lunch by myself in the gents' loo. I'd go back to the bakery in a flash, but Jeff's found someone new now, so it's either stick with the factory or go back on the dole, and with a baby on the way, I really need a steady income. Seeing this light-hearted anecdote in print would go a long way towards convincing me that my life choices have not been entirely moronic.

MY hubby and I are the perfect match. You see, he hates the crusts on his bread and always cuts them off, whereas I hate the middle bit, and only eat the crusts! We've been together 41 years now and, although he's slept with three out of four of my sisters, I refuse to divorce him because of the crusts thing.

Ada Kamikaze, Dudley

I ABSOLUTELY love bread. In fact, I love it so much that I recently changed my name from Deirdre to Barbara and married a man called Martin Read. I despise the name Barbara, and Martin is a violent alcoholic who I suspect is stealing from me, but it was all worth it so that I could resemble my favourite foodstuff when I sign letters.

B Read, Lincoln

CHECK this out. Bread is an anagram of 'beard', right? And what regularly gets stuck in people's beards? Bits of *bread*. A simple coincidence? Maybe. But I for one am not taking any chances. If you feel the same way, meet me by the dogshit bins in Hyde Park at midnight tonight. I will be wearing a red carnation in my lapel and will have some bread in my beard. We are through the looking glass here.

Anonymous, London

YOU always hear people say that such-and-such is the "best thing since sliced bread". Well, speaking as a wheat intolerant Luddite, I hate sliced bread more than almost anything else on Earth. Consequently, from this day forward I will make sure to call shit things the "*worst* thing since sliced bread", or even the "best thing since the exact opposite of sliced bread." I'd be intrigued to know how the so-called 'PC Brigade' will handle that.

Nathanael Ferrington-Fuck, Devon

Bjorn & Bread

EACH week, we ask a famous Bjorn to pose for a picture with a loaf of their favourite bread.

This week:
Bjorn BORG with a French stick.

Next week: Bjorn Ulvaeus with a farmhouse granary loaf.

THAT'S LOAF!
with Cyril Fletcher

THANK-YOU, Esther. This week I am indebted to a Mr Prepuce of Deal, who was somewhat taken aback by this slice of bread that he discovered in his loaf of Mother's Pride the other day....

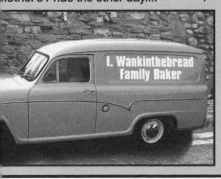

...And I don't fancy making my sandwiches with the loaves baked by *this* baker, whose van was snapped by my eagle-eyed correspondent Mrs Edna Gleet of Pudenda-on-Sea.

...Esther.

Give us this day our... DALEY BREAD

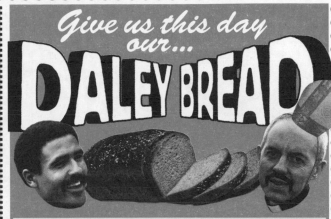

Each week, the Archbishop of Canterbury **JUSTIN WELBY** answers YOUR theological questions about either bread or Daley Thompson or both.

Dear Justin,

In Anglican Communion, is the bread supposed to be the literal body of Christ, or is it merely a symbol for Christ's love? Also, how many Olympic gold medals has Daley Thompson won?

Ethel Troutmask, Hull

Justin says: Thank you for your letter, Mrs Troutmask. I'm afraid Anglican Eucharistic theology is extremely diverse in practice, so I can't give you one definite answer to your first question. In one interpretation, those who receive the bread and wine in faith also receive the spiritual body and blood of Christ, whilst those who receive it without faith consume merely the physical signs of the Son of God. Other Anglican theory has it that there exists the real objective presence of Christ in the Eucharist, whilst a third and final strand conforms to the Eucharistic theology of consubstantiation, which holds that during the sacrament, the fundamental 'substance' of the blood and body of Christ are present alongside the substance of the bread and wine. And Daley Thompson has won two Olympic gold medals.

Dear Justin

What sort of bread do they have in Heaven? It's just that I've got a wheat allergy, you see, so I can only eat rye bread or German-style pumpernickel. It's fine if they don't have those up in Heaven, but I'll need to know now so as I can ask my children to put a few packets of rye into my coffin with me. Also, how tall is Daley Thompson?

Agnes Safeasmilk, Carlisle

Justin says: Thanks for getting in touch, Mrs Safeasmilk. In Heaven, they have absolutely every kind of bread you can imagine - and a few more to boot. And the good news is there's no such thing as wheat intolerance in Heaven, either, so you'll be free to enjoy any sort of baked foodstuff you like - for all eternity. Daley Thompson is 6ft tall.

Dear Justin

Can the Holy Ghost eat bread, or does it just fall straight through him? Also, how big is Daley Thompson's moustache and how long has he had it for?

Dolly Clearspot, Warrington

Justin says: I'll tackle your first question first, if I may, Mrs Clearspot. The Holy Ghost probably couldn't eat bread, as he's not really a person, he's more of a divine state: an ethereal realm beyond the ability of earthly description. That said, the Holy Spirit is sometimes depicted in ancient iconography as a dove, and birds love bread, don't they, so if he was in his dove form I suppose he probably could eat bread, yes. As for your other questions: I can't find any concrete information online about the size or age of Daley Thompson's moustache, but my best guess from looking at pictures would be that it's roughly 6"x1"x1", and he's had it since about 1978.

Have YOU got a question about bread and/or Daley Thompson that's also in some way related to religion? Please, please write in to: Justin Welby's 'Give us this day our... Daley Bread!', c/o Viz Comic, PO Box 841, Whitley Bay, NE26 9EQ

Farmer PALMER

KNOCK! KNOCK! KNOCK!

KNOCK!

PLEASE HELP. MY HUSBAND WENT OUT TO WALK THE DOG... AND THEN THIS BLIZZARD SET IN... HE SHOULD HAVE BEEN BACK HOURS AGO..!

DON'T YOU'M WORRY, MUZZ. ME AN' MOY BOY JETHRO KNOWZ THEEZE MOORZ LOIKE THE BAAAACK UV UR AAAAAANDZ.

CUM ON, ZUNN.

THERMOS O' FLASK

HE DRESSES AS A FLASK AND HE CAN'T STOP GOING WITH PROS

CHRISTMAS MORNING...

WAHAY! GRANNY HAS SENT ME A TENNER FOR CHRISTMAS

WELL, SHE'LL BE VERY DISAPPOINTED IF YOU SPEND IT ON A HANDJOB OR PROTECTED FRENCH OFF A PROSTITUTE, THERMOS

DON'T WORRY, MUM

I'M GOING TO GO TO A BOOKSHOP AND BUY MYSELF A NICE STORY BOOK

I'M GLAD TO HEAR IT

SHORTLY... BUSINESS IS PRETTY SLOW, PERKINS... WALK UP AND DOWN THE STREET WITH THIS ENORMOUS SIGN TO TRY AND DRUM UP SOME TRADE

YES, MR. THOM

THOM'S BOOK SHOP NOW OPEN

AHA!

THOM'S BOOK SHOP NOW O

The Snowcan

BIFFA BACON

THERE WE GAN... ANOTHER FAWATY TIN O' FUCKIN' SPESH AN' TWO 'UNDRED EMBASSY REGAL

CHAMPION! JUST A TIN O' CHOCCIE BICCIES T'GET, AN' THAT'S AALL THE FUCKIN CHRISMUSS FOOD SHOPPIN' DONE!

HEH! HEH!... I FUCKIN' LOVE CHOCCIE BICCIES, ME!

CHOC BISCUITS!

HAD ON... WOT THE FUCK'S AALL THIS?. DENTED TINS O' BISCUITS IS FIFTY PERCENT OFF, MUTHA

PUT THEMS FUCKAZ BACK, BIFFA, SON... WUZ'LL GET W'SELLS A DENTED TIN INSTEAD

BROKEN BISCUITS 50% OFF!

FUCK OFF! THEMS DENTED 'UN FUCKIN' SUPERMARKET URN BR THEZ'RE NOT AS NICE AS THESE.

AH DIVVENT GIVE A SHITE

THAT'S AS MEBEES BUT THEZ'RE HALF PRICE

WELL AH FUCKIN' DIV!

PAAA! PAAA! OVER YURR...! 'URRY!

THANK GOD! AUDREY! I THINK I'VE BROKEN MY ANKLE!

GERALD! I'D NEVER HAVE FOUND YOU IF IT WASN'T FOR THESE KIND...

BLAM! BLAM!

BORDELLO
THE ACHING WRIST KNOCKING SHOP
WANKS FROM £10

HELLO... I'D LIKE SOMETHING THAT WON'T TAKE TOO LONG TO FINISH... THAT'S GOOD AND EXCITING, WITH A NICE HAPPY ENDING FOR ABOUT A TENNER

I'VE GOT JUST THE THINGS, DEARIE

ONE FOR YOU, ROXY

COME ON, THEN, LOVER BOY...

OH, THERE'S NO SOAP IN THE BOGS AGAIN, LIL.

3 MINS LATER...
RATS' COCKS!
GRANNY IS GOING TO BE SO DISAPPOINTED WHEN SHE GETS MY 'THANK YOU' LETTER

NEXT DAY...

Dear Nan,
Thank you for my £10 note. I spent it on a lovely wank off a whore.
Love, Thermos x

...OP BICKERIN' THE PAIR O' YEHZ A SIMPLE WAY T' ...IS OOT SO AS YUZ CAN 'AVE Y' AAN WAY!

IS THERE, MUTHA?.. HOO?

GRMH!

OOYAH!

THERE W' GAN. FUCKIN' SORTED

EEH! YUZ'RE LIKE KING FUCKIN' SOLOMON AT TIMES, MUTHA

Y' FUCKIN' BASTAADS

HAD ON, MUTHA... D' YUZ THINK THIS LAGER'D BE HALF PRICE AN' AALL IF THE TINS W' DENTED?

HMM! IT'S WORTH A TRY, FATHA

GRMP!

GNN!

SHORTLY...
ER....

HOO, YEE!.. THEZ TWO 'UNDRED TINS O' SPESH AALL DENTED T' FUCK, AALREET?

AN' AH'VE GORRA COUPON F' TEN PENCE OFF THE FUCKIN' BICCIES AN' AALL

WA-HEY IN A M

FORGET the stockings, sprouts and sleigh bells – nothing truly says "Christmas is here" like the sweet sound of carol singers on the doorstep. The ancient British tradition of entertaining the neighbours with a medley of Yuletide hymns has made the holiday season special for centuries.

And one man who's certainly helping to keep this jovial pastime alive is 63-year-old bachelor MELVIN GAVISCON. Morbidly obese Melvin has been warbling festive songs door-to-door in his Tamworth cul-de-sac every Christmas for the past twenty years. But while most was-sailers are treated to just a warm glass of mulled wine or a mince pie, during his carol-singing career Melvin has enjoyed FULL SEXUAL IN-TERCOURSE with some of Hollywood's biggest stars!

"It's true," chuckles unemployed Melvin. "I've literally lost count of the number of sexy A-List celebs I've done the dirty with whilst out carolling. Believe you me, the roll call of sultry superstars I've romanced during the Yuletide season reads like a Who's Who of Tinseltown's hottest totty."

This Christmas, Melvin has decided to finally tell his full, barely believable story in an explosive new autobiography – *Wa-Hey In A Manger (£0.99, Fabrication Books)* – which he hopes will rocket straight to the top of the festive bestseller charts. In these tantalising exclusive extracts, he recounts the star-studded sexcapades that happen once the festive music stops.

O, COME ALL YE SPICE GIRLS

" It all started back on Christmas Eve, 1996. I'd just that day been laid off from my job as a janitor at the local gym, following a misunderstanding at a women-only yoga class. However, I was damned if I was going to let my work worries dampen my Christmas spirit, so I sank a few cans at home, and with the festive cheer well and truly coursing through me, I decided to head out and bring some joy to the world... or, at the very least, the cul-de-sac!

neighbours

I've always had a sublime singing voice – I reached the open audition stage of *The X-Factor* three years running – so I decided a spot of carolling would be just the job. I stuffed a few more tins into my overcoat pockets, and headed off down the street, belting out *We Wish You a Merry Christmas* at full volume whilst my neighbours looked on merrily through the gaps in their curtains.

I'd been at it nearly two hours – my throat was sore, my lips were chapped and I was just about ready to head home and curl up in bed with a big bottle of White Lightning, when I noticed a quaint little bungalow at the end of the street that I'd never seen before.

Deciding I probably had one more tune left in me, I rang the bell, and you can imagine my surprise when who should open the door but none other than Posh Spice herself – **VICTORIA BECKHAM**! I listened in amazement as she explained that she and the rest of the Spice Girls had rented the bungalow as a low key, out-of-the-way spot for their Christmas party.

Spicely does it: Beckham gave Gaviscon an early Christmas present.

Now, I won't lie to you – on a freezing night, Posh was truly a sight for sore eyes. She was dressed only in a skimpy silk kimono that left precious little to the imagination. It kept flapping open invitingly in the howling winter wind, offering me a tantalising glimpse of her curvaceous bare breasts.

'I just adore Christmas carols,' the raven-haired pop princess cooed seductively. 'The other girls have nipped to the garage to get some more fire-lighters, but I'll tell you what I want, what I really, really want – and that's to hear a traditional Yuletide hymn sung just for me.'

'Tis the season to get his jollies: Melvin's festive flings have guaranteed him numerous merry Christmases.

I can't – and won't – pretend I wasn't nervous. Posh is an internationally respected vocalist, with scores of chart-topping hits under her belt, so the idea of performing a one-off solo concert on her doorstep was daunting to say the least.

Knowing that the pressure was on, I cleared my throat, closed my eyes, and launched into a hauntingly moving rendition of *We Wish You a Merry Christmas*.

home and away

By the time I reached the final, pitch-perfect note, Posh's eyes were quite literally brimming with tears. 'That was beautiful, Melvin, just beautiful,' she whispered huskily. 'Why don't you come inside and warm up a bit?' She shot me a wink that suggested she had something more in mind than a glass of brandy.

She led me inside to the living room where a roaring gas fire was blazing in the hearth. Within seconds, animal passion had got the better of us, and we were both writhing naked on the carpet, our throbbing bodies intertwined, our lips locked in a sensuous, vice-like grip.

young doctors

I'm too much of a gentleman to reveal exactly what happened next, but suffice it to say that we *Let Love Lead The Way*, and *2 Became 1* as I inserted my penis into her vagina.

'That was easily the most orgasms I've ever had in a row,' the *Zig-ah-Zig-*ah singer purred as she pulled her scuds up after I had finished. 'You're amazing at sex, Melvin.' I thanked her politely and was about to take my leave, when I suddenly heard keys jangling in the front door, and into the room strutted the rest of the Spice Girls: Baby, Scary, Ginger and Mel C.

the sullivans

'You know how the song goes, Melvin,' Posh giggled, as her four busty bandmates wrestled me back down onto the carpet whilst removing their clothes. *'If you wanna be my lover, you gotta get with my friends...'*

And suffice it to say that I did get with her friends. All of them. Twice.

Five hours later, as I wiped my battered chopper on the curtains and sauntered home, little did I realise that this erotic encounter was just the first of countless more or less identical ones that were to occur over the next twenty Christmases. "

NOT-SO-SILENT KNIGHTLEY

" After that first time, every festive season it was the same story. I'd head out onto the cul-de-sac to wish the other residents a merry Christmas and somehow end up having no-holds-barred intercourse with an internationally renowned female. **MADONNA, PAMELA ANDERSON, NATASHA KAPLINSKY, MELANIA TRUMP**...You name them, I bedded them. And many, many more besides.

ANGER

"My nuts were roasting", says Tamworth ex-janitor

The whole thing was so unbelievable that people in the pub often thought I was making it up when I told them about it.

That said, I remember one Xmas Eve a few years back when I thought my luck had finally run out. I was out doing my usual rounds, but none of my neighbours were answering their doors. I assumed they must all be out buying last-minute gifts, despite the fact that their lights were on and I could definitely see shadows moving and people whispering behind the curtains.

skin

I was about to give it up and head home when I noticed one house I hadn't ever tried before. I knocked at the front door and must admit I nearly jumped out of my skin when it was opened by none other than top Hollywood actress **KEIRA KNIGHTLEY**.

ace

The elegant beauty explained that she had rented the house with fellow A-List star **ORLANDO BLOOM** so that they could rehearse a big snogging scene for the forthcoming blockbuster *Pirates of the Caribbean*. However, Bloom's fan belt had carked it halfway up the M40, and he'd just called Keira to say he wasn't going to make it.

cass

I told the sexy star I was sorry to hear this, and she gave me a coy smile in return. 'I suppose the one thing that would make it better would be to hear a beautiful Christmas carol, sung just for me', she cooed suggestively. What else could I do but

oblige? I cleared my throat, finished my tin of Special and set about performing an utterly mesmerising version of *We Wish You a Merry Christmas*.

mia

When I'd finished, the *Pride & Prejudice* stunner was in floods of tears, literally clutching the doorframe for support. 'Oh my God, Melvin,' she gushed. 'That was the most beautiful thing I've ever heard.' I thanked her and asked if there was anything else I could do for her on this cold, dark Christmas Eve. 'Well...' she purred naughtily, 'Since Orlando's not coming, perhaps you could come in and help me practise that kiss...'

barbara

Now, I'm as red-blooded as the next man so I didn't need asking twice. I followed Knightley upstairs to the bedroom, where she began to slowly and seductively remove her clothes. As she kicked her lacy scuds across the room, it was clear that she had more than just a bit of kissing in mind.

monica

I won't embarrass the *Atonement* star by divulging the full details of what happened next, but suffice it to say we literally rewrote the *Kama Sutra*, adding at least fifty new positions into the mix. Probably a hundred. I may have performed a beautiful Christmas carol for her a few minutes earlier, but there was nothing silent about THIS night, let me tell you. Keira's multiple orgasms were literally ear-splitting, each one louder and more earth-shattering than the last. I'm surprised she didn't wake the whole cul-de-sac with her relentless screams of sexual ecstasy as I brought her off.

rachel

Afterwards, I went to get up and grab my kecks, but Knightley *Never Let Me Go* and after begging to me to *Begin Again* we were once more making sweet, sweet *Love, Actually*. And ironically, *Never Let Me Go*, *Begin Again* and *Love, Actually* are also the names of some of her films.

> *I'm surprised she didn't wake the whole cul-de-sac with her relentless screams of sexual ecstasy as I brought her off.*

Pleasure palace: Kate's saucy invitation caught Melvin off-guard.

TWICE ON ROYAL WILLIAM'S SETTEE

"Last Christmas Eve, I decided to take my carolling skills a little further afield. I'd received a few pretty unfestive complaints from neighbours about 'excessive noise', 'disturbance of the peace' and 'habitual public urination'. Some hatchet-faced local Scrooges had even gone so far as to take out a restraining order that prevented me coming within 20ft of their front doors to sing. I suppose the phrase 'goodwill to all men' means nothing to some people.

phoebe

Anyway, with my trusty carol sheet in hand, I hopped on the Megabus down to London. It was pitch dark when I got there, and the sixteen tins I'd sunk en route had made my vision go a bit blurry. I was wandering around, looking for a door to knock at, when I finally came upon a huge white marble one with all gold leaf round the edges. It opened and I nearly wet myself in shock when I saw who was stood there in front of me: none other than the Duchess of Cambridge herself – **KATE MIDDLETON**. I'd only gone and knocked at Buckingham ruddy Palace!

enceladus

The picturesque queen-to-be informed me that her hubby and the rest of the Royals had nipped out for a swift Xmas Eve half with Princess Michael and the Kents, but that she'd love nothing more than to hear a carol sung by yours truly. And as it was a particularly dark and chilly evening, she invited me *inside* to perform it...

We went into the front room, and she reclined seductively on the plush purple velvet settee, her see-through nightie fluttering open alluringly as she lay down. I forgot to mention she was wearing a see-through nightie. Trying – unsuccessfully – to banish any erotic

thoughts from my head, I cleared my throat and launched into a haunting rendition of *We Wish You a Merry Christmas*. My angelic voice rang off the marble pillars and crystal chandeliers, filling the room with beautiful music.

By the time I'd finished, the Duchess was weeping openly whilst delivering a frantic standing ovation. 'Wonderful, just wonderful, Melvin,' she sobbed uncontrollably. 'One doesn't know how one can ever repay you for that performance.' Then she shot me a saucy wink that sent the blood rushing straight to my nether regions: 'Actually, one does have *one* idea...'

bergelmir

Next thing I knew, the see-through nightie had hit the deck – along with top-of-the-range Victoria's Secret scuds – and the future queen of England was standing stark bollock naked before me.

Modesty, not to mention the Treasons Act 1534, forbids me from going into too much detail about what happened next, but suffice it to say we painted that sofa fifty shades of royal blue.

erotic

And then, once we'd got our breaths back, we did it again. The knowledge that if we were discovered I would be publicly hung, drawn and quartered only heightened the erotic excitement of our tryst.

As I was pulling up my trackie bottoms afterwards, I suddenly heard a key in the front door. Let me tell you, I was out the window and high-tailing it across the Buckingham Palace lawn like my arse was on fire!

I had to chuckle the next day, though, as I watched the Queen giving her annual speech on telly – she was sat on the very sofa where I'd had my double portion of right royal oats just a few hours previously! It may have been a trick of the light, but I'm sure I could see a couple of fresh maps of Africa on the velvet."

NEXT TIME:
SUSANNA IN SEX-CELSIS: Melvin spills the beans about the time he sang 'We Wish You a Merry Christmas' for GMTV milf Susanna Reid, before having full sex with her, twice.

'Twas the Knightly before Christmas: Keira granted Melvin Xmas wish while A-list Orlando struggled home.

HAPPY NEW BEER!

BRITAIN'S drinkers could be in for a very merry Christmas this year, after the government announced plans to temporarily raise the safe drinking allowance by 600% over the festive period.

Current official advice is that UK adults should drink no more than 14 units of alcohol - just 7 pints of beer - each week. But once the temporary legislation is passed, the safe limit will rise to 98 units, allowing drinkers to sink 7 pints each day throughout December with no adverse effect on their health.

reality

"We know that the reality of the situation is that people will drink more at this time of year," said Prime Minister Theresa May. "So it's only common sense that we should reflect that fact by raising the safe alcohol consumption level during the Christmas period."

widescreen

Mrs May stressed that the revised limits would only be in force between December 1st and January 1st. "Anyone drinking at raised Christmas levels in the new year will be putting their health at serious risk," she warned. "Temporary means temporary."

EXCLUSIVE!

The decision to increase the safe alcohol amount was warmly welcomed by Britain's drinking community.

"This is great news for British tipplers," said Sir Turpentine Nudger, head of pub trade body the UK Institute of Licensed Victuallers.

apple

"Our customers want to celebrate the festive season properly, but nobody wants to spend Christmas in hospital with acute liver failure. I am delighted that the government has seen sense and decided to raise the safe drinking limit to a level that reflects the spirit of the holiday season."

And drinkers were also quick to praise the decision. "At last the politicians have seen sense and done something for British boozers," said Grimsby pub goer Barry Tanktop. "Last Christmas, I

Plan to raise safe drinking limit over festive season

Christmas spirits: Drinkers can safely enjoy more booze over the festive season.

had 85 units in two days and ended up in the infirmary on a drip."

"It's nice to know that this year I'll be able to sink even more than that and still be safe," he added.

cream

Meanwhile, Labour leader Jeremy Corbyn was last night calling on the government to suspend nut allergy over the festive season.

"Everyone should be able to enjoy a few nuts on Christmas afternoon without going into anaphylactic shock," he said whilst sitting on the floor of the House of Commons because he said all the seats were taken.

114

Red Arrows Announce New Pilot Line-up

Pilot scheme: *Celebrities will take control for the 2016 display season.*

THE RED ARROWS yesterday unveiled their brand new pilot line-up for the 2016 display season. And in a radical departure from the RAF's usual practice of picking experienced frontline fighter pilots to fly the iconic scarlet jets, this year there will be nine CELEBRITIES at the controls. *And none of them has ever flown a plane before!*

No business like airshow business: The rookie stars line up on the runway at RAF Scampton for their first taste of life as a Red Arrows pilot. From left to right: Rees, Balls, Fargas, Ruddock, Fish, Harriot, Bazar, Mallet. (Gemma Collins not shown as she was on the toilet when this picture was taken).

"It's going to be really steep learning curve for our rookie pilots," said Red Arrows Squadron Leader Siddley Armstrong. "Low level aerobatic flying in tight formations at speeds approaching 600mph is really going to put them to the test."

margin

"There's no margin for error when you're doing a barrel roll fifty feet above the ground wingtip to wingtip with eight other planes."

"The celebrities will have to bear in mind that, unlike on television, there are no second takes at a Red Arrows display," he added. "There's no margin for error and failure is not an option."

board

But Red 1, *TOWIE*'s **Gemma Collins**, said she was relishing the prospect of getting behind the controls and taking to the sky as part of the world famous flying team. "I'm really excited and can't wait to get in the driving seat, you know, the cockpit thingie," she told *Take a Break* magazine.

"I'd never really thought about piloting a plane before, as I always wanted to work in a nail bar or be a dancer on a cruise ship. But when the opportunity came up to join the Red Arrows I grabbed it with both hands. It's going to be really outside my comfort zone, but that's good."

polo

Red 2, former shadow chancellor **Ed Balls**, was equally keen to get airborne. "I'm looking forward to doing that bit where all the smoke comes out the back," said the ex-MP, who lost his safe Morley and Outwood seat in the 2015 election. "Hopefully my plane will do Labour red smoke rather than Tory blue," he quipped.

Balls also admitted that aerobatic flying would be a challenge for him, as he suffers from severe air-sickness. "The slightest bit of turbulence on my

Celebrity re-vamp for RAF display team

holiday flight and I go green at the gills," he said. "So trying to keep my breakfast down during a twenty-five minute full throttle Red Arrows show is going to really test me to my limits."

rates

At the controls of Red 4 will be veteran actor **Antonio Fargas**, who rose to fame as loveable pimp Huggy Bear in classic US cop show *Starsky and Hutch*. "It's going to be a blast," said Fargas, 69, who hasn't always found work easy to come by since the series was axed in the late seventies.

"Flying a fighter jet will be just like driving a car, but instead of just going left and right it'll go up and down too. I mean, how hard can it be?"

infection

Former Dollar singer **Theresa Bazar** will be flying Red 5. "I'm really nervous," said the *Hand Held in Black and White* vocalist, 60. "Singing in front of dozens of people doesn't faze me at all, but controlling a Hawk jet at close to the speed of sound whilst performing a 4g inverted loop into low cloud will be real seat of the pants stuff."

"We'll have an instructor with us on the first flight to show us where all the controls are, but after that we're on our own," said Bazar. "It's going to be a once-in-a-lifetime experience for all us celebrities."

Squadron Leader Armstrong also announced that bumbling Welsh *Driving School* star **Maureen Rees** would be taking control of Red 6.

"Maureen has failed her driving test ten times, and doesn't know the right way to go round a mini-roundabout," he laughed.

"If she gets as flummoxed flying a jet in close formation as she does when she's at the wheel of a car, crowds are in for some classic comedy moments during the coming display season."

sports

Finally, Red 9 will be piloted by TV chef **Ainsley Harriott**. "Let's hope it's not a case of Can't fly, Won't Fly with

me," he told reporters, whilst sticking out his chin and gurning.

"If I can get a cheese soufflé to rise, I shouldn't have any difficulty getting a fighter plane in the air. I know my way around an Arctic roll, but I'm not too sure about a barrel roll."

"Every time smoke comes out of the back of the plane I'll think I've burnt the toast. There's a tail on a lobster and a tail on a plane, and they've got wings like a spatchcock chicken" he continued as the reporters wandered off.

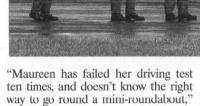

Stars in Your Skies
Meet the celebs who are going to turn the air red!

RED 2
Ed Balls,
ex-politician,
49

RED 1
Gemma Collins,
TOWIE star, 35

RED 3
Timmy Mallett,
TV presenter,
60

RED 4
Antonio Fargas,
actor, 69

RED 5
Theresa Bazar,
pop singer, 60

RED 6
Maureen Rees,
reality star, 74

RED 7
Neil Ruddock,
17th hardest ever
footballer, 47

RED 9
Ainsley Harriott,
TV chef, 58

RED 8
Michael Fish,
former weather-
man, 71

BIG TOP BILLY
King of the Three Ring Circus

Stuck in a dead-end job as a trainee invoice ledger clerk at a building supplies wholesalers, young Billy Bailey had just one dream... *to run away and become a circus accountant...*

The Greatest Show on Earth had come to Barnton, so Billy Bailey took his chance...

~Knock-Knock!~

SPINETTI'S CIRCUS

Vincenzo Spinetti Ringmaster

I've not come to see the show, Mr Spinetti...

Sorry, sonny. Ticket office opens in an hour.

...I want to join the circus!

Is that right? Well, what do you do, kid... tumbler?... acrobat? ... knife thrower? You don't look like a strongman, that's for sure. Heh-heh-heh-heh!

No sir. I'm Billy Bailey and I've got a balancing act...

...a *book-balancing* act. You see, I'm an accountant.

An accountant, eh? Well, Billy, we can always use someone who's good with figures round here, I guess...

Well I'm good with figures, Mr Spinetti...

...and one day I'm gonna be the very best circus accountant in the world!

I admire your spunk, kid. Come on, there's someone I'd like you to meet.

This is Mr Wallendo who does our books, Billy.

Not *the Great Wallendo?* - the most famous circus accountant there's ever been?!

That's me, Billy. How do you do.

Gee! I heard you once did a triple entry audit!

I sure did, Billy, with a double purchase invoice ledger finish! They said it couldn't be done but I proved them wrong!

But I only did it once. I busted my wrist pretty bad totting up the final Returns Outwards column. I never tried the Triple again.

CIRCUS ACCOUNTANCY NEWS

Wallendo to Attempt Triple!

Feat of accountancy never before attempted

Well, Billy, we've got the VAT man coming tomorrow. Why don't you help Mr Wallendo with those books while I go and thrash some chimpanzees with my belt?

Okay, Mr Spinetti.

Right, kid. If you want to be a circus accountant, you're going to have to start at the very bottom...

...and I mean the bottom...

...cleaning up after the elephants.

See here, the costs for all the shovels, buckets and wheelbarrows have to be entered here, into the Sundry Purchases (Outgoings) column in the General (Nominal) ledger.

Wow! I sure am learning lots, Mr Wallendo.

And don't forget to include them in the Trade Creditors ledger, as they're a capital asset and we can lease them back to ourselves and claim the depreciation against tax as an allowable business expense.

Gee! Working at the circus is even more exciting than I ever dreamed!

And what's more...

Quick Wallendo! The big top's on fire! The elephants have spooked and trampled down the lions' cage. All the big cats have escaped and run amuck! All hell's broken loose out here!

Oh my God!

You stay here, Billy, and keep working on those books. I'll be back just as soon as we get that fire and all these wild animals under control.

For the next two hours, Billy went over the figures again and again, battling to get it right...

Okay. This shovel cost £13.99, so I enter that as a credit in the Purchase Invoice column in the Returns Inwards daybook...

...and as a debit in the General Ledger... no, wait! Does that figure include VAT or not...?

I'll have to check it against the receipt...

Now where is it...?

Ah, here we go. It does include 20% VAT after all, so I have to enter a subtotal of £11.66 here in the Supplier ledger, and carry £2.33 forwards into the Purchase Invoice (Sundries) column.

Gosh! This circus accounting sure is harder than it looks!

Suddenly...

Gasp!

Mr Wallendo! What happened?

We were putting out the fire when we were attacked by the lions, Billy... I managed to escape by climbing up the trapeze. But a tiger followed me and it was on fire ...

Gee!

I inched out along the tightrope to get away from the burning tiger, but the wire gave way and I fell sixty feet into the ring below.

Wow!

I landed on one of the dancing bears and it hit me round the face and I fell... It was standing over me, about to kill me, when luckily a terrified elephant stood on it.

Crikey!

I thought I was saved, but then I saw a load of stampeding liberty horses heading straight for me, so I tried to escape in a clown car. But I'd only gone a few yards when it backfired, the doors fell off and all custard came out of the radiator.

As the horses thundered past I somehow managed to grab hold of one of them and ride it bare-back out of the burning big top.

Gee! Well, thank goodness you're safe!

I'm beat up pretty bad, Billy, and my glasses got smashed by one of the camels...

...so you'll have to do those books for the VAT man tomorrow!

Wh-what? Me?

B-b-but I'm just a trainee accountant. I'm not even an associate member of the Society of Professional Accountants...

...I can't do it.

You can do it, Billy. Do it for me. Do it for the Great Wallendo!

Okay... I'll... I'll try.

Oh, Billy. Just one more thing...

...you've got to do a triple entry audit with a double purchase invoice ledger finish!

SID the SEXIST

HOO LADS.

HOO SID.

WOT THE FUCK ARE YEEZ AAL GRINNIN' ABOOT?

D'YUZ NOT KNURR WOT DAY IT IS, SID?

WOT, MONDEE?

NAH MAN, SID, IT'S FUCKIN' MARCH THE FAWATEENTH!

MARCH FAWATEENTH? STEAK AN' BLURJOB DAY, SID MAN! BEST DAY O' THE FUCKIN' YEAR BY A COUNTRY MILE!

WOT'S STEAK AN' BLURJOB DAY?

IT'S THE BLURKS' VORSION OF VALENTINE'S DAY, SID... THE ONE DAY O' THE YEAR WHERE LASSIES HEV TU MEK FELLAS A NICE JUCY STEAK AN' THEN GIVE 'EM A BLOWIE.

FUCKIN' GET IN! WHY DID NEEBODY TELL ME?

HOO PET. HAPPY STEAK AN' BLURJOB DAY, LIKE. SO...WE GANNIN' TU MY PLACE OR YOURS? BEST YOURS, PROBABLY, 'COS ME MAM'S GOT 'ER BRIDGE CLUB ROOND THE NEET...

I LIKE ME STEAK WELL DONE, BY THE WAY AN' THE SAME GANS FOR THE BLOWIE...

ARE YOU GOING TO LET HIM TALK TO ME LIKE THAT, DAVE?

GRRR!

LATER...

WELL, YUZ GOT THE STEAK AT LEAST, EH SID? HO! HO!

GUMPH!

WINCE!

PRICELESS TROPHY FOUND!

Cup discovered safe and sound in bushes

GREAT BRITAIN'S World War II trophy, stolen last month in a raid on the Tower of London, has been discovered in north London... *by a DOG!*

Branston, a 3-year-old Sealeyham terrier, found the eight-inch high cup in a hedge whilst out walking with his owner in Camden.

hedge

"He did a bob in a hedge, and when he turned round to sniff it, he found the cup," said Branston's owner Hampton Plywood.

ground

The trophy which was taken from its display case in the Tower of London was awarded to Sir Winston Churchill by the United Nations at the end of the war. Experts believe it could be worth as much as £800 on the black market.

wart

Reacting to the news, Prime Minister Theresa

War-kies: Branston (above) and the WWII cup (above above) he found in a hedge.

May said it was wonderful news. "Rejoice! Rejoice!" she said outside her Downing Street home.

Line Managers 'making it up as they go along'

IF YOU think your line manager is the person to go to with problems at work, then think again. Because they are just as baffled as you, and are simply making it up as he or she goes along, according to a survey released today.

A study of over 3,000 line managers showed that the vast majority of their time was spent trying to maintain a semblance of credibility in the face of utter confusion.

"My life is a sea of meetings with people who say things like 'increase in real-time productivity on a man-to-hour-to-seat basis'," said one respondent. "I just say the same thing to my team and if anyone questions it, I simply promise them all one of those tubs of chocolate orange mini-bites from M&S."

cupboard

The survey also revealed that once a week, an average line manager will be struck by a sudden realisation of what their life has become and will disappear

EXCLUSIVE!

into the stationery cupboard for a good long cry. "I wanted to be a ballet dancer," said one respondent, poignantly.

traffic

The public reacted to the survey with some sympathy. "It explains a lot," said one office drone. "I used to think my line-manager was a hateful, sadistic, bullying woman with questionable personal hygiene," he added.

"Now, I realise she's utterly clueless, too."

I RECKON piranha fish wouldn't be half as dangerous if they didn't always go around mob-handed. If they split up and got themselves a bit better organised, like the way that only a certain number of schoolkids are allowed into a supermarket at any one time type of thing, then they wouldn't be nearly so dangerous, I reckon.

Wellington Boot, Harpendon

MY grandad was always telling me "A hard day's work never did anybody any harm," and yet he never stopped banging on about his time in a Japanese prisoner of war camp building some railway line, or whatever.

Frank Dayglow, Leeds

I KNOW that during the war, kids were evacuated to the countryside to avoid all the bombing and what-have-you. So wouldn't it have made sense to move the navy there as well? Perhaps Churchill wasn't the military genius some proclaimed him to be.

Franklyn Parmisan, Bootle

SLAP-headed drummer Phil Collins said that it was just another day for you and me in paradise. Maybe it is for him, boozing it up in the sun with topless birds and what-have-you, but surely he should spare a thought for those poor fuckers who live in Luton. I'm pretty sure they'd agree it's anything but paradise.

Iain Devenney, Oxford

FOR years I was addicted to porn, watching it online for up to 18 hours a day, until one day I discovered that if I banged one out during the first scene, my enthusiasm for watching the rest of the action diminished drastically, allowing me time to get on with the rest of my life for an hour or so.

Tubby Tanks, Northampton

I DON'T know why MI6 is called the 'Intelligence Service'. If they are that smart, why do they only spy on people in really cold places like Russia and East Germany? What's so wrong with spying on them in Ibiza or Benidorm? I think there would be a lot more young people trying to get into the secret service if they sorted that aspect of the job out a bit.

Maidstone Kent, Bedford

MY mate who's a Stoke City fan recently purchased some goldfish and named one of them Geoff Cameron after Stoke's distinctly underwhelming USA international carthorse defender. Have any of your other readers ever paid a more crap tribute to an utterly mediocre hero of theirs?

Toastie Brown, Harpur Hill

I READ recently that in Germany during the thirties, the economy was in tatters with a loaf of bread costing about 500,000 Marks. Well excuse me, but in my opinion, if people can afford that kind of money for a loaf, they're not doing too badly for themselves.

Ollie Massage, Manchester

WHY do we have signs warning cars not to smash into deer, yet nothing to warn deer from prancing about in front of cars? Again, it's one rule for drivers and another for deer.

Dave Whittle, email

IN the same way that fag packets have graphic pictures of the effects of smoking on them, why don't pipe tobacco packets feature a picture of some boring old fart working on an allotment, or perhaps gazing lovingly into the window of Greenwoods Men's Outfitters? It'd put me off smoking a pipe, I can tell you.

Oliver Cramwell, Buxton

IF the BBC ever had to tighten its belt and start making cuts, they could do a lot worse than starting with *Question Time*. They could merge it with *Gardener's Question Time*, and mix all the controversial questions with a few about re-potting and compost and what have you. This would bring that much-needed variety to the show and also calm down some of the overly-excited audience members.

Barry Ileum, Cardiff

WHY do these astronomers go on about meteorites coming dangerously close to earth and then in the same breath tell us that it passed something like 100,000 miles away? That's really far away in my book. I'd love to see one of those silly twats try to park a car.

Edam Cheese, Glossop

I'M supposed to be going to France this summer, but I'm nervous that they don't do kippers. I don't know what's wrong with these continentals. I went to Southampton recently and you can get kippers there.

Heinrich Von Butty, Hu...

* Have any of our readers ever been to France, and if so, did they do kippers? Write and let us know one way or the other so as Mr Von Butty can decide whether or not to cancel his trip.

I DON'T know why lion tamers are held in such high esteem. I watched one on telly the other night and the lions didn't seem tame at all, in fact they looked fucking furious. Either they should be done under the Trades Descriptions Act, or they should call themselves something else. I had one of those 'Federation of Master Builders' stickers on the side of my van and got done when someone sussed it was all bollocks.

Pardew Fibreboard, Hu...

I MET someone once who lived in Chelsea but supported Arsenal! Can any of your readers beat that?

Wayne Statham, Borehamwood

* There's a challenge for our readers. Perhaps you're a Port Vale fan who lives in Stoke. Or maybe a Nottingham Forest fan who lives north of the Trent closer to Meadow Lane. Or perhaps you're a Manchester United fan who lives within 250 miles of Old Trafford.

THESE "sci-fi" films try to convince us that one day robots will take over the world. However, most British contraptions come with a 1-year manufacturer's guarantee, and then they're fucked. So I reckon if we can hang on for 12 months, we'll be alright.

Basil Treetop, Luton

STING FOR A DAY

WE'VE ALL wondered what it would be like to be a lute-plucking pop arsehole. But if you were suddenly transformed into one, how would you spend 24 hours? We rounded up four of the planet's best-loved megastars and asked them one simple question: what would *YOU* do if you were *STING* for a day?

Peter North, *cumshot icon*

Being Sting for a day would be a total disaster for me. I earn my crust by ejaculating - the more pop shots I perform, the more cash I collect. As such, being suddenly and inexplicably transformed into a Tantric sex guru, who can take up to TEN HOURS to achieve orgasm, would represent a serious dent in my finances. On the plus side, I've always wanted to know what it'd be like to write a shit musical about Tyneside shipyard workers, so I could at least scratch that one off the Bucket List.

Kim Jong-un, *supreme leader of DPRK*

As a child I always dreamed of playing the lute, but my chunky little sausage fingers soon put paid to that idea. Consequently, if I were Sting for a day, I reckon I'd spend most of my 24 hours plucking away delicately at his vast array of medieval stringed instruments, creating the kind of beautiful, timeless melodies I fantasised about in my youth. Then I'd probably stop in on Trudie for a quick 4-hour knee-trembler before it was time to turn back into me again.

Bono, *lead singer of U2*

I'd love to be Sting for a day - it would represent a fascinating new experience for me. I cannot begin to imagine what it'd be like to spend 24 hours as a successful pop star who is regarded by most people as a talentless, self-important twat. It would certainly be a far cry from my usual existence to be thought of as a posturing, hypocritical bell-end who lectures on the environment whilst simultaneously flying about in a private jet. However, I'm sure that after a whole day of having everyone on Earth consider me a useless arsehole with a stupid made-up name, it would be a blessed relief to get back to being good old me again!

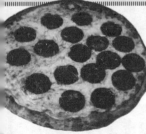

APPARENTLY, the pizza I've just had is 25% of my recommended daily allowance in fat. Well, I 'recommend' that these so-called experts who make this bollocks up re-sit their GCE maths because when I was at school, 100% of anything was the most you could have.

Pat Bastard, Matlock

MY first pet was a hamster called Jimmy and I grew up on Savile Terrace. How the hell am I expected to progress in the porn industry after being dealt that hand?

Gerry Paton, London

IF we could only start a rumour that someone high up in Isis had called someone high up in Al-Qaeda's mum a slag, then we could shit stir a kind of internal terrorist war where they all kill each other. I might get the Nobel Peace Prize for coming up with this idea, but I'd be happy with a fiver.

Lewis, email

WHAT is it with water, finding its own level all the time? Come on water companies, get control of this stuff and show it who's boss.

Steve Fatnacka Meek, Cramlington

WHY do people go to the trouble of advertising things for sale, yet when you call them they say 'sorry it's been sold'? If it's sold, why bother putting it up for sale in the first place? It wastes everyone's time and it really gets on my tits.

Keith Queef, Llanllyfni

WHY are wasps so angry? Its not as if they have to get up in the morning to do the school run, or watch their football team lose every week. Come on wasps, take a leaf out of caterpillars' books and chill out a bit!

Desulph Daz, Middlesbrough

HOW about printing a picture of Lemmy meeting Emperor Hirohito? If not, what about a hovercraft? Cheers,

Freeman Hardy, Willis

＊ *Nothing is too much trouble for our readers, Freeman. Here's a picture of Lemmy meeting Emperor Hirohito... on a hovercraft.*

I RECENTLY spotted what looked a bit like 8 Ace drinking a can of his favourite cheap lager in the clouds above Leeds. Have any of your other readers seen any vague *Viz* character pareidolia?

Steve Lovell, Leeds

HE'S been called a genius, a visionary and a folk hero. But I'm just wondering if there are two Bob Dylans out there because the miserable, tuneless sod I've just heard on the radio moaning about having wind or something doesn't fit any of those descriptions.

Otis, Reading

REMEMBER a few years ago when those Chilean miners got stuck underground and there was a massive media circus surrounding the rescue attempt? Everyone was willing the emergency services on and the miners conducted themselves bravely. Even the guy whose wife and mistress showed up at the scene got away with it, such was the feel-good spirit of the occasion. Nowadays it's all bad news, with Islamic State beheadings and wars and global recessions. So come on Chileans, get stuck underground more often.

Neil Palmer, Leicester

ACCORDING to the Psychedelic Furs song, women are "Pretty In Pink." Well, I've just spent 2 hours trying to bang one out over a photo of Dame Barbara Cartland, and have only succeeded in dislocating my shoulder. That's the last time I take sexual advice from forgotten pop stars.

R.R. Rasputin, Merthyr Tydfil

THIS is crazy, employing car thieves in a car park. Talk about asking for trouble. Why don't they just give them the sack and take the signs down?

D. Twose, Leamington Spa

WHISTLE STOP

ON page 99, Danny Volume asked readers to keep an eye out for his auntie's ACME Thunderer referee's whistle which she dropped overboard whilst on the Newcastle to Bergen ferry in 1954. And the sightings have flooded in...

I AM serving aboard the submarine HMS Vigilant and after reading Danny Volume's touching letter I kept my eyes peeled for his Auntie's ACME Thunderer referee's whistle. Last week while I was on periscope watch I actually spotted it on the sea bed, next to a crab. However, as Vigilant forms part of Britain's nuclear deterrent, only the Captain and Navigator are allowed to know our exact position and not even the Prime Minister knows where we are. So all I can say is it was somewhere between England and Norway.

Petty Officer R Jessop, email

I WAS a commercial deep sea diver working in the oil industry off the coast of Bergen and I did indeed find his Aunt's prized Acme Thunderer whilst welding at the base of a rig. I was astonished by its beauty and carried it with me for a number of years. However, sadly I too lost it overboard on the Dover to Calais ferry whilst on a fag run. Please inform the submarine captains they're looking in the wrong place and direct them to the Channel.

Jockey Scotsman, Monton

COCK SUCKER

ER... I'VE BEEN SENT DOWN FOR A LONG WEIGHT? | PARTS | UH? | WHAT?!?

THE DOPEY DICK! | NO PROBLEM, JUST STAND THERE. | WHAT'S SO FUNNY, LADS?

ISIS in Crisis!

Terror outfit fail management systems audit

TERRORIST group *ISIS* will not be granted ISO 9001 certification after failing a recent management audit. Western governments have hailed the news as a decisive blow against the so-called 'new caliphate.'

"This will really strike at the heart of ISIS," said Defence Secretary Michael Fallon. "ISO 9001 certification is the baseline for any credible organisation which tests and audits the management procedures and structure within a company. Without it, ISIS are going to look pretty foolish."

Sharia we go: Hardline terrorist organisation failed to meet statutory regulation requirements.

"Their report was pretty poor, if I'm honest," said one of the ISIS auditors who wished to remain anonymous.

planning

"Their corporate planning system was non-existent. It was just a cave with loads of scraps of paper with instructions to 'blow things up' and 'hate everyone'," he said.

"Their system for appraisals was also very informal," he continued. "There were no SMART targets and rather than verbal and written warnings, poorly performing employees were simply immolated."

stepladders

"The outfit also scored poorly on health and safety, with unattended stepladders, loose carpets and bombs on the premises. To be honest, the whole place was just a death trap."

A spokesperson for ISIS told reporters: "Death to the West. The poisonous nest of infidel wasps will be crushed."

ISIS join the Taliban, Syria and rock group Limp Bizkit who all failed recent ISO 9001 management audits.

Cliff "Could be 400"

Peter Pan of Pop may be oldest living vertebrate

SCIENTISTS researching *Sir Cliff Richard* say that the veteran pop star could be much older than previously thought. A study carried out by Cambridge boffins that used state-of-the-art technology to count the rings in Richard's neck concluded that the *Congratulations* singer could be between **350 and 450 years old!**

"Previously, the top estimates of Richards's age, based on radio carbon dating and the colour of his hair, ranged from 65 to 75 years," said lead researcher Johnny Kwango, head of the University's Cliffological Biology department. "But our results now suggest that he is much older than that. In fact, we believe he could have been alive for four centuries or more."

"It's amazing to think of all the history he has lived through," the Professor continued. "For example, when Cliff was born James I was King of England, he was al-

ready 100 at the time of the Act of Union in 1707, and Queen Victoria didn't come to the throne until well after his 200th birthday."

"And he didn't have his first top ten hit, *Expresso Bongo,* with the Shadows until he was 354," Kwango added.

Congratulations: Young Ones singer Cliff is very old one.

ACE NEWSPAPER REPORTER BARRY BROWN IS JUST FILING HIS FINAL SCOOP OF THE DAY...

THANKS FOR THAT PULITZER WINNING EXCLUSIVE TODAY, BARRY.

NO PROBLEM BOSS.

OUTSIDE BARRY'S OFFICE...

I'D BETTER GET STRAIGHT HOME. I WANT TO MAKE SURE I'M IN WORK TOMORROW MORNING, NICE AND BRIGHT AND EARLY!

BUT...

FREEZE! THIS IS A HOLD UP!

UH-OH! THE TRUCK CARRYING TOMORROW'S MORNING EDITIONS OF THE PAPER IS BEING ROBBED! I'D BETTER DO SOMETHING - AND QUICKLY!

BARRY QUICKLY DRINKS SIX BOTTLES OF NEWCASTLE BROWN...

GULP GULP GULP!

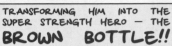

TRANSFORMING HIM INTO THE SUPER STRENGTH HERO — THE BROWN BOTTLE!!

REET! REET! YA FUCKAAZ!

I'LL TEK YUZ AAL ON! REET FUCKINN' NOO!

UH OH! IT'S THE BROWN BOTTLE!

...ONCE I'VE HAD A PISS, LIKE.

AH, THIS IS FUCKINN' NECTAAH.

REET THEN! COME AAHN THEN!

BAAP!

AH, NO. HAD ON SONN. WAIT THERE...

HURGHHH!!

HURP! HURP! HUUURP!!

AAHH...

JESUSS...

BRAP!

BETTER OOT THAN IN, EH, LADS?

AW FUKKIT, I THINK I'M GANNA FOLLOW THROUGH...

AAHH, SORRY ABOOT THIS LADDDS...

THRAAP! PLAPP!

HUUURP!!

HEY, THE BROWN BOTTLE HAS FALLEN ASLEEP! WE CAN MAKE GOOD OUR ESCAPE!

GOOD THINKING, LEFTIE!

SNORE!

THE ROBBERS TAKE OFF IN THEIR GETAWAY VEHICLE...

SCREEEEECH

BUT THEY HADN'T RECKONED WITH RUNNING OVER THE BROWN BOTTLE'S EMPTY GLASS BOTTLES!

BANG!

A PUNCTURE!

WE'LL HAVE TO ESCAPE ON FOOT!

CURSES! WE'VE TRIPPED OVER THESE BOTTLES!!

WELL DONE BROWN BOTTLE! WE'D HAVE NEVER CAUGHT THESE CRIMINALS IF IT WEREN'T FOR YOU.

EH?

BROWN BOTTLE! YOU'VE SAVED ALL OF TOMORROWS PAPERS! YOU'RE A HERO!

NOW TO SEND THEM ALL BACK TO THE PRINTERS AND HAVE THEM PULPED. WE'VE GOT A NEW FRONT PAGE STORY!

THE NEXT MORNING...

THANKYOU BROWN BOTTLE — WHOEVER YOU ARE!

OH, JESUS... ME FUCKIN' HEAD...

123

EVERYONE AGREES that the Moon landings were faked. Despite NASA's insistence that astronauts really walked on the lunar surface in the late sixties and early seventies, it is now clear that the whole Apollo space programme was nothing more than an elaborate hoax. Designed to distract the public's attention away from the war in Vietnam, the assassination of JFK by a CIA agent hiding on the grassy knoll and the murder of Marilyn Monroe with a poisoned suppository inserted by Frank Sinatra on the orders of Bobby Kennedy, the whole episode was shot in a specially built film studio in the middle of the Arizona desert. That much is clear. But how was it done? What tell-tale clues did the perpetrators leave? And how exactly have those in the know been kept silent for so long? It's time to open...

TH

with

THE STUDIO...

The studio where the sham Moon landing footage was shot is a giant hangar in the middle of the Arizona desert. But don't try looking for it on Google Earth, because all evidence of its existence has been erased from the web by the Bilderburg Group and an international cabal of bankers. Emails to Google asking why the giant hangar where the Apollo landings hoax was staged doesn't show up on the internet either bounce back or are met with a stony silence.

THE FILM CREW...

The director, cameraman, sound recordist and lighting technicians have never been identified and no-one has ever come forward claiming to be responsible for shooting the fake lunar surface footage. This can only mean that everyone involved is now dead. Whether they died in a "road accident", perished a "house fire" or succumbed to "natural causes" or "old age", nobody knows or can ever say for sure. What is absolutely certain is that they were all murdered in cold blood on the orders of the head of NASA. Dead men tell no tales and the film crew's half century of complete silence speaks louder than any words.

THE HEAD OF NASA...

As the man who gave the orders to have the film crew killed, the head of NASA was a loose cannon; a wild card who simply knew too much. Such a public figure couldn't simply be done away with, so instead his brain was wiped clean using extra-terrestrial technology found in the crashed Roswell flying saucer and stored ever since at Area 51.

NEIL ARMSTRONG...

After "returning from the Moon", Armstrong retired from public life and turned to religion. Fearful that he may confess the truth about the Apollo hoax to his priest, who would then in turn spill the beans to the media, NASA decided to silence him ... permanently. Using a poisoned umbrella, Armstrong was injected with an undetectable chemical that caused him to have a fatal heart attack whilst recovering from coronary bypass surgery at the age of 82.

BUZZ ALDRIN...

Buzz Aldrin is the only man still alive who knows the real truth ... or does he? For the truth is that the real Buzz Aldrin is at the bottom of the Marianas Trench, his feet encased in a pair of concrete boots. Meanwhile, NASA's puppet Aldrin - a *Manchurian Candidate*-style dopelganger, his face altered with plastic surgery to exactly resemble the late astronaut - travels the world perpetuating the Moon landings myth on talk shows, magazine interviews and public appearances.

FOOTPRINTS...

Step in mud here on Earth and your boot will leave a clear print. But there's no gravity in space, and that's where the Moon is. So how could a weightless man leave a footprint on the lunar surface? It doesn't make sense.

SHADOWS...

In the Apollo landings footage, the astronauts are clearly seen casting shadows on the ground. But the Moon only comes out at night, when the sky is dark. In fact, here on Earth, the only shadows you get at night are by the light of the Moon. How can the Moon cast shadows upon itself? It doesn't make sense.

FLAG...

There's no air on the Moon, so why does the Stars and Stripes flag planted by Armstrong and Aldrin appear to blow in the breeze for a few moments? NASA dupes would have you believe the following ludicrous explanation, and I quote: "The fabric hanging down from the rod acts like a pendulum, moving back and forth under its own momentum, restrained by the elasticity of the fabric attaching it to the rod above. The result is that the fabric undulates or ripples rhythmically, while the stiffness of the fabric resisting deformation gradually slows it." But the conspirators are damned by their own words, for even if that were true, the flag would have kept flapping in the solar wind, which continually blows through all of space.

CONSPIRACY FILES

pendent conspiracy researcher Dr TIM FOILHAT

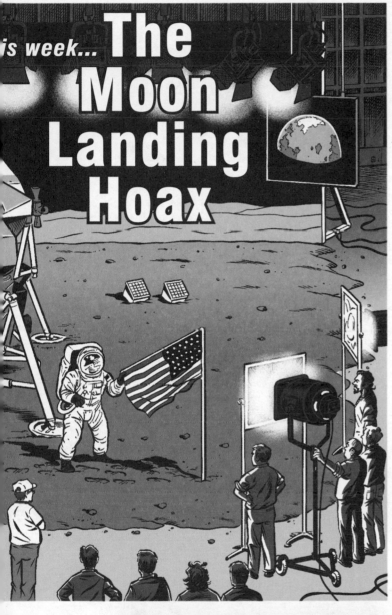

is week... The Moon Landing Hoax

LAUNCH...

Hundreds of thousands of people swear blind that they saw Apollo 11's giant Saturn V rocket blast off from Cape Canaveral on July 16th 1969. They are wrong, but how is it that so many people fell for such an obvious hoax? It's a simple matter of perspective. Instead of watching a 360 ft-high rocket take off 10 miles in the distance, what they actually saw was a 6 ft-high model taking off just 83' 4" in away. The thundering sound they heard was reproduced using loudspeakers hidden in nearby bushes relaying the sound of a man playing the kettle drums. The drummer was later killed in a staged motorcycle accident and all records that he had ever existed were destroyed by dark-suited men wearing sunglasses, who were themselves then killed by even more dark-suited men wearing sunglasses.

LUNAR LIFT-OFF...

As the Lunar Module takes off from the Moon to rendezvous with the orbiting Command Module, the camera tilts to follow its progress into the dark sky. But just stop and think for a moment - with Armstrong and Aldrin aboard,

who is working the camera? NASA claim that an electric servo was fitted to it that kept the lens pointing in the right direction, but that's clearly *BS*. The technology to develop such an automatic system simply didn't exist in the 1960s. They'll be telling you they went to the moon next, which they didn't.

LASER REFLECTORS...

Faked NASA photographs show a reflector array supposedly left on the lunar surface by Neil Armstrong and Buzz Aldrin. However, if you point a laser pen or keyring at the Moon, you won't see its brilliant beam bounce back 2.5 seconds later. That's because the laser reflectors simply aren't there. Why? It's simple. Because they never went to the Moon in the first place.

CROSSHAIRS...

In one famous photograph taken "on the Moon", the camera crosshairs appear *behind* a piece of equipment held by astronaut Buzz Aldrin. This shows that the crosshairs weren't in the camera at all. Instead, they were painted on a large sheet of glass that was held in front of the camera. For this particular picture, Aldrin must have accidentally stepped in front of the glass sheet. NASA have tried to explain this gaffe away with techno-babble about film emulsions, lens flare, exposure times and light levels on the lunar surface. But none of this can be true, because they never went to the Moon.

HOTOS...

of the most ic photographs d as evidence of Moon landings is 'Earth rise' over Sea of Tranquility. look closely at picture and you'll e something is sing. Whoever le the model of Earth that hung the studio ng may have embered to paint string black, but clearly forgot clude the Great of China which, veryone knows, sible from space. ted!

NEXT WEEK: *Dr Tim Foilhat explains why the Twin Towers couldn't have fallen down the way they did.*

SHAME, SET AND MATCH!

EXCLUSIVE!

TENNIS ACE *Andy Murray* yesterday issued a shame-faced apology after 'doing a runner' from a private jet. The British number one and fellow tennis ace *Rafa Nadal* had chartered the luxury plane to bring them home from the recent Rio Olympic games, and had agreed to split the cost between them.

Take flight: Murray's supersonic sprint with tennis pal left pilot gasping.

Murray apologises for Olympic jet runner

But when the flight landed at Stansted airport, the tennis pros pretended to go through their pockets looking for the £50,000 fare before sprinting off in different directions. The pilot, Captain Keith Burtons told reporters how he gave chase as Murray and Nadal vanished across the tarmac.

bat

He said: "I grabbed the baseball bat I keep under my seat and ran after Murray. But I'm obviously not as fit as him as I spend all day sat on my arse eating crisps in my cockpit, and he easily managed to shake me off on some waste ground near a trading estate when I stopped to get my breath back."

tip

However, not to be outdone Captain Burtons turned up the next day at the home of Murray's mother.

"I explained what her son had done, and she was very apologetic," he said. "She immediately coughed up the full 50 grand fare and a £2.50 tip on top. So that was nice."

"Mrs Murray said she would be going round later to see Rafa's mum and get his half of the fare off her," Captain Burtons added.

sorry

A contrite Andy Murray later appeared alongside his mother at a press conference. He said: "I'd like to take this opportunity to say sorry to the pilot and the airline for me and Rafa's bad behaviour. It was a moment of madness, and I promise it won't happen again."

games

And Murray also apologised to his fellow Team GB members for tarnishing what had otherwise been a very successful games for the national squad. Mrs Murray read a prepared statement, in which she apportioned equal blame for the incident between the two players.

"I have spoken to Rafa's mum, Mrs Nadal, and she is as cross with her Rafa as I am with my Andy," she said.

"They have both been very silly, but it was a case of six of one and half a dozen of the other."

mistake

She continued: "But I would just like to say that they are not bad boys. They have accepted their mistake and learnt their lesson. Now they'd just like to put this whole silly incident behind them and get on with their tennis."

Mrs Nadal later confirmed that Rafa had been grounded and sent to his bedroom, and would therefore be missing the WTA Finals in Singapore.

129

"THIS JOB'S A PIECE O

Queen Comes Clean on Royal Duties

Royal rant: *The Queen used barrac room language.*

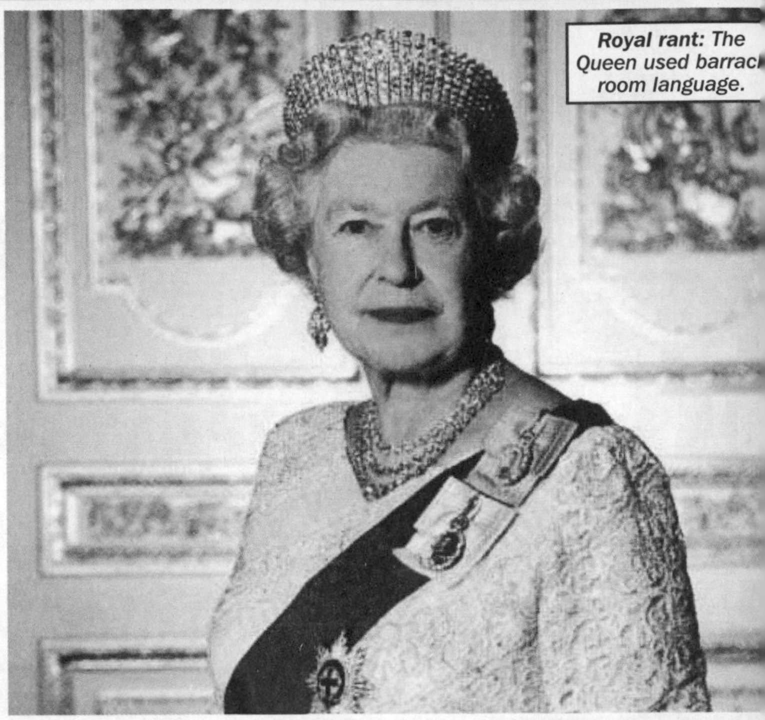

AFTER 64 YEARS on the throne, Queen Elizabeth II has earned the respect of a grateful nation. She has been a wonderful figurehead for the country during many turbulent times and her tireless service and devotion to duty have been a shining example to us all. But now a series of indiscreet remarks, apparently made by Her Majesty and recorded on a mobile phone by a member of the public, have cast a different light on her attitude to her role as monarch.

In an unguarded moment during an official visit to Manchester to open a bus station, the Queen was caught boasting that her job was nowhere near as difficult as it was painted, bragging that ruling the country was actually *"a piece of fucking piss."* Her shocking comments were overheard by cleaner Maureen Mimblehulme, 56, who was in a nearby cubicle.

effing

The mum-of-two told us: "Her and the Lady Mayoress had come in to

EXCLUSIVE!

powder their noses, and while they were washing their hands the Queen started mouthing off about how easy her job was. I couldn't believe what I was hearing. She was effing and blinding, using terrible language that I would never have expected to hear from her."

"I knew no-one would believe me if I told them, so I decided to record the conversation on my mobile phone," Mrs Mimblehulme added.

Our reporters have seen a transcript of the recording, in which the Queen repeatedly **GLOATS** over t lightness of her daily workload. a series of four-letter outbursts, t monarch **BRAGS**

* *"I just sit on my fat arse all c waving. It's not like I'm digging fucking coal."*

* *"There's lackeys to do all the s jobs. I've never washed a fucking p in my life."*

* *"I'm on forty-five mill a year, free, I shit you not, and I literally fuck all for it."*

blinding

Mrs Mimblehulme, who ins she has always been a staunch mo archist, said she was shocked to core by the Queen's cocky attitu and foul language. "I was liter ly gobsmacked," she told us. I hadn't got the recording on

Dirty words: *The Queen's outbursts turned the air royal blue, claims cleaner Maureen.*

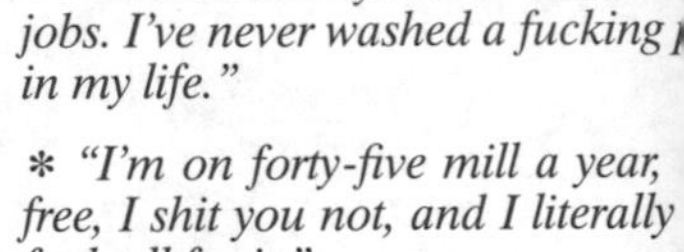

WORDS OF SHAME

Part of the transcript that will shock the nation...

On her Christmas Message...

Queen: "...it's just the same pile of old wank every year. Fucking state visit this, fucking family and friends that, blah-blah-blah, know what I mean? And I don't do it on Christmas day neither, fuck that, they just stick a tree up and record the fucker in the summer ... [laughs and coughs] ... 'ere, giz one of them fags."

Mayoress: "Yes ma'am."

Queen: "...don't even watch the fucker, neither. Fucking boring as fuck."

On taking a break...

Queen: "... I don't stand in no queues at the airport, fuck that. I've never stood in a fucking queue in me life. We get drove out onto the runway, no passports, no customs, no nowt. Straight onto the fucking plane."

Mayoress: "That's ..."

Queen: "... [inaudible] ... a fucking red carpet, it is, straight onto the plane. And it's me own fucking plane too, mind. No other fucker can come on it. Fuck that for a game of soldiers [laughter]."

On her daily duties...

Queen: "...I mean, I just have to go out and cut a fucking ribbon, know what I mean? It's what, ten seconds? Not even that, and then I'm back in the fucking Roller, feet up, G and T, off home to the fucking Palace. Job done."

Mayoress: "Yes, ma'am. It sounds ..."

Queen: "And it gets better. I don't even have to make me own fucking dinner. Four courses, on the fucking table when I get there and a ... [inaudible] ... in a fucking tailcoat, and he brings it me on a silver fucking tray with one of them big fucking dome things on the top."

Mayoress: "How very..."

Queen: "Some other fucker clears the dirties off the table, takes 'em away. Honestly, I don't know where the kitchen is. Then it's feet up in front of the telly all night."

On keeping up with the news...

Queen: "... and when I read the papers, some fucking flunkey's ironed the fuckers first. Ironed them! Can you fucking believe it?"

Mayoress: "Yes ma'am, you must ..."

Queen: "Honest, you couldn't make this shit up."

PISS" TREASON!

Royal whistleblower Maureen exposed as serial love-rat benefits queen!

Tape worm: Unscrupulous cleaner Mimblehulme's home life is less than spotless.

THE MANCHESTER lavatory cleaner who secretly recorded a private chat between Her Majesty the Queen and the Lady Mayoress of Urmston last night got a taste of her own medicine when she was *EXPOSED* as a *SERIAL LOVE RAT* living high on the hog on *STATE HANDOUTS*.

Last week, *Maureen Mimblehulme* betrayed the Queen's confidence by taping a confidential conversation that allegedly cast Her Majesty in an unfavourable light, before hawking the salacious story to a downmarket magazine. But now the tables have been turned and Mimblehulme has found herself in the media spotlight, with some very uncomfortable questions to answer.

Exposed by our chief investigative reporter
MAHATMA MACAROON

After hacking Mimblehulme's mobile phone, accessing her Facebook page and rifling through her bins, *Viz* chief investigative reporter **MA-HATMA MACAROON** came up with a picture very much at odds with the one that the 56-year-old Urmston housewife likes to portray in public.

toyboy

"The Queen's rock solid marriage to the same man has been a shining example to us all for more than seven decades. What a contrast when we compare it to Mrs Mimblehulme's own tangled love life. Only 56 years old, she is already onto her second husband, following the death of her first in 1995. Neighbours told us that present toyboy husband Frank, 18 months her junior, was recently diagnosed with a chronic pulmonary illness, so it's surely only a matter of time before fancy man number three hoves into view and moves into her £35,000 council flat.

Whilst the Queen, now in her tenth decade, continues to work hard for her modest £45 million a year civil list payment, Maureen never deigned to lift a finger for the £16 weekly Child Allowance she used to shamelessly rake in during the nineties for her brood of two children by one different men.

wallet

And whereas Elizabeth II has never put a foot wrong during the course of her long and illustrious reign, the name of Maureen Mimblehulme is a familiar one to Manchester police. Indeed, in 2012, she visited her local station to report a missing cat. Not two years later, she was back through the door once more, this time to hand in a wallet that she had "found" on the seat of a bus.

Last night, Mimblehulme refused to answer my questions yelled through her letterbox, and covered her face in shame when I pushed a camera and high-powered flashgun through her toilet window. In fact she remained holed up in her house all day, leaving only to accompany her husband on a hospital appointment and to go to the three cleaning jobs she does every day."

---

phone, I wouldn't have believed it." As soon as she got home, she decided to turn whistleblower to expose her majesty's true nature, passing on a transcript of the Queen's outrageous remarks to us.

"I think it's important that people know what the Elizabeth II is really like behind closed doors," she told us. "The truth needs to come out."

"It's absolutely disgusting. She's got one face for her subjects and another one entirely when she thinks no-one's watching," Mrs Mimblehulme added.

A Buckingham Palace spokesman last night told us there was no-one available for comment. He told us: 'Well, except me I suppose, but I've got nothing to say except that there's no-one available for comment."

Have YOUR Say

WE PLAYED Mrs Mimblehulme's candid recording to people in the street to gauge their reaction to the Queen's outrageous comments.

"...I'm absolutely disgusted. I wouldn't have expected to hear such words coming from the Queen's lips. In fact, I'm going home now to smash my Diamond Jubilee mug and send Buckingham Palace the bill."

Edna Shacklady, Tring

"...I've always been a staunch monarchist, but after hearing the Queen bragging like that about how easy she's got it, I would happily get involved in a revolution like that which took place in France between 1789 and 1799."

Frank Todmorton, Bude

"...I'm really shocked. At least the Duke of Edinburgh has never made any secret of his contempt for ordinary people. But I would have expected better from Her Majesty."

Doris Rabbits, Barnstaple

"...Me and my husband spent four nights sleeping rough on the Mall to get a good position for the Queen's 90th birthday parade. If we'd have known then the contempt in which she holds her subjects, we would only have spent two or three nights sleeping rough."

Ada Cretis, Leeds

"...I've had a very hard life, with many setbacks over the years, but it's always been made more bearable by the fact that I've always felt the Queen was on my side. Now that it's clear that she is in fact laughing up her sleeve at those less fortunate than herself, she can stick my loyalty up her big fat arse."

Ada Bling, Tooting

Have YOUR Say

TRAITOROUS love rat benefits Queen *Maureen Mimblehulme* betrayed Her Majesty's confidence by slyly taping a private conversation and making it public. We went out on the streets to find out just how *DISGUSTED* the British people were by her disgraceful actions.

"... Her behaviour was abhorrent and I was abhorred by it. She is guilty of nothing more and nothing less than Treason, and she should suffer the traitor's death. She should be hanged by the neck until she is nearly, but not quite dead, then have her entrails drawn out and burned in front of her. She should then have her head chopped off and her body cut into four pieces. Her severed head should then be placed on a spike on Westminster Bridge, and the quarters of her body displayed in four cities around the United Kingdom, for instance Leeds, Belfast, Glasgow and St Asaph."

Myles Malleson, Wade

"... Whilst I agree with the sentiments expressed by Mr Malleson (above), I'm afraid that I must take issue with his suggestion that a quarter of Mrs Mimblehulme should be sent to St Asaph in Wales. St Asaph is not a city, it is a town, and a small one at that."

George Woodbridge, Ironbridge

"... Mr Woodbridge (above) is talking out his arse when he says that St Asaph isn't a city. It is too a city. It has a cathedral, and it was given city status in 2012. However, it wouldn't make much sense to send any of Mrs Mimblehulme's remains there, because there are only 3,500 inhabitants. To show the people of Wales what becomes of traitors, she should be put on display in the biggest city in the principality, and that is Swansea."

Sebastian Cabot, Chelmsford

"... I cannot allow Mr Cabot's assertion (above) that Swansea is the biggest city in Wales to go unchallenged. Whilst it is indeed almost three times larger in area than Cardiff (150 sq. miles as opposed to 54.2 sq. miles), the Cardiff Unitary Authority boasts a much higher population (just over 1 million versus Swansea's 685 thousand). Cardiff would therefore be much the better choice when displaying 25% of Mrs Mimblehulme's remains in order to deter the populace from committing acts of treason."

Alan Crofoot, Bedford

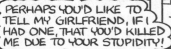

Meet the man they call... THE NOSTRA

Ex-shoe repairer Barry's prophesies keep coming true

16TH CENTURY SAGE and astrologer *Nostradamus* is famous for his visions of the future. In *Les Propheties*, a volume of quatrain verses published in 1555, he predicted with astonishing precision such historic events as the Great Fire of London, the rise of *Adolf Hitler* and the assassination of *John F Kennedy* hundreds of years before they came to pass. And now a Derbyshire father of six has been revealed as a real-life Nostradamus of the twenty-first century.

Unemployed former shoe repairer Barry Longcake of Mickleover says that, just like his ancient French predecessor, he has the power to see into the future. And in a remarkable series of harbingers and portents, he has predicted with uncanny accuracy a string of major events that have shaped recent history. Amongst other happenings, Longcake has foretold:

- *The September 11th attack on the New York World Trade Centre*
- *The election of the first black President of the United States of America*
- *The rise of ISIS following the so-called Arab Spring*
- *The success of Pudsey the dog in Britain's Got Talent*

Barry, 61, says he never knows when he's going to have one of his mysterious visions. "They just come out of nowhere at all times of the day or night," he told his local paper the *Mickleover & Egginton Daily Meteorite*. "I could be doing anything - enjoying a few cans of Spesh in the shed, having an evening in on the homebrew, or even walking home from the pub - and suddenly my mind is filled with vivid pictures of events that are yet to happen."

"When I come round I can't remember a thing, but then I

EXCLUSIVE!

invariably find that I have written down an enigmatic verse using arcane language, setting out out what I have seen. It's almost as if the spirit of Nostradamus himself is possessing me and using me as a conduit for his prognostications."

lottery

Most people would be delighted to have the gift of second sight, using their talent to predict lottery numbers and the results of horse races. But Barry maintains he rarely places bets based on his mystical prophesies. He told the paper: "I've got my fingers burned that way more times than I care to mention. My oracular verses are worded in such an old-fashioned and obscure way that I often don't work out what they are about until after the event in question has taken place."

And as a case in point, from his pocket he produces a crumpled cigarette packet on which is scribbled a cryptical verse written down during a vision he experienced at work.

express

"I'd been using strong petroleum-based glue to stick some new soles on a pair of rigger boots," says Barry. "It was a hot day and it's quite a small booth I work in, and I started to have a vision. When I came round I saw that I had written something down during my episode."

In the sixteenth year of Christ's third millennium,
Eleven warriors in blue from a city that is also red,
Shall hold aloft a silver chalice,
And be proclaimed champions of the twenty.

"I read it and immediately knew what it meant. It was a foretoken of who would be the best of 20 teams and win the Premier League in 2016. It was a team in blue, so I obviously thought it was Chelsea. But the bit about 'a city that is also red' made me think

Crystal clear: Norris's believes his visions could benefit mankind.

of Manchester, as Man United play in that colour. I was certain the verse was referring to a team in blue from Manchester. My vision was predicting Man City to take the title."

trust

"I immediately borrowed some money out of the till, shut the shop up and popped down the bookies in the precinct to put two hundred quid on Man City topping the league. I got four-to-one, so I was looking forward to an £800 payday come the end of the season."

"Of course, as everyone now knows, Leicester City were the 'eleven warriors in blue' who actually took the title. That bit about 'the city that is also red' must have referred to Red Leicester cheese, or possibly the colour of Walker's Ready Salted crisps that are made in Leicester and come in a red packet."

"Why Nostradamus couldn't have

used me to write: 'Leicester City to win the 2015/16 Premiership title' instead of farting round with a poem like something off *3-2-1* I'll never know. If only the quatrain had been worded even a bit more clearly, I'd have put my money on the Foxes at 5,000-1 and been a millionaire. I could have told the area manager to stick his job up his arse, but it wasn't to be."

"I had to forge a lot of receipts and short-change dozens of customers to make up the missing cash out of the drawer."

Diana's death foretold

We all remember where we were back in August 1997 when we first heard the shocking news that Lady Diana Spencer had perished. And Barry also remembers where he was when he learnt about the tragic high speed

Barack to the future: Could Longcake have foretold Obama's inauguration?

AMUS OF DERBY

crash in which the Princess of Hearts was killed.... *a full 24 hours before it happened!*

"I was sitting in my shed on the Saturday morning, tucking into a few cans and flicking through some mags," he recalls. "I was just finishing my sixth can when the room began to spin and I once again felt the spirit of Nostradamus taking possession of my mind's eye. I saw a black car, flashing lights, terrified faces, Lady Di and Dodi Wotsisname. It was a kaleidoscope of swirling images. When I came round, there was a strange, delphic verse scribbled across the centrefold of one of the mags I had been reading."

Beneath a mighty river across the sea,
In a town where a tower of iron doth stand,
Tomorrow shall die an English rose,
A princess with a broken heart.

"I had read in the paper that the Princess of Wales was staying in Paris - the 'town where a tower of iron doth stand' in my premonition. My blood ran cold when the meaning of the verse became clear: An English rose, Lady Diana, was going to die the very next day."

health service

"I knew I had to act fast. The clock was ticking and, if the portent was true, the Princess of Hearts had just hours left to live. I immediately pulled my trousers up, ran round to the bookies

and asked what odds they'd give me on Lady Di getting killed the next day. The woman behind the window looked a little shocked, and explained that it was company policy not to take bets on people's deaths. I tried a few more betting shops and got the same po-faced response each time."

Predictive texts: Is the spirit of Nostrodamus using Barry as a vessel?

"In the end, I went to see an unlicensed bookmaker I knew, Frankie the Hat, who worked from a pub. He gave me odds of twenty-to-one and I put a tenner on it."

enquirer

"The next morning, I woke up and heard the terrible news from Paris on the radio. My prefigurement had come to pass, and it was with a very heavy heart that I headed off to collect my winnings. But Lady Diana's death wasn't the only tragedy that occurred

that day, because when I got to the pub there was no sign of Frankie the Hat."

"He didn't come in that night, the next day, or the day after that. In fact, I've not seen hide nor hair of him - or my two hundred quid - since."

A gift... or a Curse?

Barry believes that he has been given the gift of foresight so that he can use it for the benefit of all mankind. So when he receives an augury of great importance, he usually feels duty bound to warn those who will be affected by the forthcoming events. But over the years, he has found that not everyone is pleased to hear his pronouncements. And when Barry tried to warn one prominent member of society about a forthcoming tragedy, he was left wishing he hadn't bothered.

"It was a Saturday. I'd had quite a big win on the horses that day, so I was celebrating in the boozer and I'd had quite a good night," he remembers. "When I left to walk home, the air hit me and I started to feel a bit wobbly. I nipped up an alley to have a quick piss, but as I stood there I felt Nostradamus entering my spirit. The world started spinning, my legs went from under me and I blacked out."

"The next thing I knew, a copper was kicking my foot and telling me to get up. It was light and I was lying in the

Reign check: Norris believes the Queen has less than 25 years to live

alley by a skip with my flies open. It must have been an extremely vivid vision I'd had, because it had made me be sick all down the front of my shirt."

theatre

"As I got up I noticed that, during my episode of the night before, I had scrawled a warning on the pavement by my side with a chalky stone. And when I read what I had written, my blood ran cold."

The Queen of an island race shall die,
Before one fourth of a century hath gone,
And her reign shall be passed to a man called Wales,
With ears large and a thinning pate.

"I had a thumping headache from the previous night's possession by the great seer, but even in my state I realised the gravity of the words I was reading. It was foretelling that, at some point in the next 25 years, Her Majesty the Queen was going to die and be replaced by either her son Charles, or her grandson, William."

"The copper and his mate put on rubber gloves and picked me up off the ground. I tried to tell them that the Queen was in danger, but my tongue was all dry and my head was pounding, and I couldn't get the words out properly. I tried pointing to the sibylline pronouncement on the pavement, but they didn't seem interested. It was so frustrating. I was trying to warn them of a threat to her majesty's life and they were just laughing at me."

minimum wage

"When I got to my feet, they escorted me to the end of the alley and made me stand by their car. They took my name and address

In forty years of prognostication, Barry Longcake has hit the nail on the head time and again with startling accuracy. Here are just a few of the momentous events which he has foretold...

In a year of twice twenty and yet two more,
A mighty contest of men shall be seen,
In a rainless realm of sand,
Where humped horses do walk upon the earth.

1973 Barry predicts that the 2022 World Cup will be held in Qatar.

People will speak into a window of light,
That once was five but is now six,
Thinner and larger shall it be,
But for all that just the same as it was before.

1992 Barry prophesies the 2014 replacement of the iPhone 5 with the iPhone 6.

For sake of meat at the end of day,
A man of many wheels shall strike his neighbour,
And the people shall cry out in woe,
When his place be taken by a red-haired pretender.

1997 Barry foretells the 2015 sacking of *Top Gear* presenter Jeremy Clarkson following a misunderstanding over a steak dinner and his subsequent replacement by Chris Evans

A rider astride a roaring metal beast,
Clothed in armour made from an ox's skin,
Shall defy death in circles,
Swifter than the spotted cat.

2001 Barry foresees the live Channel 4 show in which Guy Martin became the first man to ride a motorcycle at more than 70mph on a Wall of Death

Two jesters who make no man laugh,
Shall hail a false son of Spain,
And though he be of many years,
Besmirch his granddaughter's name for all to hear.

1983 Barry experiences a vision presaging the 2008 Sachsgate controversy in which Jonathan Ross prank-called Manuel actor Andrew Sachs to tell him that Russell Brand had fucked his granddaughter

CONTINUED OVER...

...CONTINUED and told me to go home. They warned me that if they caught me in that state again I'd be in big trouble."

"When I got home I cleaned myself up and lay down on my bed. It had been a pretty powerful omen, and it wasn't until later that afternoon that I felt more or less back to normal. I returned to the alley, popping into Boots on the way to buy a disposable camera so as I could take a snap of the warning that, through me, the ghost of Nostradamus had chalked onto the pavement. But it had rained heavily that afternoon, and when I got there the oracular poem had been washed away."

"I knew that without proof I would not be taken seriously, so reluctantly I had to let the matter drop. But living with the knowledge that Her Majesty the Queen has less than 25 years to live, and being unable to tell anyone, is a great burden."

Barry's vision of sextape

Not all of Barry's premonitions are harbingers of momentous events. Some are quite inconsequential, occasionally to the extent that he has no idea what they mean even after the event has occurred. Such a foreshadowing occurred one evening in 1990 after a particularly lucid vision.

"I'd spent the night at the working men's club in Mickleover and I'd won a bottle of Pernod in a raffle. I'd never drunk it before, so when I got home I poured myself a large glass. It wasn't exactly to my taste, but it was pleasant enough. And it was during my fifth glass that I suddenly felt a premonition coming on. I collapsed in my chair and didn't come round from my possession until the following morning."

"When I did, I saw that I had written a quatrain on the back of a copy of The Racing Post which had been lying on the table."

Upon a ship in a land of golden sunshine,
A man with paintings upon his skin,
Shall consort with a maiden fair,
And you can see it going in and everything.

"I couldn't make head nor tail of it. However I tried to interpret this prefigurement, it didn't seem to make any sense. But it didn't seem to be foreboding of any tragedy, so I simply forgot about it."

tattoos

"Then, a couple of weeks ago, I locked up the shop and popped into the pub in the precinct to have a lunchtime drink, a fruit juice or something, and I got chatting to Nobby from the local greengrocers. He told me that he had watched a video the night before on his computer. Apparently, it featured Pamela Anderson and her husband Tommy Lee having sex on a boat in California. According to Nobby, Tommy was covered in tattoos and it was very explicit, so you could see it going in and everything."

"And it was when he said 'see it going in and everything' that my mind raced back to my 1990 vision. Blonde Baywatch babe Pamela... Tommy with paintings on his skin... sunny California... the boat. Had I predicted the coming of this video years before it was made? There was only one way to check."

castles

"When I got back to work, I opened up the booth and logged onto the works computer. Within seconds I had found the video that Nobby had described and I watched it to see if it faithfully fulfilled the prophesy I had made all those years before."

Club of fate: The working men's club where Barry won the bottle of Pernod.

"I was amazed at the accuracy with which my vision had described the future events, so much so that I couldn't take my eyes off the screen. Unfortunately, the area manager chose that afternoon to make a surprise visit to my booth to check up on things, and he caught me watching the video."

"I tried to explain that I was simply verifying a prediction I had made 26 years previously, but he wouldn't listen. He said that using a company computer for such a purpose was a gross breach of my employment contract. He reminded me that I was already on my third and final warning for two similar offences and sacked me on the spot."

Whilst he has never wanted to benefit financially from his gift, unemployed Barry's present circumstances mean that he has reluctantly decided to start charging for the information contained in his predictions.

fringes

"I will be holding a show at the Mickleover Miners' Welfare Club every Saturday evening," he told *Daily Meteorite* reporters. "I will be reading out my quatrains, explaining what, in my opinion, they mean and also asking the audience for their interpretations. Tickets are available on the door and will cost £5 which includes a stripper and a pie and pea supper."

Tarot No! Shame of Britain's Schools!

90 PERCENT of British 8-year-olds are unable to name any of the Tarot cards, and 50% of youngsters leave school without being able to name more than 2. And now the government has pledged to increase funding in order to tackle the problem.

"These statistics are shocking," Education Minister **Nicky Morgan** told *Good Morning*'s Phillip Schofield. "If we don't act now, the present generation will grow up without the ability to look into the future."

Ms Morgan promised that the government was going to put Tarot Illiteracy high on the educational agenda. "We want every schoolchild by the age of 11 to know their Tarot cards off by heart," she said. "They are the basic tools needed if our children are to have the ability to successfully prognosticate in the modern world."

However, when challenged by Schofield to name five Tarot cards herself, the Loughborough MP became flustered and refused to be drawn. "I know my Tarot cards, of course I do," she said. "But I'm not going to get into that."

When pressed by Schofield to just name three Tarot cards, Morgan removed her microphone and stormed out of the studio.

A bright future?: Could a generation of children grow up without Tarot knowledge?

HARBINGER OF DOOM

"I saw the tragic stars' fates" says Clairvoyant Edna

THIS year's unprecedented spate of star deaths came as a shock to us all. *Lemmy, David Bowie, Prince, Victoria Wood...* the roll call of celebrities who unexpectedly met their maker was literally endless. But to one Nottingham woman, these deaths came as no surprise at all.

For every single one of the household names who perished in the first few months of 2016 had recently been to see professional fairground clairvoyant Edna Blavatsky, and she had foreseen their tragic fates as clear as day.

Palmed off: Edna Blavatsky's star-studded clientele all met unhappy endings.

"I was at Nottingham Goose Fair in October and I'd got the stall between the Haunted House and Mousetown, so business had been a bit quiet. But one of my customers was **DAVID BOWIE**. He came in the awning and crossed my palm with £2.50. He wanted to know if his new album was going to go to number one in the hit parade.

balls

Clairvoyants have a variety of techniques for looking into the future at their disposal, including Tarot cards, tea-leaves and crystal balls. The *Space Oddity* singer went for the tea-leaves reading, so I made him a brew with a teabag, and made sure I burst it with the spoon. He drank his cuppa and handed it back to me.

When I looked in the bottom of the mug, my blood ran cold. For the story of the future that the tea leaves told was unmistake-

Sign o' the end times: Pint-sized singer's palm revealed chilling fate.

able; Bowie was going to die on January 10th. Obviously, I didn't tell him that in case it spoilt his Christmas a bit. Instead, I told him that the new year would bring travel, an interesting piece of news and a stroke of good fortune."

June last year was particularly memorable for Edna, as another doomed star made his way to her tent for a reading.

johnson

"I was at the Hoppings fair on Newcastle's Town Moor. It had lagged it down solidly for five days, like it usually does, so the place was a quagmire. So I have to admit that I was quite surprised when pint-size pop star **PRINCE** poked his head through the flap and asked if I was doing readings. I told him it was £2.50 and he came in and sat down at my folding table.

He explained that he didn't believe in tea, as he was a Jehovah's Witness, so he held out his hand and asked me to read his palm. When I examined the lines on it, my blood ran cold. For the tale it told of the *Purple Rain* singer's fate was unambiguous; the lifeline stopped dead on April 21st.

As I looked into his little face, with his bright eyes full of hope for the future, I realised I couldn't tell him the terrible news. Instead, I told him that the next twelve months would see a stroke of luck, an interesting piece of news and a journey of some sort."

darling

Over the next few months, as Edna travelled Britain appearing at different fairs, her tent was visited by a *Who's Who* of doomed celebrities, including **RONNIE CORBETT, VICTORIA WOOD, PAUL DANIELS, LEMMY** out of Motörhead and **TERRY WOGAN**.

She told us: "Each time, the fate I foresaw for my celebrity clients was one of death. But nobody wants to know when they are going to die, so I make it a rule to keep it to myself when I see the Grim Reaper looming in someone's future."

Stirman: Bowie's tea-leaves revealed chilling fate.

But Edna almost let a terrible secret slip when *Harry Potter* actor **ALAN RICKMAN** called on her for a reading during the Shiremoor Children's Treat fair.

"Him who played Professor Snape came in. He wanted to know what the fates had in store for him. I told him it would be £2.50, handed over

my pack of Tarot cards and told him to shuffle them. I dealt the first three cards off the top of the deck; they were Death, the Serpent and the Magician. As an experienced clairvoyant I knew exactly what it meant. Rickman's fate was sealed; he would depart this earth on January 14th.

I froze in shock, and without thinking blurted out: 'I see death.' Rickman's eyes widened in alarm. 'What?' he said. 'When? I must know.' Thinking on my feet, I told him: 'I was just talking about your character Professor Snape and how he gets bit off a snake and dies,' I explained. He seemed relieved, and I went on to tell him that in his future I had seen a piece of interesting news, him going on a journey of some sort and a piece of unexpected good fortune.

osborne

But in reality, I knew that his fate was sealed and his days were numbered."

Chillingly, Edna's says that the stars who have passed on so far this year are not the only ones whose fate she has foretold. She told us: "Many more showbiz celebs have also recently crossed my palm with silver to have their futures read, and I have seen that some of them will die this year."

"It wouldn't be right for me to name them here. But they include a man who used to be on the television, a woman who has appeared in films and a famous musician. Mark my words, they will all meet their maker before 2016 is out."

"And I should know. I'm the third daughter of a second son," she added.

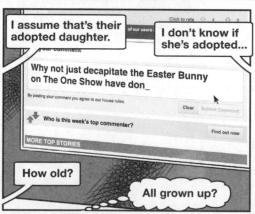

138

BIG VERN

RAFFLES the GENTLEMAN THUG

PESTS AND BUGS AND ROCK 'N' ROLL!

Mice work if you can get it: Basil Cataract looks back on a glittering forty-year career of exterminating rodents for top celebrities.

IT'S EVERY homeowner's worst nightmare. You return from a hard day's graft to find evidence of verminous creatures prowling your property. From bedbugs and birds to rodents and roaches, feral pests stalk Britain's kitchens, bedrooms and bathrooms day and night, soiling our clean surfaces, nibbling our wiring and crapping in our cornflakes packets.

But take heart. It's not just the ordinary man in the street who is plagued by these nuisance animals - the biggest stars of stage and screen also find their luxury homes prey to pest infestations. And one man who knows this better than most is 64-year-old **BASIL CATARACT**. Bachelor Basil has spent the past forty years exterminating vermin for Tinseltown's best and brightest, and his rollcall of clients reads like a Who's Who of the most famous names in showbiz.

"I've obliterated vermin in so many glitzy celeb mansions that I'm beginning to lose count," chuckles Fileyborn Basil. "But I never allow myself to get blinded by the fame of my customers; I just knuckle down and get on with the killing."

Now, to mark his glittering fourth decade in the pest control business, Basil is set to release an explosive new autobiography, *Simply The Pest* (£4.99, Lisab Books). In these tantalising exclusive extracts, he lays bare the wildest stories from his many years of A-List pest extermination...

Posh Begged Me to 'Becks-terminate' Seagull

❝ I'LL NEVER forget a call I got back in 2002. A terrified-sounding female voice informed me that a seagull had got into her house through an open window, and was now flapping about wildly inside. She begged me to come as quickly as possible, and gave me the address of a swanky-sounding mansion in Cheshire.

I deal with a lot of bird ingress cases, they're

> **"I've topped vermin for the biggest stars around,"** says A-List exterminator Basil

bread and butter to a seasoned pro like me. It's usually pigeons that have got in through an open window. Now pigeon droppings are one thing - you just have to wait for them to dry before picking them off the soft furnishings and giving everything a going over with a brush and a bottle of Febreze - but seagull shit is in a whole different league. It soaks in, it stinks of fish, and there's generally loads of it flying around once the bastards get panicked and the bomb-bay doors open. This was a code red emergency.

Gull power: Basil was called to swish Cheshire mansion when angry seabird invaded Posh's boudoir.

I arrived at the palatial residence to be greeted by none other than **VICTORIA BECKHAM** herself! Poor old Posh was trembling uncontrollably in a half-open dressing gown, her face a twisted mask of panic and fear. She explained that her husband David was out playing football, but before he'd gone, he'd carelessly left the remains of a chip butty on the master bedroom windowsill. A greedy herring gull had spotted the discarded scraps, and was now trapped inside the room, flapping about and squawking.

Posh showed me through to the bedroom and, I won't lie to you, it was a mess. The petrified bird had turned the Beckhams' priceless four poster bed into a steaming collage of white liquid faeces.

Recognising the urgency of the situation, I got straight down to business. With birds, the best thing is to make the room as dark as possible, so they're attracted to the window. I switched off all the lights and asked Posh to fetch me a broom, which I promptly used to smack the bird about a bit until it finally flapped back out into the open air.

I slammed the window shut, and poor Posh was so relieved I thought she would faint. She handed me my fee and said, "I can't thank you enough, Basil. There's your payment... Now it's time for your tip." I asked what she meant, and she threw me a cheeky wink. "I mean, if you "wannabe my lover... that can be arranged," she said, slipping out of her silky nightgown and reclining on the bed.

> ❝ ...if you wannabe my lover... that can be arranged, she said, slipping out of her silky nightgown... ❞

Now, I'm as red-blooded as the next man, so the sight of a former Spice Girl writhing nude on a the duvet was tempting to say the least. But with the window shut, the room was beginning to hum from all the seagull shit everywhere. Not only that, anyone who knows me will tell you that I'm not in this game for the sexual perks - the thrill I get from slaughtering vermin is more than enough for me. I was about to tell Posh this, when the front door slammed, and a high-pitched Cockney voice called out: "Posh, love, I'm home!"

It was her husband - David Beckham! Frantically, the *Zig-A-Zig-Ah* singer pulled her knickers back on. "You'd best do one, Basil," she hissed. I didn't need telling twice, I can tell you. I was out that window quicker than the ruddy seagull! ❞

'Hard Man' Kemp Shat It off Mini Mouse

❝ IT NEVER fails to surprise me how different from their on-screen personas celebs can sometimes be. And one incident that happened a few years back illustrates this perfectly.

I'd got a call about a mouse problem in a ritzy-sounding London mansion. Now, rats and mice are a pest controller's bread and butter, so as I sauntered up the path I certainly wasn't anticipating any major bumps in the road. Needless to say I was surprised to be met at the door by notorious TV hard man **ROSS KEMP**.

The slap-headed ex-*Eastenders* star looked troubled to say the least. He

was carrying a badminton racquet and chuntering on agitatedly about a giant rat on the loose in the house. Before I could reassure him that the situation was under control, a tiny grey dormouse came scurrying along the skirting board. To my surprise, telly's Mr Tough let out an ear-splitting shriek and leapt up onto a nearby stool, screeching "Get rid of it! Get rid of it!" in a terrified high-pitched voice. He was so scared, he was actually crying.

I wasted no time baiting a heavy-duty spring-loaded steel bar trap, and set about pumping every gap in the skirting board with ammonia spray and naphthalene. All the while the petrified *...On Gangs* 'hard man' continued to whimper on his stool.

Eventually, the noxious chemicals proved too much for Kemp's unwanted guest, and it came sprinting out of the wall and straight into the jaws of my expertly-laid trap. This one certainly wouldn't be stealing any more cheese.

The emotion was too much for Kemp. He tumbled off his stool in a relieved heap, and starting weeping like a baby at my feet. I had to chuckle as I looked down at Grant Mitchell himself, blubbing like a toddler all because of a furry little mouse no bigger than his thumb. It was a convincing display of emotion. I knew he wasn't putting it on because I've seen him act and he's not very good.

"Don't tell anyone about this," he pleaded, wiping his tear-stained eyes. "My hard man image will be in tatters and I won't get any more telly work." The bald-bonced megastar then reached for his chequebook. "I'll make it worth your while," he added.

Now, anyone who knows me will tell you that I'm not in the pest control caper for the cash. The satisfaction I get from chemically massacring feral animals is more than enough for me, so I told the gibbering star to put his chequebook away - I wouldn't squeal.

And, true to my word, I've never told a soul to this day about cowardly Kemp's terrifying mouse-based ordeal. And what's more, I never will. 99

Silverfish Caused Nightmare for Silver Fox Paul

66 IN FORTY years of clearing celebrity houses of vermin, I've noticed that pests are most often found in the kitchen. These warm, damp, food-filled areas are like heaven on earth for your average rodent or bug.

On one memorable occasion, I'd got a call about a silverfish infestation in a swanky-sounding mansion on the Wirral. Silverfish - or, to give them their scientific name *Lepisma saccharina* - are horrible little fuckers that live under lino and behind loose wallpaper. They typically feed on carbohydrates such as sugars and starch, so I was certain they'd have set up shop in the kitchen.

I arrived at the million-pound Tudor-style mansion; clearly this was the home of a big-shot. Parked on the pristine gravel was a black, top-of-the-range Range Rover with the registration number BAKE1. And who should open the door but silver-haired *Great British Bake-Off* judge **PAUL HOLLYWOOD**. The twinkle-eyed pastry-meister was in a right old state. He told me he was due to host a star-studded dinner party that very evening for his fellow celebrity silver foxes **GEORGE CLOONEY**, **GARY LINEKER** and **RICHARD GERE**. Clearly, having swarms of scaly, wingless insects scuttling around his food preparation area was less than ideal, so I set to work immediately.

Silverfish can be dealt with using natural methods, such as cedar shavings or lavender oil. But with the clock ticking and the TV baker's superstar guests and Gary Lineker due to arrive in less than an hour, the clock was ticking. I knew that chemical extermination was the only sensible option. I ushered Paul out into the corridor, strapped on my protective mask, and vapourised ten pints of liquid pyrethrin into the air. For belt and braces I topped this off with another 600g of boric acid, then sat back and waited for nature to take its course.

Thirty minutes later, the room was a sea of shimmering silvery exoskeletons; the war had been won, and Paul's swanky dinner party was back on. The tidy-bearded master baker's relief was palpable. By way of repayment, he made me a truly astounding offer: he would fix it so that I won the next series of *The Great British Bake-Off*. He made the prospect sound tempting; I'd earn the respect of the nation, plus countless million-pound book and television deals. If I played my cards right, I might even get to bake a big wonky birthday cake for the Queen like this year's winner did.

Horrible little bastard: A silverfish on some woodchip wallpaper yesterday.

I'd be lying if I said I wasn't tempted by the prospect, but as I've mentioned before, I did not get into the pest control business for fame or fortune. I got into it because I enjoy killing small animals, it's as simple as that. I turned Paul's offer down flat - though as I wandered back to my van I did regret not asking him to set an extra place at the table - that would have been quite some dinner party! 99

No Insects Please, We're Tittish

66 IT NEVER fails to amaze me how even the biggest celebs think they're somehow immune to household pests. An insect or rodent knows nothing of human fame or money; all it cares about is satisfying its insatiable lust for eating and breeding.

Word had clearly got out in the celeb community that I was the go-to guy when pests needed sorting out. Even so it was a little bit out of the ordinary when I was called over to California USA to deal with an infestation of flies. Once in LA, I made my way to the address I'd been given: 10236 Charing Cross Road, Westwood. I recognised it immediately from the telly - it was the Playboy Mansion! The door was answered by a trio of glamorous pneumatic blondes wearing babydoll nighties - **BRIDGET MAR-QUARDT**, **KENDRA WILKINSON** and **HOLLY MADISON**. I didn't know where to put my eyes, so I looked down their tops.

They explained that the week before, Kendra had won the meat raffle at a pool party thrown by **EDDIE MURPHY**, and she'd brought her prize home in the boot of her Cadillac and then forgotten about it. After the motor had been left parked in the baking sun for several days, she'd remembered and thrown the now rancid meat into the bin round the back of the kitchen. I went out to take a look, and it wasn't a pretty sight out there, I can tell you. It looked like the entire Tinseltown bluebottle population had caught the scent and decided to up-sticks and move in. The whole bin was hidden in a buzzing black cloud, and the swarm had even found its way into the downstairs bog through an open window.

I fought my way into the khazi, braving the furious mass of hungry flies, and spraying my piperonyl butoxide aerosol like my life depended on it. Pipertox is a quick-kill, contact insecticide, and I knew it would soon have the swarm dropping, well, like flies. Afterwards I went outside and gave the buzzing bastards round the bin a taste of the Basil Cataract treatment too.

As I emerged from the bathroom, covered head to foot in sticky, twitching bluebottle corpses, the girls could not have been more thankful. "I don't know how we can ever repay you," purred Bridget, to which Kendra and Holly responded: "We've got an idea..."

The sexy trio then began a slow and seductive striptease, removing my insect-spattered overalls whilst gently rubbing their preposterously large breasts in my face. Suddenly alarmed, I asked them what would happen if their boyfriend - *Playboy* founder **HUGH HEFNER** - should catch us *in flagrante delicto*. But the girls assured me that he was on the other side of town having his bunions shaved at a glitzy Beverly Hills chiropodists. As I've said before, I'm a red-blooded man, so to say I wasn't tempted to let the three blonde bombshells have their wicked way with me would be a lie. But as I've also said before, I didn't get into the extermination game for the four-way orgies. I got into it out of a pure and simple love for killing.

The girls groaned with disappointment as I stood up and pulled my overalls back on. But how could I have forgiven myself if another top celeb had been overrun by pests while I was slipping three 36DD skin-mag centrefolds a length of my chopper? 99

> ...The sexy trio began a slow and seductive striptease, removing my insect-spattered overalls...

Calliphora girls: Basil flew to LA to kill flies for Bunnies.

Next week: PEST CONTROL TO MAJOR TIM. Cataract recalls an amazing rocket flight to outer space when a flea infestation on the ISS leaves British astronaut Tim Peake scratching his ankles and shins.

LeTTERbOcKS

email: letters@viz.co.uk

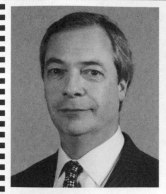

ST★R LETTER

A PEST control officer told me recently that mice aren't that keen on cheese and much prefer jam or chocolate biscuits. Well, that may be the case, but until they buy a 350 grand house and let me move in behind their skirting board, they can eat whatever the fuck I decide to put in the traps.
Bartholomew String, Devon

NIGEL Farage reportedly quit politics after receiving death threats following the Brexit vote. But according to his Wikipedia page, the former UKIP leader has survived cancer, being knocked over by a car, the wheels coming off his own vehicle at high speed on a French motorway and a plane crash in a Northamptonshire field. He really shouldn't worry about getting killed, as he appears to be the Captain Scarlet of British politics. That being the case, he wants to be very careful around electricity.
FE Breakfast, Travelodge

I HAVE a great fear of over-tightening nuts until the head of the bolt shears off. I know that using a torque wrench would prevent that happening, but as an insurance salesman I don't need to tighten that many bolts on a day-to-day basis, so it wouldn't really be worth the money.
Albert Dendron, Hull

THEY say that politeness costs nothing. Well neither does rudeness, and sometimes that's the better fucking option.
Ben Le Foe, London

ON Father's Day, every Dad receives a card stating they are "The Best Dad in the World." This cannot be true, and surely it would be better and more honest to display each father's true world ranking. It's just another example of the liberal 'prizes for all' mentality, which is holding our country back.
A Nova, Derby

I DON'T know why the Hermit Crab is so named. Those wildlife people only film them during the daytime so for all we know they might come out at night with their mates and have a right old laugh.
M. Beaujangles, Tring

I REALLY feel sorry for the homeless these days. Years ago, I would always be happy to hand over a 'spare' cigarette when they asked. But now they are nearly a tenner a packet, I'm forced to tell them to fuck off.
Fred, Middlesbrough

I'VE just been to Tesco's and bought a twin pack of recycled toilet paper. I have to say, they've done a really good job. There isn't a single skid mark to be seen on the whole roll.
Pete Sweeney, Burnley

WHAT a scam these department stores are running. I was recently browsing the Debenhams women's section when I noticed a sign reading "Bra Fitting." The notice failed to mention what time the event started, so I asked a sales lady, who looked at me strangely and walked off. The sign was clearly a ploy to get more blokes into the store. Incidentally, I've found it's best to browse lingerie departments when you're with the missus; that way they can't touch you for it.
Mr. L. Buzzard, Bedfordshire.

I'VE just spilt balsamic vinegar over a book on the history of English poetry. Have any of your readers ever had a more middle class accident?
Rob Stuart, Staines Upon Thames

✱ *Well, readers, can you beat Mr Stuart's middle class mishap? Have you burnt your finger on the Aga whilst baking artisan bread? Perhaps you slipped on an avocado skin whilst wearing leather moccasins. Or maybe you had a truly upper class accident and choked on some caviar whilst watching La Traviata at The Royal Opera House. Write and let us know.*

I DON'T understand the phrase 'gravy boat'. By my reckoning, a gravy boat should be used for floating around in massive gravy seas or gravy lakes, which, like butter mountains, don't exist any more since the EU sorted them out. I just wish gravy boat manufacturers would pull together and decide on a more appropriate name, such as 'gravy receptacle' or 'gravy holder', only more catchy.
Tim Buktu, Timbuktu

I FOUND a £5 note on the street the other day, and as a good citizen I went to hand it in to my local police station. But since it's quite far away I had to spend £3.90 on the bus fare. It felt rather pointless handing in £1.10, so instead decided to get myself a big hamburger from the van across the road before catching the bus back home.
Bob, South Shields

THERE are going to be countless changes to our way of life now that the UK has voted to leave the European Union. When we come out, will you still be able to print that picture of that bloke kissing that bird's arse?
Mr T Montague, London

✱ *It's hard to say, Mr Montague. The Brexit negotiations will be long and complicated and with 27 nations all wanting their say in any deal that is finally struck, who knows what will come out of them. It may be that in order to retain access to the single trading union, we may have to give up printing that picture of that bloke kissing that bird's arse. Or perhaps we can keep printing it in return for allowing free movement of EU citizens into the UK.*

PEOPLE drone on about how they'd like to swim with dolphins because they are so intelligent. Personally, I'd rather go swimming with Rachel Riley off *Countdown*.
Jamie Cuffe, Lincoln

I WONDER if your readers could help find my lost cat, Tiddles? He's a ginger Tom and he wears a brown collar with a bell on it. He was last seen in the Park Road area of Slough in 1935. He's probably dead now, but I will never give up hope.
Violet Horse, Slough

TOP TIPS

POLICE. Attach wifi-enabled body cameras to stray dogs and cats to increase your patrol area. For a more threatening Public Order situation, use tigers and wolves.
Tim Buktu, Timbuktu

GET headaches or migraines? Use Ibuprofen cream on your hair instead of hair gel.
Jamie Cuffe, Lincoln

CONVINCE your neighbours you are not an alcoholic and by leaving balloons and birthday party banners in the bin beside your bottle recycling each fortnight.
Martin Jacobs, St Albans

COFFEE table books can also be put on a sideboard.
Henry, London

A YELLOW baseball cap placed in a freezer overnight makes a great temporary hard hat.
Will Mylchreest, Leamington Spa

RECENTLY purchased a helicopter and have nowhere to park it? Simply tie it to your TV aerial and leave the engine running.
Wesley Reid, Tewkesbury

WHEN switching from any position during sex to doggy style, do not yell "Beast mode!" Similarly, when you are using anal beads with your partner, do not pull them out and say "And tonight's winning Thunderball number is..."
Graham Thubron, Crewe

MAKE your wife feel like she's with Richard Gere by saying to the Greggs assistant, "We'll be spending an obscene amount of money in here, so I'm going to need you to be extra nice to this 'Pretty' woman..."
Mark Stewart, Derby

STRUGGLING to find local tradesmen? Simply walk into a pub at some point in the afternoon.
James Wallace, Belper

GET all four colour nibs to come down at once in those multi-coloured pens by sawing the tapering end bit off until there's a big enough hole to allow all four nibs to come down together.
Justin Lee Hawkins, Jesmond

AVOID wasting your GP's valuable time by stripping naked in the reception area before going in to see them.
Peter Dennis, Chorley

THE GREAT DEBATE

IT'S the great debate that's splitting the country down the middle: *Should men be allowed to dry their bollocks using changing room hairdryers?* Everyone has an opinion on this most divisive of topics, but who is right? We asked two of Britain's most eminent thinkers – Oxford evolutionary biologist **PROFESSOR RICHARD DAWKINS** and Archbishop of York **DR JOHN SENTAMU** – to examine both sides of the argument from their very different perspectives.

PROFESSOR RICHARD DAWKINS

OUR HUMAN SPECIES is around 100,000 years old - a mere blink of the eye in evolutionary terms - and it is our large brains and our ability to reason that have set us apart from the other animals. Indeed, from the moment that the first Neanderthal used a sharpened flint to skin a dinosaur to make himself some new trunks, man has been creating, adapting and refining tools to make his life easier.

The changing room hairdryer is merely the latest stage of this aeons-old progression. It may have been developed for a specific purpose – the drying of damp or wet hair – but just like that piece of prehistoric flint, *Homo sapiens*'s ingenuity has found for it a new use, namely the drying of clammy testicles following a shower.

Whether putting a changing room hairdryer to such a use offends society's petty shibboleths is neither here nor there. Anyone who wants to refrain from drying their damp clockweights in this way is free to do so. But what they cannot do is impose their irrational beliefs and prejudices on the rest of us. Indeed, to accede to such people's demands would herald a return to the dark ages of ignorance, superstition and fear.

DR JOHN SENTAMU

THE PATH OF LIFE is many-forked, and along its rocky way we face many trials and tribulations. We must think carefully to decide which way to turn, and which direction is the right one for us to follow. The changing room hairdryer presents one such moral crossroads: After emerging from the shower, do we use it to dry our hair alone before switching it off, as its maker intended, or do we also play it around our damp jizzbags? To make the right choice, we must look deep into our own hearts.

But even as we do, let us remember that the manufacturer designed and built the hairdryer for one purpose alone - the drying of wet hair. And in the same way that we wouldn't use a soup spoon to eat our cornflakes, or a screwdriver to open a tin of paint, we should ponder long and hard before electing to use the wrong tool to dry our knackers.

However, even as we take the right path, we should not sit in judgment on those who stray. Rather, we should embrace them, offering our love and guidance in the hope that one day they will see the error of their ways and stop drying their crown jewels with the changing room hairdryer.

What do YOU think? Is it ever acceptable for men to dry their personal areas with the changing room hairdryer?
Text **HAIRDRYER BOLLOCKS YES** or **HAIRDRYER BOLLOCKS NO**
to **01-811-8055**

Next week's Great Debate:
Germaine Greer and **Rabbi Lionel Blue** debate the ethics of pissing in the shower.

□ **DOES** anyone know what bra size Margaret Thatcher was? Despite how good the so-called internet is, I can't seem to find it anywhere.
N Roondiscus, Lanark

□ **WHENEVER** I fart alone, I always raise my left leg (never the right) at an angle and expel the gas quite violently and noisily. Then I yell "Git oot, ya dirty baastad, away wi re!" in a Scottish accent. I was wondering if any of your other readers also enhance the act of expelling wind in a similar fashion. If not, I might trademark it, a bit like Usain Bolt's 'Lightning Bolt' or Mo Farah's 'Mobot'.
'Mad' Heinrich Prolapse, Germany

□ **WHILST** in a bus queue last week, I noticed that the attractive young lady in front of me had such thin leggings on that I could easily see her French style knickers underneath. I could even make out the intricate lace pattern on them. Luckily for her, I was blocking the view of any sad perverts behind me who would have loved to have a good gander at her lovely, pert bottom.
Bobby, Clayton

□ **IT'S** no wonder that grey squirrels kill red squirrels, after I heard one wildlife commentator saying that the grey ones were very common whereas the red ones weren't at all common. I didn't realise that there was such a class divide between squirrels, but reinforcing it with that sort of talk is always going to cause friction and resentment.
Ivan Terrible, Dorchester

□ **IT'S** no wonder spiders are always hungry. They spend all their time spinning webs in haunted houses and ghost trains. They should build a big web right over the top of a fresh dog shit. In no time they'll be inviting their mates round for a slap-up bluebottle barbecue.
Desulph Daz, Middlesbrough

□ **I HAD** a dream last night where me and my family went on a 2-week holiday to Crete with the broadcaster Louis Theroux and his family. When we went to pick up our hire cars, Louis insisted on having the larger and more comfortable car of the two. I suggested we swapped after the first week, but he flatly refused. I thought it was really selfish behaviour and, as a fan of his documentaries, he really went down in my estimations. I know it was only a dream, but there's no smoke without fire.
Gilbert Privet, Nottingham

□ **I RECEIVED** a letter today which had 'THIS IS NOT A CIRCULAR' printed on the front. When I opened it, I had to laugh because it WAS a circular. I bet whoever sent it will be kicking themselves when they realise their mistake.
Maldwyn Palmer, Milton Keynes

□ **IT** has recently come to my attention that some morally uptight Christians actually call their daughter Chastity. Well, I'm sorry, but that just sounds like an ironic name for a pornstar who loves it up her spam fritter. It's just asking for trouble, if you ask me.
James Wallace, Belper

□ **I READ** in the paper this morning that former Wimbledon champion Novak Djokovic has a tennis court in his back garden. And as if that weren't enough, he also gets his racquets and trainers for free. Is it any wonder

he's so good at tennis with advantages like this? I dare say I could win a Grand Slam or two with a few freebies like that.
Chad Mufti, Walton-on-the-Naze

THE LAUGHING POLICEMAN

OH HO HO HO HO HO HO HO HO HO HO HO HO HO!

SHAKE!

OH HO HO HO HO HO HO HO HO HO HO HO HO HO!

HA HA HA HA HA HA HA HA HA HA HA HA HA HA!

HA HA HA HA HA HA HA HA HA HA HA HA HA HA!

SLAP!

WHEN YOU'VE QUITE FINISHED SEEING THE FUNNY SIDE, CONSTABLE, COULD YOU ESCORT THE VICTIM'S WIFE FROM THE PREMISES?

WHIMPER! TWITCH!

CRIME SCENE DO NOT CROSS

HESTON BLUMENTHAL'S BURGER VAN

CHAMPION. I'M STARVIN'!

HONK! HONK!

TSSSSCH!

SAUSAGE, EGG AN' BACON BUN PLEASE... AN' A CUPPA TEA.

DO YOU HAVE A RESERVATION?

EH? I'M 'UNGREH. I'VE GOT BE IN LEEDS BE 3. GOT PICK SOME FRIDGES UP AN' DROP 'EM OFF IN CARLISLE.

I'LL JUST CHECK TO SEE IF WE HAVE A TABLE AVAILABLE...

AH YES, IF YOU'D CARE TO TAKE A SEAT BY THE CONDIMENTS, I'LL BE ALONG TO TAKE YOUR ORDER IN PERSON.

OUR BASIC LUNCHTIME TASTER MENU STARTS AT £255 A HEAD, NOT INCLUDING DRINKS, AND WE ADD A COMPULSORY 12.5% SERVICE CHARGE WHICH IS, OF COURSE, DISCRETIONARY.

CAN I RECOMMEND TODAY'S SPECIAL DISH..? A TRIFECTA OF PEAS COATED IN A LIGHT WINE GUM BATTER, GARNISHED WITH A SPRING ONION THINNING, AND DRIZZLED WITH A ROAST YEAST JUS...

...THE WHOLE IS SERVED ON AN EAGLE'S FEATHER, AND IS ACCOMPANIED BY AN AMUSE PORTEFEUILLE OF 3 MICRO-CROUTONS WITH WHIPPED DRIPPING.

WHAT'S THIS... FISH?

AH! THAT'S A STICKLEBACK FIN, FLASH-FRIED IN LIQUID NITROGEN, ENROBED IN GOLD LEAF AND SERVED ON A TIMBALE OF PIGEON CHEEK ICE CREAM... COMPLEMENTED BY A PORK PIE JELLY CRISP SANDWICH.

OR PERHAPS YOU'D LIKE TO TRY THE QUAIL STOMACH HAGGIS PRESENTED ON A BEACH STONE, WITH A BABY CARROT COIN, RICE GRAIN AND BRAISED SWEETCORN KERNEL SALAD MEDLEY...?

IT REALLY IS A FEAST FOR THE SENSES!

CAN I 'AVE BREAKFAST IN A BAP? FAT BOB USED DO BREAKFAST IN A BAP.

NO. THE SPECIAL SET MENU IT IS, THEN.

GOT BE ON AGG BE 4, MIND...

AN HOUR AND A HALF LATER...

..ET VOILA!

CHOMP

SWALLOW

...AND HOW WAS YOUR MEAL, SIR?

I'M STILL 'UNGRY.

THAT'S WONDERFUL, THANK-YOU.

TSSSCH! VV VROOM!

TWO MINUTES LATER...

P
WC

SWERVE!

OOH, BLOODY 'ELL...!

ON BOB

SQTHRRRP! SQUIP! SQUIT!

OOF!

LAST TIME I GO THEE

144

OH, LORDY! IT'S THE FAT SLAGS...

AYUP, GIRLS. GET Y'SELVES SAT DOWN, QUICK...FILM'S ABOUT T'START

SOZ WE'RE LATE, BAZ

NOT TO WORRY... I'VE GOT THE POPCORN IN...

...AN' YOU'LL FIND A SPECIAL TREAT AT THE BOTTOM, IF Y'CATCH MY DRIFT

WOT YOU ON ABOUT?

I'VE DONE THE OLD 'POPCORN' TRICK...I'VE CUT A HOLE IN THE BOTTOM O' THE BOX AN' POPPED ME CHOPPER THROUGH...

SO Y'CAN PICK Y'WAY DOWN THROUGH THE POPCORN, AN' THEN GIVE ME A NICE LITTLE TUG WHEN YOU'RE FINISHED

EEH, Y'KINKY BUGGER, BAZ. TROUBLE IS, WE DON'T LIKE IT...

...IT'S TOO SALTY, AN' IT'S ALL SMALL AN' GETS STUCK IN Y'TEETH.

AYE...AN' WE'RE NOT FUSSED ON POPCORN MUCH, NEITHER

NA-AA-AA-AA!

AYE, VERY FUNNY...

WELL, I WISH I'D KNOWN Y'DIDN'T LIKE IT BEFORE I SPENT A FORTUNE ON A BUCKET O' THE FUCKIN' STUFF AN' STUCK ME COCK INSIDE IT

DON'T WORRY, BAZ...THERE'S PLENTY OF OTHER STUFF WE DO LIKE!

ALRIGHT!

'ERE, LUV...D'Y'MIND IF I SWAP THIS POPCORN FOR SUMMAT ELSE?

SHORTLY...

Y'COULDN'T EAT THEM NACHOS A BIT QUICKER, COULD YOU? THE CHEESE IS REALLY STARTIN' TO BURN ME BELL END.

NOM! NOM!

NOM! NOM!

CURVY KIM LEAVES LITTLE TO IMAGINATION

Will not: Kim leaves sweet FA to soul outfit.

SEXY REALITY STAR *KIM KARDASHIAN* shocked fans at a glitzy film premiere last night, when she revealed that eighties soul band *IMAGINATION* would barely feature in her last will and testament.

Busty Kim, 35, stunned onlookers at the star-studded Los Angeles event by claiming that the now-defunct funk outfit - whose hits include *Just an Illusion* and *Music and Lights* - stand to inherit only a minuscule slither of her multi-million dollar fortune in the event of her death.

bung

The curvaceous reality queen told reporters: "I'll probably bung Imagination a few quid when I pop my clogs - maybe enough to cover an eight-pack of AA batteries or a Wetherspoon's

EXCLUSIVE!

curry - but they certainly shouldn't expect anything life-changing."

She added: "Sorry, guys."

Speaking to journalists outside his London home this morning, vowel-greedy Imagination frontman **LEEE JOHN** said he was "shocked, saddened and confused" by the revelation.

duck

John, 59, claimed: "Neither me nor the other two out of Imagination have ever met Kim

Kardashian, so we obviously weren't banking on top billing when it came to being remembered in her will. But to discover that we'll only be left about eight pounds fifty between the three of us is a real blow, I won't lie to you."

At the time of press, it was revealed that the members of both **SHAKATAK** and **LIQUID GOLD** understood that Kardashian has promised her ormolu clock to them after she goes.

BAXTER BASICS MP

THE PEOPLE HAVE SPOKEN, AND THEIR DECISION IS CLEAR. I FOR ONE RESPECT THAT DECISION... BUT I AM AFRAID THAT I CANNOT...AND WILL NOT...ACCEPT IT.

IN MY OPINION IT IS A WRONG DECISION, BASED ON A WOEFULLY INCOMPLETE UNDERSTANDING OF AN EXTREMELY COMPLEX QUESTION...

COMPOUNDED BY THE WILFULLY MISLEADING STATEMENTS, HALF-TRUTHS AND, YES, OUTRIGHT LIES THAT HAVE BEEN PRESENTED AS THE SO-CALLED "FACTS"..!

THE CONSEQUENCES OF BLINDLY FOLLOWING THROUGH AND ACTING ON THIS ILL-INFORMED AND CRUDE PLEBISCITE DO NOT BEAR THINKING ABOUT..!

IT IS MY CONTENTION THAT WISER COUNSEL SHOULD IN THIS INSTANCE PREVAIL, AND THE RESULT OF THIS VOTE SHOULD BE SET ASIDE FORTHWITH...!

...THEN, AND ONLY THEN, WILL WE BE ABLE TO DRAW A LINE UNDER THIS WHOLE EPISODE, AND MOVE ON!

HMM... WELL, THE JURY WAS UNANIMOUS, MR BASICS. THEY HAVE FOUND YOU GUILTY ON ALL SIXTEEN COUNTS OF GROSS INDECENCY, LIVING OFF IMMORAL EARNINGS AND KEEPING A BROTHEL FOR THE PURPOSE OF PROSTITUTION.

FUCKING BASTARDS.

BACK AT THE HOUSE OF COMMONS...

...A £6,000 FINE AND 200 HOURS COMMUNITY SERVICE! CAN YOU BELIEVE IT..!?

HAVE YOU EVER HEARD ANYTHING SO RIDICULOUS...? I'M A MEMBER OF PARLIAMENT!

OH CHRIST! THIS IS GOING TO BE ALL OVER THE PAPERS TOMORROW "MINISTER FOR FAMILY VALUES CAUGHT RUNNING S AND M BROTHEL"!

IT'S GOING TO TAKE A PRETTY BIG STORY TO BURY THIS BIT OF BAD NEWS.

I MEAN, THE MONEY'S ONE THING... WE'LL TAKE IT OUT OF THE DUCKHOUSE FUND...BUT COMMUNITY SERVICE..!?

HMM... I WONDER...

PASS ME THAT BOOK OF EUROPEAN CONSTITUTIONAL LAW, WILL YOU..?

CERTAINLY, MR BASICS.

LET ME SEE...EUROPEAN COMMUNITIES ACT 1972...BLAH-BLAH...BOLLOCKS... BLAH-BLAH...BOLLOCKS... AH!... YES, HERE WE GO.

"EXERCISE OF THE SOVEREIGN PREROGATIVE."

BINGO! IT DOESN'T NEED THE PM OR AN ACT OF PARLIAMENT...

ANY MEMBER OF HER MAJESTY'S GOVERNMENT CAN TRIGGER ARTICLE 50 AND SET THE FULL BREXIT SHITSTORM IN MOTION..! PERFECT!

BOOK ME ON THE NEXT FLIGHT TO BRUSSELS.

LATER, IN BRUSSELS...

...SO, I JUST SIGN HERE, DO I, AND THAT'S IT?

OUI, MONSIEUR BASIQUES.

SKRIT! SKRIT!

NEXT DAY... ...YESTERDAY'S UNEXPECTED TRIGGERING OF ARTICLE 50 HAS SENT MARKETS INTO FREEFALL, AS THE THREAT OF A RECESSION, MASS UNEMPLOYMENT AND THE BREAK-UP OF THE UK PUSHED THE POUND TO ITS LOWEST EVER VALUE..!

FUCKING GET IN!! NOT A WORD ABOUT ME RUNNING THAT KNOCKING SHOP!

DRING! DRING!

I WONDER WHO THAT IS...

HELLO?... OH, PRIME MINISTER...ERM, YES... YES...RIGHT AWAY...

SHORTLY... ...YOU BLOODY IDIOT, BASICS! DO YOU HAVE ANY IDEA WHAT YOU HAVE DONE..!? YOUR STUPID ACTION HAS SINGLE-HANDEDLY DERAILED THE GOVERNMENT'S CAREFULLY FORMULATED BREXIT PLAN...

I DIDN'T REALISE THERE WAS ONE, PM.

OF COURSE THERE WAS.

WE WERE GOING TO JUST KEEP SAYING "BREXIT MEANS BREXIT" AND THEN ANNOUNCE A ROYAL WEDDING SO EVERYONE FORGOT ALL ABOUT IT.

SORRY, PM.

BASICS, YOU ARE A THOROUGHLY UNTRUSTWORTHY, CORRUPT AND DISHONEST POLITICIAN, NOT TO MENTION A CONVICTED SEX OFFENDER, PERJURER AND THIEF...

...I AM AFRAID YOU LEAVE ME WITH NO OPTION.

NEXT DAY...

LORD BASICS OF FULCHESTER...!

ANYBODY KNOW WHERE I GO TO PICK UP MY £300 DAILY ATTENDANCE MONEY?

Dr Alex Comfort's
The Joy of Flatpack Furniture

"*Putting together flatpack furniture* is a natural and fulfilling activity that we should all enjoy without embarrassment or prurience. Over the years, many people can become bored with furniture assembly, regarding the process as nothing more than a chore. But when two or more people come together to construct a pre-cut particle board table, cupboard or bookshelf, it should be a pleasurable and rewarding experience for everyone. In this series of frank instructional features, I will show you how to add a new and exciting dimension to sectional furniture construction, making each new project that you undertake as thrilling as the first time.*"

This week: The Faltskøg Chest of Drawers

1 For him: Remove all the components from the packaging, and check them off against the list provided. If any items are missing or damaged, call the helpline. Most flatpack furniture manufacturers are happy to provide replacements. For her: Make sure all the tools you will require for the construction are at hand. You will need two screwdrivers (flat-bladed and cross-headed), a 6mm hex key and a small hammer. For both: Do not feel the need to rush this part of the process. You and your partner should relax and enjoy the sensation of exploring the various pieces of your chest of drawers.

2 For him: Fasten the runners onto the side panels, aligning the grub screws with the pre-drilled holes. Ensure that they are correctly oriented with the bearing at the front and the retaining flange uppermost. For her: Construct the main cabinet carcass, aligning the top battens, side and base using the 8mm dowels before tightening the locking screws to hold the framework rigid.

3 For him: Offer up the hardboard back panel to the completed cabinet, dropping it into the rebate. For her: Check that the carcass is square by measuring the diagonals and making sure they are equal. For both: Fasten the backboard in place using the 20mm panel pins provided. Start with a single one in each corner before driving in the rest at intervals of approximately 10cm. You may even like to invite a friend to join you during this part of the assembly. Threesomes are not for everyone, but don't be afraid to experiment.

4 For him: Construct the three drawers using the smaller dowels, before affixing the runners. Slide the baseboards into the rebate on the front and sides, laminated surface upwards, before fitting the rear piece using the allen bolts. For her: Fix the handles onto the drawer fronts using the 30mm machine screws, before putting the drawers into the finished cabinet carcass. For both: Ensure that the drawers run freely and sit squarely. Adjust by loosening off the grub screws and moving the runners slightly up or down in the slots before re-tightening.

x48 x48 x12 x1 x12 x24 x24 x24 x12 x48 x10

Next week: The Ülvaeus TV Stand

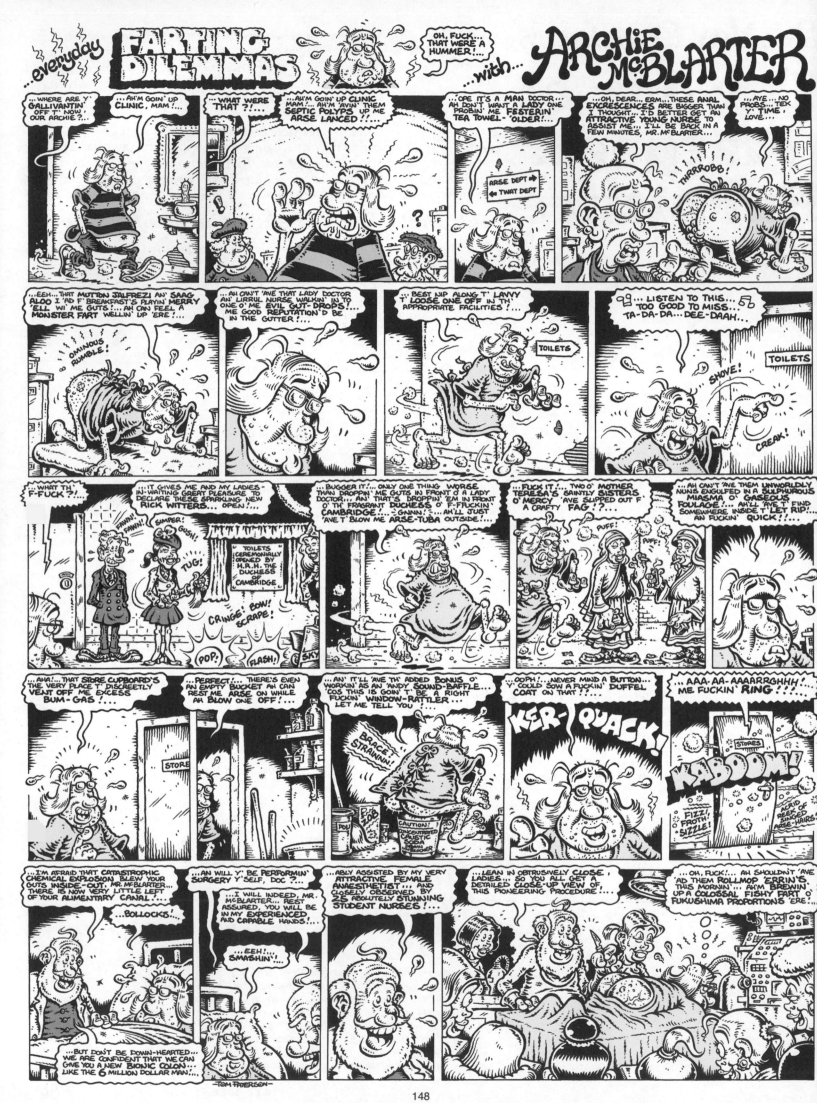

Sid the SEXIST

TYNESIDE'S SILVER-TONGUED CAVALIER

TITS OOT!

SCAMMED BY CYBER ROMEO

POLICE yesterday warned single women to be on their guard after a Halesowen spinster was conned out of £2000 by a man she fell for on an internet dating site. Librarian Janice Bunions, 52, met the heartless conman after posting her profile on a lonely hearts website. "Almost as soon as I uploaded my details, I got a message from this man, who called himself Barry," she told us.

"He seemed perfect. According to his profile, he was the same age as me, a school teacher who liked country walks, reading and trips to the theatre. He ticked all the boxes, and we agreed to meet up for a drink at a local country pub the very next evening," said Janice.

"We hit it off straight away, and we went on several more dates over the next few weeks. Eventually, we got married, bought a house and had three children. Barry played the part of a happy husband to perfection. He even took me for a surprise weekend in Paris to celebrate our tenth wedding anniversary. I never suspected for a moment that it was all an act."

"I feel such a fool after my internet lover swindled me out of £2000!" ~ Janice, 52

EXCLUSIVE!

But it was after the couple had been married for fifteen years that Barry let the pose drop and finally revealed his true colours.

conned

"I came home from work one day to find a note on the kitchen table, saying he'd left me," Janice told us. "He said we'd grown apart and, although he hoped we'd always be friends, he just didn't love me any more."

"Even worse, he'd taken the bank book containing our £2000 life savings. At that moment I realised that he was a fraud and I'd been conned."

"I felt such a fool, but he'd seemed so plausible during all the years we'd been together," she said.

Janice immediately reported the scam to West Midlands police, who said they would look into the matter although they held out little hope of recovering her lost cash. "They told me he would be long gone and was probably already lining up his next victim," said Janice.

And the police's suspicions turned out to be correct. Janice told us: "A friend told me that she'd heard on the grapevine that Barry had moved in with a chemistry teacher from his school. When I heard that, my blood ran cold."

Eiffel for it!: Dream French holiday soon turned into nightmare for librarian Janice.

"I only wish I could warn her that she'll wake up in twenty years and he'll have made off with her cash too," Janice continued.

prosed

A spokesman for West Midlands Police told us: "This man was prepared to carry out a well-orchestrated long-term scam on an innocent woman over a period of fifteen years with the sole intention of swindling her out of £2000 life savings."

And he had this warning for any single women contemplating embarking on an internet romance. "This ruthless conman is still at large, and we would warn all women to be on their guard. If you are contacted on the internet by someone who seems too good to be true, then he probably is."

"More often than not, the man of your dreams will turn out to be a nightmare," the spokesman added.

Finbarr Saunders (& his) DOUBLE ENTENDRES

FINBARR & HIS MUM HAVE CALLED IN ON MR. GIMLET...

HELLO, MR. GIMLET. WE'RE JUST ON OUR WAY TO THE LOCAL CARPET WAREHOUSE AND WE WERE WONDERING IF YOU'D LIKE TO COME ALONG AND...ER...SAY THINGS...

I'M SORRY, MRS. SAUNDERS. I'M A BIT BUSY TODAY.

YOU SEE, I'M TRYING TO GET A COMB THROUGH MY WIFE'S BIG, HAIRY CROWLER.

FNURK! FNURK! — HOD! HOD! — NAMP! NAMP! — YIT! YIT!

IT GOT RATHER MATTED AFTER FROTHING AT THE PROSPECT OF A MEATY BONE THE OTHER DAY.

CHUP! CHUP! — ANK! AHK! — YOD! YOD!

SHE'S BEEN COMPLAINING THAT IT'S LIFTING WITH FLEAS, SO I DECIDED TO GIVE IT A THOROUGH SHAMPOO IN THE BACK GARDEN.

YAK! YAK! — SPON! SPON! — FNUB! FNUB!

HOPEFULLY THAT'LL GET RID OF THE TRIPEY WHIFF IT'S BEEN GIVING OFF IN THIS RECENT HOT WEATHER, TOO.

NIB! NIB! — HEMP! HEMP! — YURT! YURT! — NYK NYK — HOOP! HOOP!

WELL, IT WAS EITHER THAT OR SHAVING IT COMPLETELY AND LEAVING IT BALD WITH ALL ITS UNSIGHTLY PINK DEWLAPS HANGING DOWN, I SUPPOSE...

NUP! NUP! — LILT! LILT! — SPANG! SPANG!

...BUT THAT WOULDN'T HAVE LOOKED VERY NICE.

...AND THE POSTMAN IS SCARED OF IT ENOUGH ALREADY AFTER HE CAUGHT SIGHT OF IT WHEN IT WAS ALL IN A LATHER OVER A NEW RUBBER TOY.

YOK! YOK! — FNARR! FNARR! — WIB! WIB! — K-YAK! K-YAK! — NUG! NUG! — FLAD! FLAD!

WHAT'S IT CALLED?

WHAT'S WHAT CALLED?

WHY YOUR DOG, OF COURSE, MR. GIMLET!

DOG? WE HAVEN'T GOT A DOG, MRS SAUNDERS.

WHATEVER GAVE YOU THAT IDEA?

FONTWELL! COME BACK HERE AND FINISH COMBING THE TATS OUT ME MINGE!

I'LL BE RIGHT WITH YOU, DEAR.

THE BINMAN THAT FEAR FORGOT!

9.30 on an ordinary morning in Barnton. The municipal binmen are on their rounds, going from house to house and taking away the rubbish.

Suddenly...

Wooooh! We'll have to leave that bin, lads.

Why, what's wrong?

There's a lion by it!

RAAAARGH!

Pah! I'm not scared of lions.

Municipal binman Todd McNabb - a former SAS Commando and Navy Seal - had seen service in Iraq and Afghanistan, and he wasn't about to let anything come between him and his bin round.

Leave this to me, lads. That overgrown moggy doesn't scare me!

But Todd, it could be a maneater!

I can't watch!

Oi, puss! Get off that ruddy bin or I'll give you a fourpenny one up the bracket!

RAAARGH!

GRAARGH!

Come on then, Tiddles, let's have you! I'll knock you into the middle of next week!

RAAAARGH!

Look out!

The blood and fur flew as McNabb and the lion grappled by the bin ...

It looked like the fierce maneater was going to come off on top, until...

K-RAK!

Yelp!

Take that, you flea-bitten chump!

Gertcha!

And if you show up on my bin round again I'll turn you into a ruddy hearthrug!

Don't worry, lads. That's the last we've seen of him.

Well done, Todd! You fighting that lion was the bravest thing I've ever seen.

Oh-oh...

I'm afraid you've wasted your time, Todd.

Why?

The lid's not down properly... look.

Is it open more than the regulation three inches?

Yes, by nearly half an inch.

Tchoh!

Barnton Council Refuse Dept. Your bin could not be emptied. Please ensure the lid is fully closed before putting it out for collection.

***Next week in the Binman That Fear Forgot:
McNabb braves an ISIS training camp to collect their recycling bin.***

THE 666 O'CLOC

WE ALL LOVE the news

WE ALL LOVE the news. It's the timeless topical telly show that keeps us updated on current affairs from Tyneside to Timbuktu. Whether it's in-depth reports from far-flung war zones or light-hearted footage of cats waterskiing, the news is everyone's first port of call for our daily dose of international info.

And at the forefront of this iconic small screen institution are the news reporters themselves: fearless anchormen and women who work tirelessly to bring us the daringest dispatches and the steamiest scoops. We welcome these seemingly friendly faces into our living rooms every evening, but how much do we REALLY know about the people behind them?

According to one man - **NEVILLE HADDO** - the answer is "very little indeed". Driffield-born Neville, 61, worked as a toilet attendant in the prestigious BBC newsroom for almost five weeks, and in that time he witnessed the true nature of the UK's favourite broadcast journalists up close. And what he saw left him **SHOCKED** and **DISTURBED**.

"The list of BBC news anchors I've worked with reads like a Who's Who of BBC news anchors," says recently divorced Neville. "To see them on telly, you'd think they wouldn't hurt a fly. But what Joe Public doesn't realise is that they are all harbouring a terrible secret: namely, that each and every one of them worships the dark lord Satan!"

According to Haddo, witchcraft, devil worship

Devil woman: Bruce doled out doll-based voodoo to fellow presenters.

EXCLUSIVE!

and occult magic are at an all-time high at the BBC's News HQ - and the brave lav cleaner is now risking his own personal safety to expose it.

"Hallowe'en is the spookiest time of the year, so it seemed a perfect opportunity for me to lift the lid on the ghastly, ghoulish goings-on at the Beeb," he told us. "The fact that I've just this week been sacked after being falsely accused of stealing cleaning products has nothing to do with it," he added.

In this exclusive interview, Haddo reveals the eye-popping extent of the Satanic scandal lurking inside Auntie's newsrooms.

EDWARDS SAW RED OVER HUW-MUNCULUS

*With his gentle blue eyes and soft, lilting Welsh voice, **HUW EDWARDS** is the very picture of the calm, trustworthy newsman. But Haddo saw a very different side to the silver-haired presenter during his five-week stint at the Beeb...*

❝ Huw makes Aleister Crowley look like Ben Fogle," Neville told us. "He can regularly be heard chanting Satanic incantations before he steps out in front of the cameras, and his dressing room is literally chock-a-block with inverted crucifixes, pentagram-emblazoned cowls and gargantuan, rune-inscribed altars - all courtesy of the British licence-payer.

I did my best to steer well clear of the guy, but unfortunately things came to a head in my first week on

BBC Devil-ision: Neville's close shaves with the dark arts left him fearing for his life.

the job, when Edwards moved his demonic doings into my domain - namely, the cleaning storage cupboard. I was nipping in there one morning to get a fresh batch of caustic soda after Gavin Esler had blocked the second-floor gents again, when I heard what was unmistakably Huw's muffled velvety tones through the door. Only he wasn't droning on about the post-Brexit pound or the Labour leadership battle like he does on telly, he was intoning what sounded like Latin curses. Now, my Latin's a little rusty these days, but I did catch one word clear as a bell: *"Diabolus."*

Suddenly, the door opened, and out stepped Huw. He was dressed in a black hooded robe, his hand clutching a gnarled wooden staff with a rotting goat's head strapped to the top. He swept past me, still muttering under his breath, and with some trepidation I entered the closet. What I saw inside chilled me to the very bone. There were several large glass jars on the top shelf, next to where I keep the Toilet Duck, and in each of them floated a twisted creation so horrific I can scarcely bear to describe it. But I suppose I should have a go, otherwise people might accuse me of making the whole thing up, which I haven't.

These creatures were broadly humanoid in shape, but there was something hideous, something profoundly ungodly, about each one - giant bulbous heads; warped, spidery limbs; pallid, clammy skin. It

was clear as daylight to me, Edwards was raising a half-human homunculus army to do his devilish bidding for him. Any doubt that these unclean specimens were Huw's handiwork was instantly erased when I spotted the Post-It notes stuck to each jar, with 'HUW EDWARDS'S HOMUNCULI - DON'T TOUCH' scrawled on them.

Not wanting my precious cleaning products anywhere near these despicable abominations, I stuffed six bottles of Ecover limescale remover and a big wad of J-cloths under my jumper and sprinted out the door. The BBC security team caught me as I was leaving the premises and searched me. I tried desperately to explain that Huw Edwards was using my storage closet as an incubator for

Army of darkness: Huw kept dark secret in Neville's closet.

demonic foeti, but they'd already put two and two together and made five.

...K NEWS

I was given a verbal warning and placed on probation, but, still, I counted myself lucky. Lucky to have escaped with my life. **"**

BEELZE-BRUCE WAS VOODOO VIXEN

Haddo's run-in with Edwards's bizarre homunculi left him badly shaken. But it was small potatoes compared to what he would experience the following week at the perfectly manicured hands of none other than **FIONA BRUCE**...

" On telly, Fiona Bruce seems intelligent, professional, and - let's face it - not unattractive for her age," says Haddo. "But her many fans would be horrified if they knew what I know about their favourite anchorwoman's true nature.

One night, after dealing with a minor incident in Nicholas Witchell's private bathroom, I passed Fiona's dressing room to see her clutching what looked like an innocent set of Barbies. I thought she was a bit old to be playing with dolls, but then, suddenly, the realisation hit me: these particular dolls *weren't* for playing with.

They were stuffed with straw, and stained with what looked like fresh animal blood. Over each one's head was glued the face of a rival newsreader: Alastair Stewart, Jon Snow, Krishnan Guru-Murthy and Sophie Raworth. I watched in horror as Bruce gleefully inserted long hatpins into each of them, whilst hissing bizarre Haitian curses. There was no doubt in my mind: Fiona was practising the ancient occult art of voodoo.

I must have literally gasped in terror, because she looked up suddenly from her diabolical work to see me at the door. I bolted quick as a flash, but there was no doubt she'd spotted me, for when I passed her room the next day, a new doll had been added to her collection.

And this one had *my face* on it.

I began to notice the effects of Fiona's fiendish practice straight away. I was locking up the storage cupboard when I was suddenly consumed by a burning fever that told me Fiona was torturing my wretched effigy, holding it over a tallow candle, playing the flames across it sadistically. In a zombie-like trance, I stuffed four bottles of bleach and a big box of Domestos Turbo Fresh Rimblock into my bag and stumbled out.

Thankfully, by the time I was stopped by security, the trance had worn off. I tried to explain that I had been acting under the influence of Fiona Bruce's arcane black magic, but they simply wouldn't listen. I was given a dressing down by my supervisor and issued with a final written warning. But as I left the building, I reminded myself that my fate could have been much, much worse. **"**

SPELLS WEREN'T SUNNY FOR BLACK WIZARD SCHAFERNAKER

With his sharp suits, cheeky grin and testicular surname, **TOMASZ SCHAFERNAKER** *is, without doubt, Britain's favourite meteorologist. After Carol Kirkwood. However, Haddo soon learned that the "sunny spells" Tomasz spoke of in his weather reports weren't the only spells he was interested in...*

" As the days passed, I saw more and more terrible things occur in the bowels of the BBC newsroom," Haddo recalls. "Some of them were so mind-bendingly preposterous you'd think I was making them up, despite the fact that I'm not. I saw Emily Maitlis perform a six-hour Black Mass in the canteen; I heard George Alagiah recite the Lord's Prayer backwards; I witnessed Nicholas Owen slaughter a live goat before bathing in its still-warm blood and offering the carcass up to Beelzebub, the dark angel-prince of the abyss.

Everywhere I turned, the Beeb's anchormen and women were prostrating themselves at Lucifer's cloven hooves. But all this was nothing compared to what the weather forecasters were getting up to...

I was passing the meteorology department one afternoon, having spent three hours shifting a stool the size of a Pringles tin from Will Gompertz's U-bend, when I heard strange noises coming from inside Tomasz Schafernaker's dressing room. I peered through the crack in the door, and what I saw inside was so unbelievable you might accuse me of lifting it wholesale from the beginning of *Ghostbusters*, which I haven't because that happens in a library, and this happened in a BBC office.

Schafernaker was sat at a table covered in bits of paper with all different letters on them. Suddenly, he began speaking in a strange guttural voice, much deeper than his usual one. 'O great prophets of the unseen world,' he intoned, 'O Paracelsus, O Nostradamus, O noble prognosticators of the ethereal realm, tell me, pray, what shall the weather be like tomorrow?'

I watched in horror as the papers suddenly began to flutter about the room of their own accord, flapping round Schafernaker's head like a flock of ghastly A4 birds. They rearranged themselves on the wall, spelling out a terrifying message:

'CHILLY AT FIRST WITH MIST OR FOG PATCHES CLEARING. A DRY DAY TO FOLLOW WITH PATCHY CLOUD AND LIGHT WINDS. HIGHS OF 12 DEGREES.'

It was painfully clear what was happening: rather than relying on satellites and charts like a normal weatherman, Tomasz got his infernal forecasts by communicating directly with his Satanic majesty the Antichrist himself.

Horrified, I bolted for my storage cupboard, but the scrotally-named dark wizard spotted me and gave chase. He came sweeping into my closet, and began chanting mystical incantations that caused my cleaning products to fly off their shelves and whirl madly around the room. Ducking a hellish hail of airborne lavatory cleansing equipment, I grabbed my duffel bag and barged straight past him.

The Beeb security guards stopped me before I could exit the building, and emptied my bag to find ten urinal cakes, a big bottle of tank freshener and six packs of bog roll. I tried to explain that these items had been magicked in there by the necromancer known as Tomasz Schafernaker, but it was no use. I was handed my P45 right there and then.

But my nightmare was far from over. Still apparently under the influence of Fiona Bruce's voodoo sorcery, I stumbled to the nearest pub and drank 9 pints of lager, before hiring a prostitute and taking her home with me. When my wife arrived back from her night shift the following morning, she put two and two together, made five, and filed for divorce.

My whole life has been turned upside by my brief stint in the wretched recesses of Auntie's diabolical abyss. I don't know what I did to deserve it, but I *do* know this: *I'll never watch BBC News again.* **"**

Forecasting shadows: Weather wizard Tomasz received devilish divinations.

NEXT TIME: *Neville gets a new job as a toilet attendant at Radio 2, only to discover that Ken Bruce, Lynne Bowles and Desmond Carrington are shape-shifting alien lizards.*

Hen Cabin

Should've done this years ago.

Cunts want choice!

Chicken ★ Burgers ★ Kebabs ★ Hala

Pizza - Indian - Jerk Chicken
Burgers - Thai - Vietnamese
Chinese - Italian - Eskimo stuff
Moroccan - Caribbean - Greek
Tex Mex - Seafood - Vegan
Polish - Spani___ - Fish & Chips

Here's the new menu.

M-menu?

Fuck me.

I ain't heard of half this, let alone know how to cook it!

Piece of piss, I got the fuckin' lot out back!

There's your pizzas.

But those are all ham and pineapple –

– suppose someone orders this 'Four Seasons' thing?

Throw an handful of peas on the fucker.

Once it's battered and fried no cunt will know.

Them on those shelves are the Chinese, the rest are for Indians.

If in doubt mix two up.

What about the meat?

If anyone orders a madras or vindaloo just put a bit less water in, so it's hotter.

Then tip it over four raw wings.

They cook in the sauce.

What if they want lamb, or prawn?

Or rice?

Cunts'll get wings.

We'll have *just* run out.

What's *jerk* chicken?

Hot wings in shitloads of brown sauce.

Piri-piri?

Brown sauce and ketchup.

And what's all this Indonesian stuff?

Fuckin' hell pal! Stop *looking* for problems!

There's mace, marjoram, sage, a fuckin' *nutmeg* –

– not to mention sachets of soy sauce in the noodles!

If you can't make everything on that menu with *that lot* you got no business calling yourself a fuckin' chef!

I don't!

Soon

Can I *get*...

Won ton soup...

The salt and pepper ribs...

Peking duck for two. Some *har gow*. A portion of *sui mai*. And for main courses...

Just an *ayem goreng*, an *empul gepuk*, and a *gado-gado*.

Er...

Chop fuckin' chop then.

156

ROGER MELLIE
FTV
THE MAN ON THE TELLY

MORNING, ROGER

MORNING, TOM... JUST POPPED IN TO PICK UP MY POST... CAN'T STAY LONG, I'M OPENING AN ORPHANAGE ACROSS TOWN IN HALF AN HOUR

IT'S ALL THESE CELEBS DROPPING LIKE FUCKING BLUEBOTTLES... THERE'S A REAL SHORTAGE OF TALENT ON THE OLD UNVEILING CEREMONY CIRCUIT. I CAN NAME MY PRICE... FUCKING GREAT.

OKAY, WHAT HAVE WE GOT HERE?... SPEARMINT RHINO MEMBERSHIP RENEWAL... SPEEDING TICKET... STRINGFELLOWS MEMBERSHIP RENEWAL... ANOTHER SPEEDING TICKET

...WHAT'S THIS ONE?

...FIVE GRAND **CASH** ON THE DAY, TOM, AND FIVE PERCENT OF ANY DONATIONS THEY GET OVER THE NEXT TWELVE MONTHS... NOT BAD, EH?

LONG MAY IT CONTINUE, I SAY

OH, SMASHING, IT'S MY RESULTS

RESULTS!?... WHAT RESULTS?

HEALTH CHECK, TOM...

THE CELEBRITY DEATH STAMPEDE MADE ME THINK IT MIGHT BE AN IDEA IF I WENT TO THE QUACK'S FOR AN M.O.T...

...YOU KNOW, HEIGHT, WEIGHT, BLOOD TESTS, PISS INTO THE BOTTLE... THE FULL MONTY.

GOOD IDEA, ROGER

IS EVERYTHING OKAY?

YES, LOOKS ABSOLUTELY FINE, ABSOLUTELY FINE...

HEIGHT, 6' 2" WEIGHT, 18 STONE 3...

BMI INDEX 38.3, CLINICALLY OBESE...

EH?

WELL **THAT'S** BOLLOCKS, I'VE GOT A BIG FRAME

AH, I SEE WHAT'S HAPPENED. HE'S PUT MY ACTIVITY LEVEL AS 'LOW', THE DAFT TWAT...

...I **TOLD** HIM I PLAY DARTS THREE TIMES A WEEK

ANYWAY... BLAH BLAH, BLAH... LIGHT SOCIAL DRINKER... NON-SMOKER...

EH!?... YOU TOLD THE DOCTOR YOU'RE A LIGHT DRINKER AND A NON-SMOKER?

WELL I **AM**, TOM... I NEVER DRINK IN A MORNING THESE DAYS, NOT UNLESS IT'S HAIR OF THE DOG... AND I DON'T INHALE THESE FUCKERS.

BLOOD PRESSURE 180 OVER 120...

CHRIST, ROGER... THAT'S THROUGH THE **ROOF!**

NO, THAT'S ALRIGHT, TOM... YOU'VE GOT TO HAVE HIGH BLOOD PRESSURE IN THIS GAME TO SURVIVE... YOU NEVER SEE A TELLY PRESENTER WITHOUT A PURPLE FACE AND WIGGLY VEINS IN HIS TEMPLES... IT'S ALL PART AND PARCEL. I CAN HANDLE IT... I'M A **PRO!**

CHOLESTEROL, 17.8...

JESUS! 17.8?

STOP FRETTING, TOM

...IT MIGHT BE A BIT ON THE HIGH SIDE, BUT I'M A BIG BLOKE... THERE'S PLENTY OF BLOOD TO DILUTE IT.

ANYWAY, MY DAD'S CHOLESTEROL WAS HIGH... IT'S IN THE MELLIE GENES

LIVER ENZYME FUNCTION, WHATEVER THE FUCK THAT IS... TEN TIMES NORMAL..., KIDNEY ENZYME FUNCTION, WHATEVER THE FUCK THAT IS... EIGHT TIMES NORMAL

BLAH! BLAH! BLAH!

...URINE GLUCOSE, 12 MILLIMOLES

BLOODY HELL! ...ROGER...

I KNOW, TOM... **MILLIMOLES!**...

...THEY JUST MAKE THESE FUCKING WORDS UP, DON'T THEY

FINAL STROKE AND HEART ATTACK RISK PROBABILITY... 97%

JESUS!

I KNOW... ONLY 3% OFF A PERFECT SCORE

CLEAN BILL OF HEALTH THAT, TOM...

...NOT BAD FOR A MAN OF MY AGE, EH?

RIGHT, I'M OFF TO PULL THE STRING ON A LITTLE CURTAIN FOR FIVE GRAND PLUS...

...A STAR'S WORK IS NEVER DONE, TOM

SEE YOU IN THE BOOZER LATER... DRINKS ARE ON ME

NEXT DAY...

HE'S IN HERE

HI, TOM. THANKS FOR COMING TO SEE ME

ROGER... ARE YOU ALRIGHT?

YES, JUST A BIT OF A FART ON WITH THE OLD TICKER, TOM, BUT IT'S BACK TO NORMAL

...JUST ABOUT TO PULL THE CORD ON THE PLAQUE, I WAS, WHEN I GOT THIS FUCKING GREAT GRIPPING PAIN IN MY CHEST AND I WENT DOWN LIKE A SACK OF SPUDS

TECHNICALLY DEAD, I WAS, FOR 5 MINUTES TILL THEY BROUGHT ME BACK

...BUT LUCKILY, AS I WENT DOWN, I PULLED THE CORD, SO I'D FULFILLED THE CONTRACT, AND THE MONEY'S SAFE

BREAKFAST, MR. MELLIE... EGGS, SAUSAGE, BACON, BEANS, BLACK PUDDING AND FRIED BREAD, JUST LIKE YOU ORDERED

LOVELY... THANK FUCK FOR PRIVATE MEDICINE, EH, TOM? YOU WOULDN'T GET THAT ON THE NHS.

As *The Force Awakens* breaks box office records everywhere, the world has gone *Star Wars* potty. Forget conflict in the Middle East, climate change and terrorism, the topic on everyone's lips in 2016 is the seventh installment in this sci-fi odyssey that began a long time ago in a galaxy far far away in 1977. We've all grown up with *Luke Skywalker*, *Darth Vader* and *Princess Leia*, but how much do we really know about this billion dollar franchise that tore up the movie rulebook? May the Force be with you as we engage hyperdrive, set our phasers to stun and check out...

20 THINGS YOU NEVER KNEW ABOUT STAR WARS

1 **STAR** Wars very nearly didn't happen at all. Luckily the director's mother and father, *Ada* and *Frank Lucas*, met, married and subsequently fused their DNA through sexual reproduction. Their subsequent offspring George was fortunate to be born into a relatively affluent society in which he was able to pursue his creative interests rather than eking out a desperate subsistence through backbreaking toil.

2 **IN THE** scene in *The Empire Strikes Back* where the Millennium Falcon makes its escape from the ice planet Hoth, eagle-eyed viewers may spot that Chewbacca looks more like a teddy bear than a wookiee. That's because, during filming at Elstree Studios, a careless wardrobe assistant mislaid the character's costume. Luckily, children's series *Rainbow* was being shot on a nearby set and actor *John Leeson*, dressed as Bungle, was able to pop over and double for 7'5" actor

Peter Mayhew. To make him appear taller on screen, the director asked Leeson to stand closer to the camera.

3 **WHEN** he was offered the part of Luke Skywalker, *Mark Hamill* foolishly signed over the rights to his own image to the movie's producers. Now, four decades later, he still has to pay Lucasfilms a royalty of $15 every time he catches sight of himself in a mirror, and his wife has to cough up another $10 each time she looks at him.

4 **ALTHOUGH** West country muscle man *Dave Prowse* played Darth Vader on screen, the arch villain's sinister, sonorous voice was provided by American actor *James Earl Jones*. But not before the part had been offered to, and turned down by, Wurzels lead singer *Pete Budd*, Bristol born all-in wrestler *Pat Roach* and Cornish comedian *Jethro*.

5 **IN THE** scene in *Return of the Jedi* where the rebels attack the Imperial Shield Generator, eagle-eyed viewers may spot that Wicket, leader of the Endor rebels, looks more like a teddy bear than an eewok. That's because, during filming at Elstree Studios, a careless wardrobe assistant mislaid the character's costume. Luckily, children's series *Rainbow* was being shot on a nearby set and actor *John Leeson*, dressed as Bungle, was able to pop over and double for 3'6" actor *Warwick Davis*. To make him appear shorter on screen, the director asked Leeson to stand further away from the camera.

6 **ALTHOUGH** 3'8" actor *Kenny Baker* played astromech droid R2-D2 on screen, he did not provide the robot's trademark beeps, clicks and whistles. The fandabidozi sound effects were the work of a then little-known Scottish entertainer, *Janette Tough* – later to become a household name as *Crackerjack*'s 'Wee Jimmie' Krankie.

7 **BLOOPER** alert! In the climactic scene of *Return of the Jedi*, Darth Vader, played by *Dave Prowse* and *James Earl Jones*, reveals that he is father of Luke Skywalker, played by *Mark Hamill*. However, this is simply not true, as Mark Hamill's father is actually *William Thomas Hamill*, 88, a retired US Navy captain.

8 **THE** character of Jabba the Hutt was originally intended to be computer generated. However, it was eventually found cheaper to hire a fully-grown bull elephant seal to play the part. The 2-ton animal was shipped from Whipsnade Zoo in a specially built crate, before spending three hours in make-up, during which time its handler prevented it from getting too restless by feeding it herrings.

9 **DURING** filming, actors playing Imperial stormtroopers had a rough deal when it was time to take lunch. Unable to remove their helmets, the only thing on the on-set catering menu they were able to choose was soup of the day. And on days when it was a lumpy soup, such as garden vegetable, minestrone or Scotch broth that wouldn't fit through a straw, they simply had to go hungry.

10 **AND** toilet breaks were out of the question too. The process of getting out of their rigid plastic costume trousers was so complicated that the actors simply wore *Tena For Men* incontinence pads during the long days of filming.

11 **THE** Imperial Death Star - an enormous orbiting war machine equipped with unimaginable firepower - may seem like a mere science fiction fantasy. But in fact TV star *Noel Edmonds* is currently building just such a planet-sized battle station on the other side of the Moon. "Once my Death Star is operational, I'm going to use it to rule the Galaxy through fear and unquestioning obedience to my every whim," the *Deal or No Deal* host told *TV Quick* magazine.

12 **ACCORDING** to someone who clearly spends far too much time in his bedroom writing entries for the Star Wars Wiki on the internet, the Force is "a metaphysical, spiritual, binding, and ubiquitous power that holds enormous importance for both the Jedi and Sith monastic orders." For those who possess it, the Force allows them to open doors without touching them, a bit like when you go to Homebase.

13 **THE** title on George Lucas's original screenplay for the first movie was "Star Trek". It wasn't until the film was in final post-production that a tea-boy at the editing suite pointed out that there was already a successful TV series of that name.

4 DURING filming in the scorching heat [of] the Tunisian desert, the [te]mperature inside **Anthony [D]aniels**'s C-3PO's robot [su]it reached temperatures [of] 250°C or more - *as hot as [a] meat oven*. Set technicians [re]gularly removed Daniels [fro]m the suit and basted him [wi]th goose fat to ensure that [h]e cooked evenly and crisped [u]p nicely. Filming then [co]ntinued until a skewer was [in]serted and the actor's juices [ra]n clear.

5 THE original film [s] opened to record box [of]fice receipts in 1977, but [di]d you know it also holds [th]e record for being shown [in] the smallest movie theatre [in] the world? The Tiny ABC [ci]nema was owned by world's [sm]allest man **Calvin Phillips**, [an]d made from a converted [sh]oebox, with a screen the size [of] the end of a shoebox.

6 AND the ice creams [s] in the matchbox-sized [fo]yer were the world's [sm]allest rip-offs, costing a [co]ol £5 each... for a thimbleful [of] raspberry ripple on a cone [th]e size of a golf tee.

7 THE knickers from that [s] costume that Princess [L]eia wears in *that bit* recently [so]ld at a charity auction for [£]0.3 million. The buyer [w]as the Tokyo Museum of [F]emale Science Fiction Stars'

Underwear, whose collection also includes **Jane Fonda**'s perspex bra from *Barbarella*, Leela's chamois leather loincloth from *Dr Who* and Ripley's skimpy cotton briefs from *Alien*.

18 THE part of Marty was originally played by **Eric Stoltz**, but he was replaced after six weeks of filming.

19 AT the climax of *A New Hope*, Obi Wan Kenobi is killed by Darth Vader and his empty cloak falls down onto the ground. To achieve this special effect, George Lucas drafted in TV magician **Ali Bongo**. "I haven't got a clue how it was done," Lucas told *Empire* magazine in 2005. "It was a closed set with just the cameraman, Bongo and the actors present."

20 ANOTHER scene masterminded by Ali Bongo, in which Darth Vader padlocked Princess Leia into a brightly coloured box with her head and feet sticking out of the ends before theatrically sawing her in two, didn't make the final cut.

GILBERT RATCHET

AUNTIE PAT HAS COME ROUND TO SHOW US HER NEW BABY, READERS.

COO! COO! COO!

DAD'S PIGEONS

NAPPIES & STUFF

MUM

SO I'VE INVENTED THIS **AUTOMATIC INFANT-ADMIRER™** WHICH WILL PEER AT THE TOT AND MAKE APPRECIATIVE NOISES, WHILE I PLAY MINECRAFT.

OOPS! I HADN'T SCREWED THE ADMIRING EYEBALL ON TIGHTLY ENOUGH!

CLONK!

DAD'S PIGEONS

BWWAAAHH!

YOU MADE THE BABY CRY, GILBERT — SO YOU CAN SETTLE HIM DOWN!

BWURRRR

NAPPIE & STUFF

HERE, TAKE HIM OUT IN THE GARDEN FOR SOME FRESH AIR!

AND KEEP JIGGLING THAT PRAM UNTIL HE FALLS ASLEEP!

JIGGLE JIGGLE

GOSH! THIS IS MONOTONOUS WORK!

MY PISTON-POWERED "ROCK-A-BYE-BABY-O-MATIC" WILL DO ALL THE PRAM-JIGGLING FOR ME!

AND OFF WE GO!

TOOLS

KER-THUNK!

YIPES! THAT WAS A BIT OF AN INDUSTRIAL-STRENGTH JIGGLE!

LAND'S END to JOHN O'GROATS TEDDY BEAR DELIVERIES

OH NO! I SHOULD HAVE NAMED MY INVENTION THE "ROCK-A-*BYE-BYE*-BABY-O-MATIC!" I'VE LOST AUNTIE PAT'S BABY!

THAT WAS A BRAND NEW BABY, TOO!

TOOLS

IF I DON'T FIND A REPLACEMENT FOR IT, AUNTIE PAT WILL HAVE MY GUTS FOR GARTERS!

I KNOW! I'LL GO AND VISIT FATHER O'DUBIOUS AT ST SWITHEN'S ORPHANAGE!

SAINT SWITHENS ORPHANAGE

AROMA OF PLAY-DOH, MILK AND SPEW

ABC

HE'S BOUND TO HAVE A FEW SPARE BABIES KNOCKING ABOUT THE PLACE!

GOLLY! IT LOOKS LIKE FATHER O'DUBIOUS IS IN TROUBLE WITH THE ORPHANAGE'S BOARD OF DIRECTORS!

THESE FIGURES FOR OUR FINANCIAL PERFORMANCE LAST YEAR ARE A DISGRACE, O'DUBIOUS!

FAR FROM MAKING A PROFIT, THIS ORPHANAGE IS ACTUALLY **LOSING** MONEY, DUE TO THE COSTS OF... WHAT'S THIS? "LOOKING AFTER CHILDREN?"

WHAT KIND OF A FARCICAL BUSINESS MODEL IS THIS?

I WANT TO SEE THIS COMPANY START TURNING A PROFIT, O'DUBIOUS — OR YOU'RE FOR THE CHOP!

OH DEAR — WHAT AM I GOING TO DO?

I'LL HELP YOU TRANSFORM YOUR ORPHANAGE INTO A PROSPEROUS COMMERCIAL VENTURE, FATHER ~ IN EXCHANGE FOR ONE OF THESE BABIES!

IT'S A DEAL, GILBERT!

IN TODAY'S MARKETPLACE, WHAT YOUR ORPHANAGE NEEDS IS A BRAND MANAGEMENT CONSULTANT!

TOOLS

WE'VE GOT TO MAXIMISE PUBLIC AWARENESS OF THE ST SWITHEN'S BRAND BY UTILISING DIGITAL MEDIA.

SEE, I'VE CONSTRUCTED THIS **GIGANTIC ARSEHOLE** WHICH WILL BE IN CHARGE OF PROMOTING YOUR ORPHANAGE ON SOCIAL MEDIA!

ST SWITHENZ IS KEWL

CLICK!

TWITTER

=PARP= UPLOAD PHOTO ACROSS ALL PLATFORMS =PARP=

WOW! SOMETHING'S GONE WRONG WITH THE BRAND MANAGEMENT ARSEHOLE!

BANG! SPARK! FIZZ! =PARP= ERROR! ERROR!

IT'S MALFUNCTIONING!

=PARP=

OH NO! THE STUPID MACHINE HAS GONE "EDGY!"

ST SWITHEN'S SEZ HOORAY FOR HITLER!!

CLICK

=PARP= UPLOAD PHOTO...

IT'S POSTED A HIGHLY OFFENSIVE MESSAGE WHICH WILL CAUSE WIDESPREAD OUTRAGE!

LOOK, GILBERT — THAT CONTROVERSIAL MESSAGE HAS BECOME AN INTERNET SENSATION!

TWITTER

OVER A DOZEN NARKY TEENAGE BOYS HAVE SHARED THE PICTURE ON FACEBOOK AND TWITTER!

ALL THAT PUBLICITY HAS RESULTED IS ST SWITHEN'S ORPHANAGE BECOMING A HUGE SUCCESS — THE COMPANY IS NOW VALUED AT **TEN BILLION POUNDS!**

£ £ £

WELL DONE, FATHER O'DUBIOUS!

AND FATHER O'DUBIOUS LET ME HAVE THE BEST BABY IN THE ORPHANAGE!

DIAMOND RATTLE

MINK NAPPIES SOLID GOLD PRAM

AUNTIE PAT IS GOING TO BE OVER THE MOON!

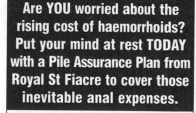

Castle Frankenstein

AT LAST, IGOR! MY CREATION IS READY AND THE STORM IS REACHING ITS HEIGHT!

YES MASTER!

THROW THE SWITCH! THROW THE SWITCH THAT WILL BREATHE NEW LIFE INTO THIS ONCE MORBID FLESH!

YES MASTER!

K-RAKK!

LIVE! I COMMAND YOU TO LIVE!

LIVE!

SEE, IGOR! HIS FINGERS TWITCH! HE BREATHES! HIS EYES OPEN! HE BREAKS HIS BOUNDS! I HAVE DONE IT, IGOR! I HAVE CREATED LIFE!

HMM... I'D BEST GET HIM A JACKET FOR WHEN I UNVEIL HIM TO THE BAVARIAN SCIENTIFIC INSTITUTE, I SUPPOSE.

YES MASTER.

SHORTLY...

I'D LIKE A JACKET FOR MY ABOMINATION, PLEASE.

CERTAINLY SIR...

THOSE FOOLS AT THE SCIENTIFIC INSTITUTE! THEY SAID I WAS MAD! THEY SAID I WAS MEDDLING WITH...

I'M AFRAID WE DON'T HAVE ANYTHING OFF THE PEG TO FIT HIM. WE'LL HAVE TO MAKE ONE TO MEASURE.

YES, YES. WHATEVER YOU SAY.

THEY ACCUSED ME OF PLAYING GOD...! OF TAMPERING WITH THE VERY FABRIC OF...

NOW, WHAT STYLE WOULD SIR PREFER? SINGLE OR DOUBLE BREASTED? ONE, TWO OR THREE BUTTONS?

EH!?

WHY WOULD I - DOCTOR VICTOR FRANKENSTEIN - I WHO HAVE BREATHED FRESH LIFE INTO A COLD, DEAD CADAVER - CARE ABOUT SUCH A TRIFLING MATTER?

OKAY. I'LL PUT YOU DOWN FOR SINGLE-BREASTED, ONE BUTTON, THEN.

ERM... ACTUALLY, NOW I'VE THOUGHT ABOUT IT, I'LL GO FOR THREE BUTTONS. I ALWAYS THINK ONE BUTTON LOOKS A BIT... WELL, NOT SCRUFFY, EXACTLY, BUT YOU KNOW WHAT I MEAN.

VERY WELL SIR. NOW, WHAT ABOUT THE LAPELS?

NOTCH, PEAK OR SHAWL?

YOU HAVE THE BRAZEN INSOLENCE TO ASK ME - A MAN WHO HOLDS IN HIS GRASP THE VERY LEVERS OF HUMAN EXISTENCE - TO LOWER MY MIND TO SUCH AN INCONSEQUENTIAL QUESTION!

WELL, IT'S JUST THAT WITH THOSE BIG BOLTS STICKING OUT OF HIS NECK, I THINK HE COULD CARRY OFF QUITE A BOLD PEAKED LAPEL.

REALLY?

OH DEFINITELY.

WELL, IF YOU THINK SO, BUT DON'T MAKE THEM TOO WIDE. I DON'T WANT IT TO LOOK TOO 70S.

QUITE, SIR. THE SLIM PEAK LAPEL IS VERY MUCH DE RIGUEUR THIS YEAR.

HAS SIR ANY PARTICULAR PREFERENCES AS REGARDS POCKETS?

NOT REALLY. YOU SEE, I MADE HIM OUT OF ABOUT 8 DEAD BODIES, SO HE DOESN'T HAVE ANY BELONGINGS TO PUT IN THEM.

WELL, YOU CAN HAVE THEM PATCHED, FLAPPED OR PIPED AT NO EXTRA COST, SIR.

REALLY? ERM... FLAPPED, THEN, I SUPPOSE. NO... PATCHED. I'VE CHANGED MY MIND. THAT WOULD LOOK NICE WITH THE PEAKED LAPELS.

SPLENDID. NOW WE'VE JUST GOT TO DECIDE ON THE CUFF BUTTONS AND VENTS BEFORE LOOKING AT SOME FABRICS.

AT THE INN...

COME QUICKLY! DR. FRANKENSTEIN HAS CREATED ANOTHER MONSTER! IT'S IN THE TAILOR'S SHOP NOW!

IT MUST BE DESTROYED!

DESTROY IT! DESTROY THE MONSTER!

COME! LET'S FORM A MOB AND ARM OURSELVES WITH PITCHFORKS!

YES, PITCHFORKS!

WE'LL DRIVE THAT MONSTER BACK TO HADES FROM WHENCE IT WAS SPAWNED!

½ AN HOUR LATER...

Hardware

...OR WHAT ABOUT THIS MODEL, WITH STAINLESS STEEL TINES AND A HICKORY HANDLE?

HMM... I DON'T KNOW...

COULD WE HAVE ANOTHER LOOK AT THE BRONZE ONE..?

I LIKED THE CHEAP ONE WITH THE PINE SHAFT. THE FIRST ONE WE LOOKED AT.

Letterbocks

★ ★ ★ ★ email: letters@viz.co.uk ★ ★ ★ ★ ★

DURING the recent Rio games, I really fell for glamorous Colombian triple jumper Caterine Ibargüen. In an attempt to impress her, I decided to take up the sport myself and built a regulation size Olympic triple jump run-up and sandpit in the back garden. My personal best jump so far is just over 2 metres, which is still about 13 metres short of Caterine's gold medal-winning effort. But for a 56-year-old, 18 stone bus driver, it's not a bad effort. Hopefully she will read this and be impressed by my efforts. If she fancies getting together, my number's in the book.

Frank Buttie, Glossop

ALTHOUGH the Olympics are over, the excitement goes on. We still have the thrill of finding out which breakfast cereals, vitamin pills, razors, and meat-free products our sporting heroes used to help them secure those gold medals.

Mike Tatham, St. Andrews

I'M confused about the elderly. Why is it they are always complaining about 'that loud music' in my cafe, but then order me to speak up because they can't hear a word I'm saying?

Mrs Fatchops, Armagh

I READ somewhere that the cost of constructing another runway at Heathrow would be over £1billion. I'm no financial genius but surely if they made runways like large roundabouts, where the planes could land and slow down in circles, the saving on concrete alone would considerably bring down these astronomical costs.

Eddie Breakspeare, Tring

THESE so-called 'environmentally friendly' wind turbines are all well and good, but surely, statistically, 50% of the time the wind is blowing the other way? This will make them spin in the opposite direction, sucking power from the grid instead. I'm only a butcher and I figured that out, so what we pay boffins like Professor Brian Cox fat research grants for is anybody's guess.

Adrian Newth, Stratford upon Avon

I KNOW we're no longer allowed to smoke on planes because of passive smoking, but surely there are ways around this? Why can't we simply open a window when we light up? I realise that if you do, you're supposed to get sucked out of the plane, but that only ever happens in James Bond films, and to be fair they're as far-fetched as fuck.

Bradley Mews, London

"THERE'S no better way to advertise your business," claim business card printers Vistaprint on their latest advert. Well in that case, why are they advertising their business on TV, rather than on the little bits of card they are so keen for the rest of us to use?

Adam Jones, Tonbridge

WHY don't MI5 give their spies a couple of Es instead of suicide capsules? That way in the event of capture and interrogation, rather than giving away secrets they would just talk a load of bollocks instead. They might even get up and bust some moves and pull a few shapes in the process, softening up their interrogators and perhaps introducing a bit of levity into the whole sorry proceedings.

Ian Fleming, Bondfordshire

WHEN I was a kid, the only blokes you saw playing snooker were on the dole, wore string vests and usually had a cigarette behind their ear. Television managed to turn this round and glamourise the game, making it extremely popular. So why don't they do the same for darts? Come on BBC, let's see some of those fat drunks scrubbed up and wearing a nice bib and tucker.

Holdroyd Fraser, Nottingham

I DIDN'T expect the lovely sunshine this morning, but when I saw it I thought it was the perfect weather for a nice round of golf. Sadly I don't play the game, nor have I any desire to do so.

William Bumbletoe, Gateshead

MY local hospital has just completed a 3 years major development of their main entrance area. The changes are fantastic and it has improved the hospital experience no end. You wouldn't know it though, by the way the gloomy and ungrateful-looking patients waddle about the place dragging their assorted medical apparatus. Some people are never happy.

DC Lewis, Sholing

I WONDER if the scientists at CERN have managed to resist the temptation to stick their cocks into the Large Hadron Collider? It's been in operation for a few years now and I'll be honest, if I worked there I couldn't last more than a week without wanting to give it a go.

Mike Fordham, Chelmsford

EVERY time Neil Young comes on the radio I reach for the razor blades - the miserable, whining get.

Peter Busby, Australia

YOU'D think all those polar explorers who got frostbite and ended up getting their fingers amputated would of thought to take a pair of gloves with them.

Archibald, Ingerlund

I ALWAYS feel sorry for parrots when I see them in cages as they always seem so lonely. For goodness sake, why can't the owners stick another parrot in there so they have someone to talk to? A mynah bird would be even better, as that way they can chat with someone from another culture, or whatever.

H Glumm, Truro

Tell your dreams to the VIZ Psychiatrist
Professor Ulf Friedrichsen analyses YOUR dreams...

LAST NIGHT I dreamt I was in a country pub where I ran into Tony Blackburn in the car park. We briefly spoke about his case against the BBC before parting ways. I proceeded to then have dinner in the pub with my family, including my grandfather who, surprisingly was alive and now from Birmingham. He chastised me for talking to Tony, insisting that I should have written him a letter instead as it was more polite. What does it all mean?

Richard, Cambridge

∗ *Well, Richard, this dream is of a predominantly sexual nature. The car park represents a bed, and the pub a woman's breasts, since you can get a drink in a pub, just like a baby drinks from its mother's teat. Tony Blackburn, with his long hair in the sixties, can be likened to the pubic region of the woman in the car park bed. Eating your dinner corresponds to you performing oral sex on her, and your grandfather being dead, or stiff, denotes your state of arousal. Birmingham is the 2nd largest city in the UK, the number 2 representing the number of balls you've got which are being forced to work hard during sex - the chastisement in your dream. The letter which you were meant to write betokens the paper you wipe your cock on when you've finished.*

● **Have YOU** had a dream which you don't understand the meaning of? Perhaps you are on a train that keeps going in and out of a tunnel, or perhaps you repeatedly dream your wife sends you go to the shops to buy a cucumber and two avocados. *Write to: Professor Ulf Friedrichsen, the Viz Psychiatrist at the usual address.*

I FOUND this wine gum today. How we laughed when we realised it looked like two eyes and a nose. More bodily-shaped wine gums please, Maynards!

Jono Watts, Harrogate

I'M literally crying about the state of the world today. Well not literally, but crying real tears on the inside. Tears of the heart. I'm literally sobbing and wailing about the state of the world, but internally. Outwardly I'm putting on a brave face, for the sake of the world.

Hampton Peabody, Bun

∗ *There, there, Mr Peabody, don't go upsetting yourself. Just think how somebody who has just had a baby feels. They must feel terrible, bringing a child into a world like this. But come on, pull yourself together. Dry the tears of your heart, have a nice cup of tea and things will seem better.*

THAT male lynx that escaped from Dartmoor Zoo was captured and, because of his irritability, was apparently given a mate. What message does that send to all the other male lynxes that didn't escape? Surely now they will all be hatching an escape plan so that they too can get hooked up and have their conjugal rights.

Ian McLean, Torquay

I DROVE down a Norfolk lane yesterday where the trees had grown over the top, creating a tunnel effect. I swear it was the same road where the Aliens in *UFO* chased Ed Straker in his flash car and Peter Gordeno blew the fuckers out of the sky in his Sky Interceptor 1, though I might be wrong. Can I have five quid anyway?

Harry Monk, Norwich

THESE dash cams are a danger to motorists. Every time I see footage from one, there seems to be some sort of accident involved.

Peregrine Measor, Hartlepool

NOVAK Djokovic might be the world's best tennis player, winning trophies and millions of pounds all over the globe, but I wouldn't swap places with him. He has a wheat and dairy intolerance, and I like cheese on toast.

Peter Dennis, Chorley

YOU'D think that all the celebrities who had the chance to meet the late great Muhammad Ali would have had a bit more respect for the frail old man. In every photo I've seen, they all seem to be taking the opportunity to chin him.

Johnny Salami, Italy

I JUST held a fart in from Warrington Bank Quay to Slough. Can any of your readers beat that?

Ronnie Turbine, Middlewich

∗ *Well, Ronnie, it's over to our readers, but at a staggering 184.04 miles, it is certainly going to take some beating*

LAST night, I dreamed that I shaved my nose off. Well, I think it was a dream. I haven't looked in the mirror yet.

Grant B Warner, New Zealand

I AM tired of commentators going on about Jessica Ennis-Hill, saying how remarkable it is that she's performing so well a couple of years after having a baby. I went back to work at my local chippie one month after giving birth, and a week later I won a medal for making the best chips in Arbroath, but have the BBC even mentioned my potato-frying achievement once? Another example of English bias from the Beeb.

Tiffany Bleach, Arbroath

WHY do you never see a hearse with an air freshener hanging off the rear view mirror? I'd have thought that kind of vehicle would need one more than most, especially on hot days.

Steve, Stockport

FOR many years I've been buying raisins thinking they are special, only to find out today, they are just dried out grapes. Unbelievable.

Larrie, Ashby-de-la-Zouch

YEARS ago I was arrested for stealing women's underwear off washing lines. I haven't done it since, but that's because people these days tend to use tumble driers. I'm now concerned that, with the recent tendency for these machines to burst into flames, people will again start hanging their washing out, once more putting temptation in my way.

Barney Plywood, Fulchester

Icebocks

"**MUM'S GONE TO ICELAND**" says the advert for the frozen food chain. But it seems as though *Viz* readers have all been to Iceland for their holidays, because you've been writing in in droves about your vacations to this little Arctic country. Here's a selection of the best we received...

❄ **I WAS** recently on holiday in Iceland, and I saw that outside the town hall in Reykjavik a life-sized photograph of the Icelandic Football team had been erected to celebrate their successful performance at Euro 2016. Seeing as it was this team that knocked England out of the tournament, I thought this was in rather poor taste, so I kicked it over and started smashing it up before trying to set fire to it. Imagine my surprise when, to rub salt in the wound, the police were called and I was arrested. Talk about being sore winners!

Barnton Lovelace, London

❄ **I'M AN** American, and my recent holiday in Iceland brought home to me what a peaceful country it was compared to where I live. My wife and I were there for a week, but we only ever saw two police officers, both of whom were helping a man to park his car in Reykjavik. Back home, they would have tasered him, or shot him if he was black.

Herb Oysterburger, Ohio

❄ **THE SCENERY** in Iceland is absolutely breathtaking, with the main attraction being the volcanoes. We have a couple of volcanoes in Scotland, but they're bust and nobody would travel five minutes to see them. Perhaps if we got our own volcanoes fired up and working again, we might be able to attract a few tourists to the place like the Icelandics do.

H McLeish, Edinburgh

❄ **I ALWAYS** thought that Nordic people were extremely tall and blonde. So whilst I was in Iceland this summer, I was surprised to see a man there who was about 5 foot 4 with mousy brown hair. I had to laugh when I realised it was my husband with whom I had come on holiday.

Ada Chelstrom, Hull

❄ **BEFORE** I went to Iceland, everyone warned me about how expensive everything was, so I took quite a bit of money with me. What they didn't tell me was that all the prices over there were in foreign, so I couldn't spend any of my cash anyway.

Frampton Lord, Crewe

❄ **APPARENTLY**, polar bears occasionally come over to Iceland on ice floes from nearby Greenland, but they are always shot by government officials. If I were a polar bear, I'd certainly think twice about visiting the ruddy place if this was the kind of welcome I'd get. I'd rather get an ice floe to the Faroe Islands or Canada or somewhere.

Dolly Burbank, Derby

STAR DEATHS SET TO DROP

THE VARIETY CLUB of Great Britain has announced that it is slashing the celebrity death rate for the third quarter of 2019, capping it at an all-time low figure of three quarters of 1%.

Celeb mortality rate pegged at 1%

Not grave news: Celebs given boost to lifespan.

The drastic move follows the highly inflated star mortality numbers experienced during the first three months of this year, which saw the deaths of an unprecedented number of high profile showbiz figures.

"January to April saw an unprecedented spike in the celebrity death rate," Variety Club chief executive Gladstone Buttifant told reporters. "It was an unsustainable level of loss, so we decided to step in and act before the situation got out of hand."

cap

Although news of the cap has been welcomed by showbusiness fans worried at the prospect of even more of their favourite stars dying unexpectedly, the Variety Club's action has been roundly criticised by the British Society of Obituary Writers, Memorialists and Necrologists, who claim that jobs will be lost if the celebrity death tally is allowed to stagnate.

tin

"A robust and buoyant turnover of household names is essential for a healthy obituary industry," BSOWMN spokesman William Duxbury told Radio 4's Eddie Mair. "Intervening to peg the drop-off rate at an artificially low level will inevitably lead to thousands of obituary writers being made redundant."

cave

However, Gladstone Buttifant rejected claims that the new death rate cap for famous faces was ill-considered. "This was no kneejerk reaction," he said. "We were faced with a runaway spiral of star morbidity and we decided to act to set a temporary cap on the death rate before it was too late."

And Mr Buttifant was confident that the present low rate would only be a temporary, short-term measure. "The public can rest assured that we will keep the situation under constant review," he said. "Figures are improving all the time as new stars are added via talent shows and reality television."

man

"As soon as the residual celebrity deficit from the first quarter of 2016 has been recouped, we will increase the death rate and the stars will start dying once again, albeit at a more sustainable level," he added.

DICKIE BEASLEY

YOUNG DICKIE BEASLEY HAD ONE AMBITION...TO BECOME AN ACCOUNT EXECUTIVE AT A TOP LONDON ADVERTISING AGENCY.

AT THE OPTICIAN...

BEASLEY...? DICKIE BEASLEY?

COME ON, DICKIE. IT'S TIME TO GO IN FOR YOUR EYE TEST NOW, SON.

YOU CAN WATCH THE REST OF YOUR 'MAD MEN' EPISODE LATER.

JESUS H. SAATCHI! IT WOULD HAVE TO BE IN THE MIDDLE OF DON'S BIG PITCH.

ALRIGHT. LET'S GET THIS OVER WITH. I'M MEETING JEREMY LATER FOR A SWIFT CAPRI-SUN AT SOHO HOUSE.

OK, DICKIE. SIT YOURSELF DOWN.

NOW JUST LOOK AT THE POSTER HERE ON THE WALL AND TELL ME WHAT YOU SEE...

HMM...

L OREM IPSUMBOLLO

NO. UH-UH. NOPE. NO GOOD AT ALL... I'M NOT GETTING ANYTHING FROM THIS, I'M AFRAID.

YOU CAN'T EVEN READ THE TOP LINE?

OH I CAN READ IT, SURE. IT'S JUST NOT RESOUNDING WITH ANY OF MY CORE VALUES OR BRAND AWARENESS RECEPTORS.

THE DESIGN CONCEPT IS AGGRESSIVELY CONFUSING, WHICH INSTANTLY ISOLATES THE CONSUMER. AND THE CONTENT - WHAT LITTLE THERE IS - HAS ZERO ASPIRATIONAL IMPACT.

I MEAN, EXACTLY WHAT MESSAGE ARE YOU TRYING TO CONVEY TO THE PUBLIC HERE?

ER..."DO YOU NEED GLASSES?" I SUPPOSE.

EXACTLY! LET'S NOT BEAT AROUND THE BUSH... YOU'RE IN THE BUSINESS OF SELLING SPECS! AND WE ALL KNOW WHAT SELLS SPECS, DON'T WE..?

OPTICIANS?

SEX SELLS SPECS! EVEN IF THE PUNTERS DON'T NEED GLASSES, THAT DOESN'T MEAN WE CAN'T MAKE THEM WANT GLASSES!

OKAY, I'LL DO IT... I'LL TAKE ON THE BRIEF. YOU GOT PHOTOSHOP ON THIS RARY?

HALF AN HOUR LATER...

THERE...IT'S FINISHED!

...LET'S FOCUS GROUP THIS MOTHER!

Regular SEX with a BEAUTIFUL WOMAN? All it takes is... **GLASSES!**

YOU, YOU AND YOU... IN YOU COME, PLEASE.

JUST LOOK AT THIS AND TELL US YOUR THOUGHTS, IF YOU WOULD.

WHAT'S ALL THIS? I'M HERE FOR AN EYE-TEST.

YES, WHERE'S THE OLD WALL CHART?

HMM...THAT'S INTERESTING.

...SUBJECTS' ARE DISPLAYING REMARKABLE BRAND LOYALTY. STILL, LET'S TRY TO SQUEEZE SOME MORE REACTION JUICE OUT. WE CAN CHOW DOWN ON AN OPINION SMOOTHIE LATER.

YOU. TELL ME, WHAT IS YOUR INITIAL IMPRESSION OF THIS POSTER? DOES IT MAKE YOU, FOR INSTANCE, WANT TO BUY A PAIR OF GLASSES?

I'VE ALREADY GOT A PAIR OF GLASSES.

RIGHT. WELL, YOU SHOULDN'T EVEN BE HERE, THEN, AS YOU DON'T FIT OUR CLIENT'S TARGET DEMOGRAPHIC. KINDLY GET OUT.

HOW ABOUT YOU GUYS? FEELING THE SUDDEN URGE TO PURCHASE SPECTACLES?

NO. I'M FEELING THE SUDDEN URGE TO FIND ANOTHER OPTICIAN, TO BE HONEST.

ME TOO. COME ON.

THANKS A BLOODY BUNCH, DICKIE! YOUR POSTER IS ONE OF THE WORST ATTEMPTS AT ADVERTISING I'VE EVER SEEN. AND NOW IT'S COST ME ALL MY CUSTOMERS. I'LL BE STICKING TO MY OLD WALL-CHART IN FUTURE, THANK-YOU VERY MUCH. AS FOR YOU, GET OUT! I'M SICK OF THE SIGHT OF YOU.

SHORTLY...

...I DON'T KNOW, MUM. MAYBE THE OPTICIAN'S RIGHT. MAYBE I'VE SIMPLY NOT GOT WHAT IT TAKES TO BE A TOP ADVAND CREATIVE AFTER ALL.

...I MEAN, WHAT WAS I THINKING OF, IMAGINING THAT THE PUBLIC WOULD BE TAKEN IN BY SUCH A VACUOUS, INANE AND PATRONISING CAMPAIGN..?

Regular Sex with a beautiful woman? All it takes is... **a Mercedes SLR V8** Mercedes Benz

"Ahhh. I love Sundays, me."

BING BONG
BING BONG
BING BONG

"Hi mum, fancy a coffee?"

"I'm up the fuckin' duff –"

"– to him."

"What? But – Where's – *Who*?"

"I'm pleased to meet you, son."

"This is Bernard, I been helping him since his wife died."

"Helping him what?"

"Have a good time, whaddyafuckin' think?"

ZZEEPP

Eeeuuaaawww!

"Er, this is Bernard..." "Hello."

"The dad of my unborn fucking kid!"

"And this time I want a daughter because *he* –"

"– has been *bastard* useless!"

"May I borrow your bathroom?"

"Yeah, cos he needs to tip out his bag."

"This is insane! You're over 60! Where's Daz? Are you far gone?"

"Six month."

"*Six* months? That can't be possible!"

"Fuckin' is though!"

"Pigs fit him up for a stabbing he didn't do, just watched."

"No, I meant you've no bump!"

"Why would I have?"

"Bernard's baby!"

Upstairs

"That sorry old cunt ain't a drop of spunk left in him, I just want him up the aisle."

"No family and fuckin' minted!"

"Best of all, *fucked*. That heart ain't his for a start, is off a car crash kid!"

"Only had it a year, he's pills dropping out of his arse."

"I reckon plenty of fry-ups and keep at his cock –"

"– by time Daz is out I'll be young, free and loaded!"

"He's been up there a while."

"She means to *murder* him..."

"Will've been full to fuck, I fried him six eggs this morning."

Eventually

"It's locked."

"Well kick the fucker in, I've no pension!"

RATTLE

LIBERTINES SLAMMED

Regulators take Doherty & co to task over pension plan failure

BRIT-ROCK bad boys the *Libertines* are adored by millions of fans for their dangerous and glamorous brand of post-punk garage rock. But now parents are being warned that the 4-piece Indie outfit, whose hits include *Don't Look Back into the Sun* and *Can't Stand Me Now*, are setting a dangerous example to impressionable children with their cavalier approach to personal finance.

According to experts the band, whose hits include *What a Waster* and *Up the Bracket*, are a personal finance time bomb after making few plans for their future. It is alleged that all four members of the group have;

*NO private pension to bolster what is expected to be a lean state payout when they reach retirement age

*FAILED to take out a life assurance for the security of family and loved ones in the event of their death

*INVESTED savings in an extremely low interest rate post office savings account, thus eroding their value

By our Financial Correspondant
Montague Aubergene

"Having no pension provision in place is a horrifying situation for the Libertines to be in," said financial advisor Beelzebub Watkins. "In the present financial climate it is madness."

inflation

"Even worse, putting money into a low interest rate account means that their savings will not keep step with inflation," he continued.

"They should be investing their capital in some kind of long to medium term savings bond at the very least," continued Mr Watkins, who stressed that he wouldn't encourage his own children to listen to such a fiscally imprudent pop group.

finances

"There's nothing cool about failing to manage your finances," he told us, whilst making imaginary speech marks with his fingers.

However, it is feared that many of the band's other impressionable young fans will look upon the Libertines as role

Doherty: Pitiful pension provision.

models and attempt to emulate their rebellious, devil-may-care attitude toward financial responsibility.

retirement

A straw poll taken at one of the band's concerts at the Brixton Academy last week showed that just one fan in ten had made any financial plans for their retirement, whilst fewer than 5% had consulted an independent financial adviser in the past 12 months.

Band frontman **PETE DOHERTY**, who once forced a kitten to smoke crack, refused to comment yesterday when asked whether he had a SIPP or was a member of a defined benefit scheme on the steps of Westminster Magistrates Court.

exchange rate

Meanwhile fellow vocalist **CARL BARÂT** said he was thinking of joining a funeral payment plan he'd seen advertised on television. "Plans start from just £4 a month, there's a guaranteed cash lump sum for your loved ones when you pass on, and you don't have to undergo a medical," he told us.

"Not only that, you get a free Parker pen just for applying," he added.

NOBBY'S PILES

169

Take a Shit

APRIL CRUEL!

"A-List pranksters ruined my life," says so-gullible Gethin

It's no joke: Gethin Cartilage's life was turned upside-down by A-list pranksters.

WE all love April Fools' Day. Whether we're chuckling at a barely-believable newspaper headline, tucking into a hollowed-out boiled egg or sticking a loved one's toothbrush up our bottoms, there's nothing us Brits like better on the first day of the fourth month than instigating - or falling for - a light-hearted seasonal prank.

However, for one morbidly obese Harlow bachelor, the first of April has come to represent the most dreaded 24 hours of the entire calendar year. Unemployed **GETHIN CARTILAGE** has had his life RUINED by a string of Easter-based practical jokes... all played on him by Hollywood's biggest stars!

❝ I've been beaten up, jailed and placed on the sex offenders' register, and it's all thanks to the A-Listers and their April Fools' pranks," says 61-year-old Cartilage. "Don't get me wrong, I like a joke as much as the next man, but after thirty years of being taken in hook, line and sinker by Tinseltown's most mischievous icons, I've decided it's finally time to put my foot down. ❞

Cartilage's metaphorical foot will come down in the form of an explosive new autobiography - *The Joke's On Me* (£0.49, Scrapheap Books) - which promises to sensationally spill the beans on his three decades of high-profile gullibility. In an exclusive series of extracts, he now reveals the extent of the damage done to him, and his reputation, by heartless Hollywood hoaxers...

STAR WARS CARRIE FISHED ME RIGHT IN

Cartilage's first brush with April Fools' agony came all the way back in 1982.

❝ I heard a clunk on the doormat one morning, and went to retrieve the post," he says. "It was just the usual junk mail - bills, court summonses and so on - but one letter stood out: a plush, purple envelope with my name

*As told to **Vaginia Discharge***

beautifully inscribed in gold lettering on the front. I opened it, and what I read inside made my heart race:

'Dear Gethin,

I am currently at Elstree Studios filming the third Star Wars movie, 'Return of the Jedi'. I've noticed you around, and I would like nothing more than for you to come and make long, hot, passionate love to me in my trailer while I'm wearing that gold bikini out the film.

Yours sincerely,

Carrie Fisher AKA Princess Leia'

My head was spinning. As a huge *Star Wars* fan, **CARRIE FISHER** was my all-time favourite actress, and I'm not ashamed to say I had spent many happy hours fantasising about her, often three or four times in a single evening. How one of Hollywood's biggest names had got hold of my home address was a mystery to me, but I wasn't about to start asking questions when Princess Leia was gagging for a shot on my little stormtrooper. I bolted straight out the door, but in my haste, I forgot to check the date on the letter: April 1st.

I arrived at Elstree Studios, and managed to cleverly outwit the security guard by hitting him hard on the head with a bit of wood. I wandered the studio backlots and eventually found the dressing room trailers. I knocked on the door of the biggest one and went in. To my consternation, there was no sign of Princess Leia in her Jabba the Hutt sexy slave outfit; there were just two women in their underwear. I later learned that they were there to film a shampoo advert.

When they spotted me, one of them screamed while the other one ran at me and kicked me really hard between the legs. It didn't half hurt, as I had already taken my trousers down

in anticipation of my forthcoming sexy session of intergalactic rumpy-pumpy. Before I knew what was happening, the security guard who I had earlier knocked out burst into the trailer, roughly strong-armed me to the floor and started giving me a proper leathering.

The police eventually arrived and took me to the station. As I sat in the cells, nursing my wounds, I couldn't believe I'd been so gullible as to fall for Carrie Fisher's practical joke. The thought of her, sat in her Hollywood mansion, chuckling away to herself at her "clever" April Fools' Day ruse, made me fume with anger. And my mood didn't improve when I was later found guilty of trespassing, assault occasioning actual bodily harm and indecent exposure.

I showed the prosecution her letter, but they found the handwriting to be almost identical to my own - Carrie Fisher had certainly done her homework. It was enough to sway the magistrates against me and I was sentenced to 140 hours of community service.

As I stood at the side of the motorway picking up litter, I made a vow to myself to check the date on the letter next time I got an offer that seemed too good to be true. ❞

Continued over...

STONE-COLD SHARON LEFT ME BASICALLY IN-CLINK

The years went by, and Cartilage began to assume Fisher's practical joke had been a one-off.

I fell for a few other April Fools' gags throughout the eighties, but thankfully none were perpetrated by Hollywood megastars," he recalls. "The worst was when I got a phone call from the young women who do yoga in the local park, telling me they desperately wanted to see my penis. I fell for that one good and proper, and ended up doing a fair bit of bird as a result. By the early nineties, though, I was out on probation and eager to put my gullible days behind me. Unfortunately, it wasn't long before I was hoodwinked again by one of the world's sexiest stars...

It was Easter 1991, and I'd just bought myself a new-fangled fax machine. You can imagine my surprise when the first fax I received on it was from none other than A-List Tinseltown goddess, **SHARON STONE**. How she'd got my personal fax number was beyond me, but her message claimed she was preparing to shoot a steamy new movie starring her as a nymphomaniac actress who gets stalked by an obsessive fan, and she desperately needed my help to research her role.

She said she had moved into a flat just round the corner, and she wanted me to climb over the back wall and steal her underwear off the washing line to help her get into character. She explained how she wanted to rehearse a graphic love scene from the film where the tables are turned and the stalker himself becomes the object of the sexy actress's insatiable nympho lust.

Needless to say, I was only too happy to help. I'd been Miss Stone's biggest fan ever since she'd winked her minnie-moo at me in that film. Moments later I was heading out of my front door, already in character as a sex pervert knicker snatcher. In all the excitement, though, I'd forgotten to check the date on the fax: *April 1st.*

I got to the block where Stone had told me she'd taken a flat and straight away saw the skimpy scanties flapping on the line in the yard. I scaled the wall, ripping my jogging trousers on the broken glass embedded in the cement along the top. They were ruined, but it was a small price to pay for the chance to do a torrid sex scene with my favourite silver screen siren.

I quickly got to work grabbing all the knickers and bras off the line, sniffing them just like an actual pervert would before stuffing them into a carrier bag I'd brought with me. Suddenly I heard a scream, and turned to see a woman watching me from the kitchen window with a look of horror on her face. I was taken aback; she didn't look anything like the blonde-pubed belter off the *Basic Instinct* video I had paused so many times that the tape had snapped. She was about a foot shorter, two stone heavier and had dark hair for a start. I didn't know who she was, but one thing was for certain - she wasn't Sharon Stone.

I'd been Miss Stone's biggest fan ever since she'd winked her minnie-moo at me in that film

She came running out into the yard, calling me all the names under the sun in a thick Essex accent while threatening me with a bread knife. At that moment I suddenly remembered what day it was and it dawned on me what had happened. I had fallen victim to another Tinseltown prankster's April Fools' Day set-up. I laughed, and began explaining to the woman all about Sharon Stone's hoax fax message, but she just kept jabbing at me with the knife, screaming for her boyfriend.

He came out and gave me a proper kicking before calling the police. My good-natured gullibility had been my downfall yet again. Stone had reeled me right in with her seasonal leg-pull, and hung me out to dry like those knickers on the line.

When the case reached court, exhibit A was Sharon's fax, but the prosecution got in some "expert" who claimed he could prove it had in fact been sent from my own machine. It was a technical glitch that swayed the jury unanimously against me and I got six months suspended. The judge told me I would have been looking at a custodial sentence for a sex crime and a couple of years on the nonce book if it wasn't for the fact that my jogging bottoms had been up over my semi when the woman saw me in her garden.

As I left court, I counted my blessings. Things could have turned out a whole lot worse. But I was sure of one thing: I would never again be duped by an A-List April Fooler.

TRICK ME, BABY, ONE MORE TIME

Cartilage returned home to Harlow not only a wiser man but also determined never again to be the butt of a star's practical joke. But sadly it was only a matter of time before he was deceived by yet another famous superstar.

Word must have got round Hollywood that I was a sucker, and in Spring 1999, I came home from a hard day's community service to find my answer machine flashing," he remembers. "I pressed play on the message, and I literally couldn't believe my ears. A sexy American voice came crackling over the speaker: 'Howdy Gethin, it's me... ***BRITNEY SPEARS***'.

The Mississippi-born pop nymphette told me she was shooting a new, X-rated music video in which she'd be dressed as a sexy student nurse. She needed a strapping male to play the principal of the college who'd give her a good, hard spanking on her bare behind. No prizes for guessing who she had in mind to administer the punishment to her pert young derriere when she turned up late for her shift ... yours truly!

Britney went on to explain that the video shoot was taking place in the gym at a nearby nursing academy, and I was needed on set straight away. She said to go up the fire escape round the back of the building and climb in through a window into her room, where she would meet me to go through the script. Needless to say I was out of the door like a shot; I'd been a big fan of Miss Spears ever since her sexy schoolgirl video for *Hit Me Baby One More Time*, when she was seventeen, so that was alright.

However, when I clambered into the room there was no sign of her. I thought I'd waste no time, and started rooting through a nearby chest of drawers to look for my costume. First I looked through her knicker drawer, very carefully, then I rooted through her bras and stockings, but it wasn't there either. I opened the wardrobe and climbed in; I was sure my outfit must have been in there.

However, I didn't get time to check, as the door shut behind me. Suddenly I heard someone come into the room. I assumed it was Britney, there to go through the script with me. But when I opened the wardrobe a crack and peeked through, I was surprised to see a student nurse who had just finished her shift and was getting undressed ready to have a shower.

At that moment, an awful realisation dawned on me ... it was April 1st and I'd been had again. I decided to stay put, waiting silently in the wardrobe until the nurse left the room, so I could make good my escape the same way I'd got in. Unfortunately, when the girl came back from her shower and started drying herself in front of the mirror, the wardrobe started to make rhythmic knocking sounds, probably due to woodworm. She opened the door, saw me and screamed.

I knew this looked bad and the fact that it was just an innocent misunderstanding would be hard to get across, so I pulled my trousers up and ran. I managed to make it down the fire escape, but I was apprehended at the gates by a security guard who rugby-tackled me to the ground. As he held me in a headlock and half-nelson, waiting for the police, I tried to explain that I was the victim of a practical joke by Britney Spears, but he wouldn't listen.

Britney needed a strapping male to play the principal of the college who'd give her a good, hard spanking...

As my trial date approached, I wrote a letter to Spears's record company, asking if she'd do the decent thing and testify in court that she had pranked me, but they never got back to me. I played the court the answerphone message, but the poor quality of the recording made it sound like it was just me, putting on a high-pitched American accent through a hankie. Without any evidence to back up my story, I was found guilty, sentenced to six months and put on the Sex Offenders' Register.

As I slopped out on my first morning at the nick, I reflected that yet again, my wide-eyed naivety had been exploited by a cruel and malicious A-Lister. At that moment, I made myself a solemn promise: never again would I be a megastar's April Fool.

WHAM BAM! THANKS A LOT PAM!

As the new millennium dawned, Cartilage's guard was well and truly up.

"I assumed word had got out to the glitteratis that I was an easy target for their cruel April Fools' pranks," he says. "So, I made a special effort to double check every letter, fax or voicemail I received for any trace of a seasonal celebrity hoax. The years passed largely without incident. I was tricked into exposing myself to some women in a multi-storey car park, and another time I was duped into licking some ladies' bicycle saddles outside a library, but in general my caution paid off. However, last April I let my guard slip for just a moment...

There was a knock at the door of my bedsit. I answered it to see none other than *Baywatch* beauty **PAMELA ANDERSON** and her husband **TOMMY LEE** stood on the doorstep. 'Hi Gethin, said Pam. Mind if we come in?' I was a little starstruck, but I showed them through to my kitchenette-cum-bedroom-cum-lounge.

Sitting on my bed-cum-dining-table, Pam asked me if I was aware of her and Tommy's XXX-rated sextape, filmed on their luxury yacht off the coast of California. I told them I'd heard about it, although I'd never seen it except for this one time when I'd accidentally downloaded it off the internet and burnt it onto a DVD-ROM. Pam explained that they were now planning to film a sequel, but their video camera had broken down.

She said that their Hollywood friends had mentioned that I had a camcorder, and they wanted to ask if I would come along and shoot the video. I was a bit starstruck, and I readily agreed. I never even thought to check what the date was. It was a mistake that was to cost me dear.

Like the couple's first sextaope, this one was to be shot on a boat, this one a houseboat tied up by the side of Harlow's Stort Navigation canal. I arranged to meet them there with my camera in half an hour and waved them off.

I got out my camera, that I had bought during the closing down sale at Comet, and was relieved to see that there was still some charge left in the batteries. With a rising sense of excitement, and a bit of rising elsewhere if I'm honest, I set off for the canal.

When I arrived on the towpath, I was surprised to see the boat rocking at its moorings. The pneumatic blonde *Barb Wire* star and her rock drummer fella had clearly started without me! I didn't want to interrupt them and put them off their stroke, so I gently climbed on deck, poked my camera lens up to a chink in the cabin curtains and pressed record.

My viewfinder was soon filled with the red-hot action. Tommy was giving her one from behind; they were going at it like knives! If I hadn't been so carried away by the sexy scenes I was filming, I might have noticed that Pam's hair had changed colour, her charms had got smaller and Tommy's trademark tattoos had vanished.

Pam asked me if I was aware of her and Tommy's XXX-rated sextape filmed on their luxury yacht off the coast of California...

At the time I just thought she'd put on a wig, taken out her implants and he'd had his tatts lasered off.

BayWatch out!: *Pammy's saucy sex pranks caused misery for Cartilage*

I had moved round to another window to get a better view of Tommy's famous T-bone going in, when disaster struck. The low battery beeper started going off on my camcorder, and the couple looked round to see what all the noise was. Surprise, surprise ... they weren't Pam and Tommy - they were people I'd never seen before ... and they looked mad. In my haste to escape, I tripped on my lowered tracksuit bottoms and fell overboard into the oily canal.

Every time I tried to climb out, the man on the boat stamped on my fingers, and I was still floundering around in the water when the police arrived to arrest me twenty minutes later. As they fished me out and loaded me into their van, I was too cold to explain what had happened, how I'd been the innocent victim of yet another April Fools' prank perpetrated by the stars.

During my twelve months in solitary, I had plenty of time to reflect on the fact that I'd spent the last years being put through the wringer by rollcall of celebrity pranksters that read like a *Who's Who* of Hollywood A-listers. I was mad as hell and I simply wasn't going to take it any more."

NEXT TIME: Gethin tells of his horrific experience on 1st April 2016, when a sizzling Skype message from **Kim Kardashian** *leads to him having his legs broken in the changing rooms at Dorothy Perkins in Harlow town centre.*

Take a Shit

"I Pity the April Fools!"

Mr T's round-up of this year's best seasonal practical jokes from around the world

■ **I pity the April Fool** in Peru, who was taken in by a pal who had dressed up like a space alien. Carpet fitter **Boco Perez**, from Lima, covered himself in tinfoil and put a goldfish bowl and deeley-boppers on his head, before abducting his pal, farmer **Alfonso Garcia.** Perez then took him to his garden shed, which he had decked out to look like the inside of a flying saucer, before spending two hours probing the terrified Garcia's anus using his carpet-fitting tools while making high-pitched bleeping noises. To finish off the cheeky prank, he then knocked his victim unconscious using a rubber mallet and deposited him naked in a field more than 100 miles from his home. Perez was found by the roadside three days later, suffering from dehydration and convinced he had been abducted by space aliens. He had fallen for his pal's leg-pull hook, line and sinker!

■ **I pity the April Fool** in Leeds, England, who was offered a bit of chewing gum from a trick packet. Schoolboy **Barry Duckworth** was offered a piece of chewing gum from a suspiciously unfamiliar-looking packet by an older boy who had never spoken to him before, who approached him in the playground surrounded by a phalanx of cackling sidekicks. Suspecting a trick, Duckworth refused the offer, only to be put in a headlock and told: "Do it, you fucking gaylord." As he struggled to get free, Duckworth's hand was grabbed, and he was forced to grip the strip of chewing gum and pull on it, causing a thin, spring-loaded wire to snap down on his fingers. Duckworth was then pushed to the ground, kicked in and his shoes were thrown onto the top of the maths block, before the group wandered off to find someone else to trick with their daft leg-pull.

■ **I pity the April Fool** in Malaysia, who was duped into thinking he had gone deaf. The entire population of Kuala Lumpur played the prank on **Tunku Abdul Rahman**, 68, by mouthing words at him, leading him to believe that he must have lost his sense of hearing. Even the consultant ear-specialist who the alarmed fishmonger went to see was in on the gag, and sat opening and closing his mouth noiselessly throughout his consultation at the hospital. As the clock struck noon, the 1.6 million people who live in the Malaysian capital began laughing at Rahman and shouting "April fool!" The embarrassed victim later claimed that he knew it was a prank all along, so the joke was actually on everybody else, not him.

I'll be back pitying more April Fools next year! **Mr T**

Ye April Foole!

Dr Lucy Worsley's Top Ten APRIL FOOLS' DAY TRICKS FROM HISTORY

10 At dawn on April 1st 1536, **Henry VIII** woke his wife **Anne Boleyn** and told her that she had been found guilty of Treason and Incest, and was to be executed that very morning. The unsuspecting Queen fell for the ruse hook, line and sinker, and Henry kept the joke going right until the moment the executioner's axe fell on her neck. As Anne's head landed in the basket, the King cried out "*April Fool!*", and all his courtiers pointed at her and laughed. However, the joke was on Henry, for the beheading was delayed, and actually took place at one minute after midday, when it no longer counted.

9 On April 1st 1937, as the giant Zeppelin the *Hindenburg* approached her mooring at the Lakehurst Naval Air Station, New Jersey, the captain decided to pop it with a pin to make the crowd jump as an April Fools' joke. However, he was unaware that the navigator behind him was just at that moment lighting his pipe, and instead of going off with a loud bang, the 7 million cubic feet of hydrogen in the airship caught fire and exploded. As the crowd looked on in horror, the Hindenburg was consumed in a giant ball of flames that instantly killed everybody on board.

8 At nine o'clock on the morning of April 1st 1601, **Elizabeth I** arose from her bed at Greenwich Palace and brushed her teeth as usual. At one minute before noon, **Sir Walter Raleigh** arrived at her court and presented her with a painting by **Hans Holbein**, which showed the naval hero and explorer grinning from ear to ear with her majesty's toothbrush stuck up his arse. The Queen, well known for being able to take a joke, shook her head slowly and laughed, exclaiming: "*You got me there, Sir Walter.*"

7 On April 1st 1945, **Stalin**, **Churchill** and **Roosevelt** met at Yalta to discuss how the post-war free world was to be carved up between the three Allied powers. As the conference convened, the atmosphere was extremely tense. But as Stalin shook hands with Roosevelt, the US president received a shock from a clockwork buzzer concealed in his palm. Then the Soviet leader put a cigar in Churchill's mouth and lit it, shouting "день дурака!" (April Fools in Russian) as it exploded, leaving the British Premier with a soot-covered face. Not to be outdone, Churchill and Roosevelt later sneaked into Stalin's hotel suite and left a *Naughty Fido* fake dog turd in one of his slippers. These April Fools pranks broke the ice between the three leaders and the Yalta Conference was a great success, leading to 70 years of uninterrupted world peace.

6 On the morning of April 1st 1936, **King Edward VIII** made an historic radio broadcast to his people, announcing that he was abdicating the throne because of his love for American divorcee **Wallis Simpson**. His speech was peppered with dramatic pauses, which listeners took to be his majesty struggling to keep his emotions in check. However, in reality, Mrs Simpson had earlier spiked his tea with farting powder as an April Fool prank, and the long silences were merely the king desperately battling to nip in his flatulence. In his memoirs, Edward, now living in exile as the Duke of Windsor, later recalled: "*If my people had heard me blowing off like a fucking chainsaw every other sentence, the gravitas of my historic announcement would have been somewhat marred.*"

5 At her Coronation on April 1st 1838, **Queen Victoria** was the subject of an hilarious practical joke perpetrated by the then Archbishop of York, **Edward Venables-Vernon-Harcourt**, who yelled out "*April Fool!*" and whipped the throne away from under the monarch just as she went to sit down after being crowned. *The Illustrated London News* reported: "*Her majesty took a magnificently inelegant tumble, going derriere over embonpoint and legs akimbo down the back steps of the dais to the evident hilarity of the assembled dignitaries, who were inadvertently accorded a privileged glimpse of next week's Buckingham Palace washing.*" However, the mood of merriment in Westminster Abbey was not shared by the sour-faced Queen herself, who had lost three teeth and suffered mild concussion and a bruised coccyx as a result of the light-hearted prank. "*We are not amused,*" she announced to a smirking Venables-Vernon-Harcourt when she eventually came round.

4 At the height of the Battle of Balaclava in 1854, the British Cavalry Light Brigade, armed with nothing but swords, mounted a famously foolhardy charge along the so-called "*Valley of Death*", directly into the teeth of 20 battalions of opposing Russian guns. What none of the men setting out on this frankly suicidal mission realised was that the order to charge had been made as an April Fools' Day leg-pull by inveterate joker the **Earl of Cardigan**. As the massacre ensued, his grace sat safely on his horse at the top of the Fedyukhin Heights, giggling at the naive gullibility of his men. However, the few maimed survivors who eventually made it back to camp got their own back when they replaced Cardigan's sugar with salt.

3 At the beginning of the Battle of Trafalgar on April 1st 1805, the commander of the British flagship *HMS Victory* decided to play a trick on **Admiral Nelson** by putting boot polish round the eyepiece of his telescope. As a result, Nelson spent the entire battle with a big black ring round his eye, much to the amusement of his crew. Indeed, even as Nelson lay dying on the deck after being felled by a French musketeer, he was still none the wiser and the assembled officers had to stifle their sniggers at his comical appearance.

2 On April 1st 1933, a research scientist named **Ralph Wiley**, working for the US Dow Chemical Company, finally managed to synthesise Polyvinylidene Chloride, thus inventing the transparent, flexible film that would later be successfully marketed as "*Cling-film*". As an April Fools' joke, Wiley took the first prototype length of PVdC he produced and stretched it across one of the toilets in the Michigan labs where he worked. Two minutes later, one of his colleagues went into the lavatory, emerging shortly afterwards with all piss on his shoes and trousers, to the scornful amusement of his colleagues.

1 On April 1st 1969, US astronaut **Neil Armstrong** became the first man to set foot on the Moon. Moments later, his co-pilot **Buzz Aldrin** exited the door of the Lunar Module only to discover a burning paper bag on the top step. Quickly, he stamped on the bag, only to discover that it contained a dog dirt, which went all over his boot. As the sound of Armstrong and Mission Control's mocking laughter filled his helmet, April Fool Aldrin's first job when he finally reached the lunar surface was to go and look for some grass and a puddle.

BUSTER GONAD and his unfeasibly LARGE TESTICLES

the REAL ALE TWATS

SHIP AHOY! AND SHE'S PACKED TO THE GUNWHALES WITH FINE ALE AND PRECIOUS PORK SCRATCHINGS!

FREE HOUSE

THE SHIP INN

GOOD FOOD

HOIST THE JOLLY ROGER AND STAND BY TO BOARD HER, ME CASKIES!

DRINK WELL, COMPADRES! FOR WE HAVE MANY PINTS TO QUAFF 'ERE THE TOLLING OF LAST ORDERS!

THE NIGHT IS YOUNG, AND BY THE GRACE OF CASK-CONDITIONED ALE, SO ARE WE!

UM, I'LL HAVE ONE OF THOSE, PLEASE. —

DRINK MAYPOLE CIDER

PINT OF ORIGINAL? RIGHT YOU ARE.

AH! I SEE THAT YOU HAVE OPTED FOR THE GOETHE'S ORIGINAL, RATHER THAN THEIR THUNDERING BELLEND.

HUNH?

A COMMON ROOKIE'S ERROR, IF I MAY SAY SO, YOUNG FELLOW!

YOU WILL FIND THAT THE GOETHE'S THUNDERING BELLEND IS A FAR SUPERIOR TIPPLE TO THEIR ORIGINAL BITTER IN EVERY WAY...

DUE IN NO SMALL PART TO THEIR USE OF THE TRADITIONAL DECOCTION MASHING TECHNIQUE DURING THE BREWING PROCESS, RATHER THAN THE NEW-FANGLED INFUSION MASHING...

YEAH, WELL, WHATEVER.

THIS ONE'S FINE FOR ME, CHEERS.

GETTING THE OLD E-READER OUT FOR A SPOT OF READING, EH?

——TRYING TO, YES.

STOUT

I NOTE THAT YOU'VE GOT A STANDARD OVER-THE-COUNTER KINDLE THERE...

YOU'D BE BETTER OFF WITH A CUSTOM MADE ONE. THERE'S A CHAP WHO DRINKS IN THE DOG AND GUN CALLED TECHY DAVE WHO BUILT ONE FOR ME.

STOUT

IT'S GOT 3G, 2GHZ PROCESSOR AND AN IMPRESSIVE TWO GIG OF MEMORY...

EXCUSE ME, IS IT ALL RIGHT IF I VAPE IN HERE?

SURE, GO AHEAD.

STOUT

AH, HAVING A PUFF ON THE OLD VAPORIZER, EH?

I USED TO HAVE A VAPE PEN LIKE THAT, BUT THEN I UPGRADED TO A BOX MOD. THE DIFFERENCE IS AMAZING!

STOUT

JUST TAKE A LOOK AT THIS...

ISN'T SHE A BEAUTY? THIS IS THE UTBNB-1360.

STOUT

SHE'S GOT TEMP-CONTROL COILS, PROGRAMMABLE LCD DISPLAY MEMORY SYSTEM, AND A MASSIVE 230 WATTS OF POWER!

YEAH, WELL I'M JUST TRYING TO GIVE UP FAGS, SO THIS DOES THE JOB FOR ME.

TOUT

OH, ONCE YOU'VE TRIED THE UTBNB-1360 THERE'S NO GOING BACK TO VAPE PENS.

HERE, LET ME DEMONSTRATE...

HUFF! HUFF!

PFFFFFFFFFFFFFFFFFFFFFFFFF-AH!

!

HOY! WOULD YOU MIND NOT BLOWING THAT ALL OVER ME AND MY KIDS?

Cough!

WE'RE TRYING TO EAT!

MY GOOD MAN, THIS IS A PUBLIC HOUSE, AND THE LANDLORD HAS DECREED THAT VAPING IS PERMITTED.

TOUT

MIGHT I SUGGEST THAT YOU AND YOUR OFFSPRING GO AND EAT IN A RESTAURANT?

YOU WANT TO TELL YOUR MATE TO LEARN SOME MANNERS OR I'LL FLATTEN THE PAIR OF YOU!

STOUT

HE'S NOT MY MATE!

DON'T WORRY MY YOUNG FRIEND — WE WILL CONTINUE TO VAPE TO OUR HEARTS' CONTENT.

STOUT

THIS LOUT WOULDN'T DARE ASSAULT US - TREVOR THE LANDLORD IS A PERSONAL ACQUAINTANCE OF MINE...

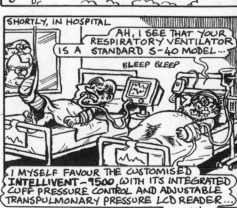

SHORTLY, IN HOSPITAL

AH, I SEE THAT YOUR RESPIRATORY VENTILATOR IS A STANDARD S-40 MODEL...

BLEEP BLEEP

I MYSELF FAVOUR THE CUSTOMISED INTELLIVENT-9500, WITH ITS INTEGRATED CUFF PRESSURE CONTROL AND ADJUSTABLE TRANSPULMONARY PRESSURE LCD READER...

...cough...

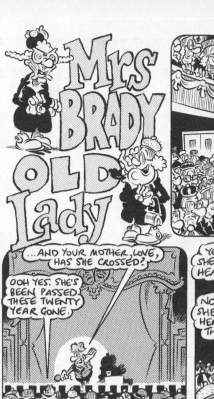

NOW, I'M GETTING A MESSAGE THAT THERE'S SOMEONE IN THIS ROOM I HAVE TO TALK TO...

DOES THE LETTER 'C' MEAN ANYTHING TO ANYONE..? OR 'E'? ...OR 'M'?

OOH! OVER 'ERE! 'APPEN THAT'S ME MOTHER COMIN' THROUGH!

AND DID HER NAME BEGIN WITH 'M', MY LOVE?

YES. IT WERE MAM.

EEH! HE GOT THAT SPOT ON!

...AND YOUR MOTHER, LOVE, HAS SHE CROSSED?

OOH YES. SHE'S BEEN PASSED THESE TWENTY YEAR GONE.

YES, THAT'S RIGHT. SHE'S TOLD ME SHE HAS. SHE'S POINTING AT HER HEART, LOVE. WAS IT 'ER HEART?

NOT REALLY. SHE GASSED HERSELF IN THE OVEN.

EEH, ADA. IT'S UNCANNY!

YES, THAT'S RIGHT...AND THEN HER HEART STOPPED, DIDN'T IT.

THE DETAIL, DOLLY.

SHE'S SAYING SOMETHING ABOUT A HOUSE HERE, LOVE... DID SHE LIVE IN A HOUSE? DOES THAT MEAN ANYTHING TO YOU?

SHE DID! SHE LIVED IN A HOUSE!

OOH, AND IT WAS A LOVELY HOUSE, WASN'T IT... SHE USED TO KEEP IT SPICK AND SPAN, DIDN'T SHE..?

SHE DID, YES.

SHE'S TELLING ME SHE DID. AND WAS THERE A CHAIR... A CHAIR SHE USED TO SIT IN..? HER FAVOURITE CHAIR. A SPECIAL CHAIR?

NO, NOT PARTICULARLY...

THAT'S RIGHT. SHE'S TELLING ME THERE WASN'T.

APPLAUSE

SHE'S SMILING... SHE SAYS THERE WERE CURTAINS... IS THAT RIGHT..?

OOH YES. WELL, BLINDS. AT THE WINDOWS, THEY WERE.

I'M GETTIN' GOOSEBUMPS, ADA.

MIND, YOU'D THINK SHE'D'VE MENTIONED THAT DOODLEBUG AS CAME DOWN THE CHIMNEY RATHER THAN THE CURTAINS, ADA.

WE AS ARE LEFT CANNOT FATHOM THE MYSTERIES OF THEM AS HAVE DEPARTED, DOLLY.

THEIR WHYS AND WHEREFORES ARE NOT FOR THOSE OF US LEFT ON THIS SIDE OF THE ETHEREAL VEIL TO QUESTION, DOLLY.

'APPEN YOU'RE RIGHT, ADA.

AND WAS THERE A CAT... OR A DOG..? SHE'S SAYING SOMETHING ABOUT A CAT OR A DOG...

ERM...

OR DID ONE OF THE NEIGHBOURS HAVE A CAT OR A DOG..? OR A BUDGIE..?

THE MAN NEXT DOOR HAD AN ORANG UTAN... YOU REMEMBER, DOLLY.

EEH, I DO. IT TOOK YOUR MAM UP ON THE ROOF THAT TIME...

MIND, YOU'VE GOT A CAT, ADA, HAVEN'T YOU..?

I HAVE. 'APPEN THAT'S WHAT SHE'S TALKING ABOUT, DOLLY.

SHE'S LAUGHING. SHE SAYS YOU DOTE ON THAT CAT. IS THAT RIGHT, MY LOVE..?

YOU DO, DON'T YOU, ADA. YOU DOTE ON IT.

I DO. I DOTE ON IT.

SHE SAYS YOU DO.

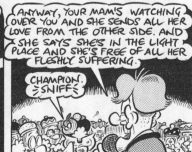ANYWAY, YOUR MAM'S WATCHING OVER YOU AND SHE SENDS ALL HER LOVE FROM THE OTHER SIDE. AND SHE SAYS SHE'S IN THE LIGHT PLACE AND SHE'S FREE OF ALL HER FLESHLY SUFFERING.

CHAMPION. ≈SNIFF≈

NOW, I'M GETTING ANOTHER MESSAGE THAT THERE'S SOMEONE IN THIS ROOM I'VE GOT TO TALK TO... DOES THE LETTER 'S' MEAN ANYTHING TO ANYONE..? OR 'L'..? OR 'D'..?

EEH, DOLLY! IT'S ME DAD!

1966 Cup Squad
COLD CASE

The members of England's 1966 World Cup-winning team speculate on some of the greatest mysteries of the age. This week...

The Disappearance of LORD LUCAN

ON THE EVENING of November 7th 1974, the bloodstained body of 29-year-old nanny Sandra Rivett was discovered slumped in the Belgravia mansion of her employer, the 7th Earl of Lucan. The playboy aristocrat - later found guilty of the murder in his absence - vanished into the night after committing his sickening crime and has never been seen since. Although many outlandish theories to explain his disappearance have been put forward over the years, none have ever been proven... *until now.* For, having spent the last fifty years investigating the world's most perplexing criminal cold cases, the heroes of England's 1966 World Cup victory over West Germany have finally turned their attention to the mystery of the vanished peer. And after sifting carefully through all the evidence, they are ready to deliver their eleven sensational verdicts on what really happened to Lord "Lucky" Lucan...

Gordon Banks, golkeeper

AS IS well known, Lucan was good friends with zoo owner John Aspinall. In my opinion, it's not beyond the realms of possibility that Lucan has spent the 42 years since committing his crime hiding in plain sight, dressed as a tiger in cage at Aspinall's zoo, only taking his costume off at night after closing time. If I am right, "Lucky" Lucan spends his evenings drinking vintage claret and playing backgammon, laughing along with his Clermont Club co-conspirators at how he has quite literally got away with murder.

George Cohen, right defender

SCOTLAND Yard detectives said at the time that it was as if Lucan had simply "vanished off the face of the earth," and perhaps that is exactly what happened. I am convinced that immediately following the murder, the fugitive peer was abducted from the street outside his plush Chester Square townhouse by a flying saucer using a tractor beam. It is my belief that the 7th Earl of Bingham has spent the last 42 years as an experimental subject on another planet, strapped to a table and relentlessly probed up the anus using bizarre scientific instruments fashioned from strange metals not found on Earth.

Ray Wilson, left defender

WHERE conventional wisdom has so far failed to solve the myste of Lord Lucan, the teachings of the mystic east may yet be able shed light on his whereabouts. For if, as many think, the fugitive pe did indeed jump overboard from cross-channel ferry in the early hou of November 9th 1974, according Buddhist teachings he would have bee immediately reincarnated as a ba born at that very instant somewhe else in the world. A simple search birth records throws up the possibili that, bizarre as it may seem, th murderous aristocrat's immortal spi could well have ended up inhabiting th earthly body of American rapper Jo C, whose hits include *Early Mornin Stoned Pimp* and *Kyle's Mom is Big Fat Bitch*. If so, tragically, it m never be possible for police to final bring Lucan to justice for the murd of Sandra Rivett, as Joe C died in h sleep in November 2000.

Jack Charlton, central defender

FOLLOWING the murder, many people think Lucan made his way to a remo Kent airfield, where a light aircraft was waiting for him to fly to a new life und an assumed name on the continent. But flying across the foggy English Chann in the dark, the inexperienced Lucan could well have become disorientated a ditched his plane into the sea, with the fuselage eventually settling on the seabed ma fathoms below the surface. If my theory is correct, just like in the obscure 1970s mini-seri *Goliath Awaits*, it is entirely feasible that Lucan is still alive today, living off fish and using th crashed plane's battery to electroly water into oxygen. But after more tha four decades below the waves, t charge in the battery must surely getting low, and it is anyone's gue how much longer he can survive in h underwater prison.

Bobby Moore, central defender

THE PRINCIPLE Occam's Razor stat that the simplest a most obvious solution to a proble is often the correct one. That's w I believe that Lucan hasn't vanish at all - *he's still living in his Belgra mansion!* He simply doesn't answ the door when the bell rings. Or the police come round with a sear warrant to look for him, he hid behind the sofa until they've gone

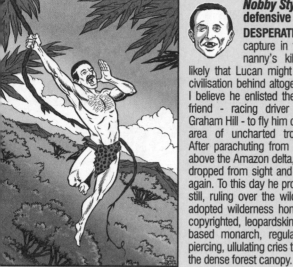

Nobby Styles, defensive midfielder

DESPERATE to evade capture in the wake of the nanny's killing, it is very likely that Lucan might decide to leave civilisation behind altogether. To this end I believe he enlisted the aid of a family friend - racing driver and keen pilot Graham Hill - to fly him out over a remote area of uncharted tropical rainforest. After parachuting from Hill's plane high above the Amazon delta, the fugitive peer dropped from sight and was never seen again. To this day he probably lives there still, ruling over the wild animals of his adopted wilderness home like a heavily copyrighted, leopardskin-trunked, jungle-based monarch, regularly issuing ear-piercing, ullulating cries that echo through the dense forest canopy.

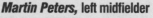

Martin Peters, left midfielder

AS A MEMBER of the Establishment, Lucan had a wide-ranging and powerful network of friends and acquaintances, including judges, Freemasons and senior police officers, and he called on some or all of these contacts to help him make his escape. One of them may well have been a government scientist working on a top secret serum capable of rendering a person injected with it completely invisible. Were a phial of this classified potion somehow to have fallen into Lucan's possession on or around November 8th 1974, he has probably spent the last 42 years living amongst us, completely naked yet entirely unseen. Detectives would only be able to spot and apprehend him if they threw a bag of flour at where they thought he was.

Bobby Charlton, attacking midfielder

WHILST detectives spent the 1970s scouring the world, following up every reported sighting of the runaway aristocrat, ironically he may have been right in front of us all along... on our televisions every Saturday afternoon in the guise of wrestler Kendo Nagasaki. The sinister ninja-masked grappler shot to fame at exactly the same time the fugitive peer disappeared, and his true identity was always kept a closely guarded secret. When Lucan was finally unmasked by Big Daddy during a 1975 bout at Wolverhampton Baths, his influential friends got to work and the rumour was quickly put about that Nagasaki was in fact Peter Thornley, a haulage contractor from Stoke-on-Trent.

Roger Hunt, centre forward

IT SEEMS to me that there may well be a time travel element to Lucan's perplexing disappearance. Just because time travel doesn't exist now doesn't mean that it didn't exist in November 1974... or that it won't at some point in the future. Could it be that a Lord Lucan from the year 2020, who came out of prison in 1994 after serving a 20-year sentence for the murder of Sandra Rivett, stole the keys to Doc Brown's DeLorean and travelled 46 years back in time to the night of the murder in order to help himself evade capture and consequently escape the life sentence he had just served? Perhaps we will never know. What is certain is that it would not have been possible for him to have gone back to the day before the crime and prevented himself from committing it, as this would have meant that he had just served 20 years in prison for a crime that never actually took place - a terrible travesty of justice for a respectable peer of the realm.

Geoff Hurst, centre forward

IT IS often said that the best place to hide a book is in a library, so where could be better for Lord Lucan to conceal himself than on the books of a celebrity doubles agency... as a Lord Lucan lookalike? The crafty Earl would have been well aware that the last place cops would expect to find him would be posing as a not particularly convincing doppelganger of himself. Indeed, in an ironic twist, the police may even have found themselves hiring Lucan to portray himself in a reconstruction of his own sickening crime for the BBC's Crimewatch programme. And when that lookalike work dried up, the moustachioed Earl could always turn his hand to being a Freddie Mercury impersonator, making a tidy living appearing as the flambouyant Queen frontman at beachfront bars in Benidorm, alongside the likes of Mr Methane and Sticky Vicky.

Alan Ball, right midfielder

VERONICA, Lady Lucan has often stated her belief that her husband would have done the decent British thing and, consumed by guilt after his terrible crime, thrown himself from a ferry into the English Channel. But that may not have been the end of his story, for it is my opinion that he didn't perish in those cold, forbidding waters on that fateful winter's night in 1974. On the contrary, like Jonah in the Bible and Pinocchio in the cartoon, straight after plunging into the freezing sea he could well have got ate off a whale. According to marine biologists, these giant marine cetaceans can easily live for 80 years or more, so if it was a young whale that Lucan got ate off of, he may well still be alive and well in its giant stomach. However, life inside a whale won't have been the luxurious experience he might have been expecting. Not only will he have spent the last four decades waist deep in a foetid soup of semi-digested squids, Lucan will also have been unable to light up one of his beloved Cuban cigars for fear that puffs of smoke emanating from the beast's blowhole might give passing police a clue as to his hiding place.

Next week in 1966 World Cup Squad Cold Cases - Sir Alf's golden boys investigate the mysterious disappearance of US Navy Flight 19 over the Bermuda Triangle in December 1945.

JUMBLEGATE!

Corruption at Cotswolds church roof fundraiser

A FIVE-YEAR investigation into the events at a Gloucestershire village jumble sale has revealed widespread corruption and mismanagement among the organisers. The report committee under Lord Chief Justice Lord Leverbrook found that the sale held in St Fiacra's Church Hall in Little Chilblaine BROKE many generally accepted rules, and was RIDDLED with malpractice and deception.

In the report, which runs to MORE THAN 2500 PAGES, Leverbrook outlined countless examples of illicit behaviour amongst the parish councillors and church members who ran the event, including

* **CARDIES** *being put aside for friends and associates of the stall holder*

* **TWO-FINGER** *Kitkats being sold at nearly the cost of a four finger Kitkat*

* **BAGS** *of crisps from multipacks being sold individually on the refreshments stall*

* **THE VICAR** *accepting free cups of tea from parishioners in the days leading up to the event*

News of the scandal was greeted with shock in the picturesque

EXCLUSIVE!

Cotswolds village, leaving residents stunned and horrified.

"I'm left stunned and horrified," said picturesque Cotswolds village resident Dolly Mixture, 64. "Like many here, I have greeted news of this scandal with shock."

skirt

But another Little Chilblaine local who wished to remain anonymous said that the contents of the report came as no surprise.

"I had my eye on a lovely skirt on the ladies' clothing stall, but I had to pop for a tuppence," she told reporters. "When I came back, Mrs Walbottle the stallholder had put it under the table with 'reserved' written on it."

"At the end of the sale, I saw it being carried away by Mrs Merquis, who happens to be Mrs Walbottle's sister-in-law," she added, while raising her eyebrows and nodding her head slowly.

sharpener

The investigation also uncovered evidence of a widespread conspiracy to manipulate prices across many of the stalls. "Items that were for sale at a certain price at the beginning of the event were routinely 'knocked down'

Unfair trade: Report documents illicit jumble practices centering around clothing, children's toys, bric-a-brac and general knicknackery.

as the sale neared its end at 3.00pm," said Lord Leverbrook.

"There was one of those dolls that go over toilet rolls for 30p on the white elephant stall," said parishioner Eda Trojan, 74, who has lived in Chilblaine all her life. "Well, I wasn't going to pay that, so I offered them 20p and was refused."

"At five to three, I saw someone offer 20p like I did, and they got it," she fumed.

case

The report findings were unable to put an exact figure on the amount of money raised by the sale, which was held on August 6th 2011. But due to the biscuit price manipulation and a massive watering down of orange squash on the refreshment stall, profits are believed to have been somewhere in the region of £50 to £60.

cold

The vicar, Tim Lettuce, told the inquiry that all the money had been put into the parish fund to pay for urgent repairs to the church roof.

But with no official financial records of the jumble sale being kept, Leverbrook concluded that the final destination of the money could not be ascertained with any certainty. And many in the village were equally sceptical of Lettuce's claims that it had gone to a worthy cause.

suit

"Yes, it might have gone into the steeple fund like the vicar said, but what's to say he didn't spend it on drugs, or funnel it into the coffers of the so-called Islamic State?" said local busybody Mavis Featherlight, 81.

Rev Lettuce was last night remaining tight-lipped in the face of mounting criticism, and would only speak repeatedly to reporters in order to flatly deny Lord Leverbrook's accusations of corruption and financial mismanagement.

Meanwhile, villagers say that since the report was published, the vicar has been holed up in his rectory, leaving only to perform regular church services, visit parishioners and pop to the shops.

Shit-stirrer beetle

I thought you should know your husband told me he thinks you've put on weight

Take a Shit

BIN THI

"They call me the Beau Brumm of Ashington" says Dandy Bin Cleaner Brian

EVERYONE likes to keep up with the latest clothing styles, eagerly scouring the rails of our local boutiques for the trendiest clothes. But one prominent North East entrepreneur says he is definitely NOT a dedicated follower of fashion. *"I don't follow fashions, I set them,"* claims Brian Lillicrap. *"They don't call me the Beau Brummell of Ashington for nothing."*

"I don't know what it is, I just seem to have a flair for style," says Lillicrap, 58, who has no formal fashion training. "I never did art at school and I failed all my CSEs. But I've always had this instinctive feel for the cut of clothing, the textures of various fabrics and for colours which complement each other."

Now, after making his first three-figure fortune in Ashington's mobile bin sanitising boom of the late 1990s, Lillicrap is set to make another, as he prepares to launch his own exclusive men's designer label in the former pit town. He told us: "Giorgio Armani and Paul Smith will be shitting themselves when they see my 2016 Autumn Collection. Believe you me, my designs will be setting catwalks alight from Ashington to New York, via Paris and Milan."

Brian first realised he had an instinctive feel for fashion when he inadvertently sparked an international style craze back in the early 1990s.

❝ It was a sweltering hot day and I was on the Cowpen Estate in Blyth. I was cleaning this young mum's wheelie bin, but there was this shitty nappy clagged to the bottom that the pressure washer just wasn't shifting. It must've been in there a fortnight or more, during the hottest part of the summer, and it had set like concrete. I charge £1.50 a bin and for that my customers rightly expect a first class, professional service,

As told to *Vaginia Discharge*

and they get it - after I've cleaned a bin, you could eat your dinner out of it - so I leaned over to get my fingers right under the nappy to try to prise it off the bottom.

As I did so, my belt snapped and my jeans dropped, revealing the top half of my arsecrack to the world. As I fished the nappy out and tossed it in the hedge, I never gave a second thought to what had just happened; if anything, it was quite nice to feel a bit of a breeze back there on such a hot, sweaty day. But as I continued on the rest of my cleaning round, dragging my pressure washer from house to house, I noticed that the women on the estate were giving me the glad eye even more than usual. Eventually I realised what it was that was getting them going... it was the new way I was wearing my jeans!

And the women of Blyth evidently weren't the only ones who noticed my bold style statement. Fashion designer Alexander McQueen must've been driving through the Cowpen that day as well, possibly after taking a wrong turning on his way to Barcelona or Tokyo. However it happened, he clearly clocked my low-riser trousers and liked what he saw, because later that week he launched his own range of "bumster" jeans at London Fashion Week. With their revealingly daring cut, these caused an international sensation, taking the haute couture world by storm and making McQueen's name as a rising star of the fashion world.

In a cruelly ironic twist, the next time I wore my own low-slung jeans, a customer accused me of ripping off Alexander McQueen's idea.

Now of course, it's

> *My belt snapped and my jeans dropped, revealing the top half of my arsecrack to the world*

Fashion victim: Brian claims his trend-setting haute couture ideas have been stolen by the industry's big players.

the biggest thing in fashion and all the youngsters are doing it. You can't walk behind a youth in the street without seeing their undercrackers or the top of their arse. ❞

Giuseppe Zanotti took this year's Milan Fashion Week by storm with his collection of haute couture jewelled fabric loafers and espadrilles. But, according to Brian, the Italian designer's daring shoes - retailing in the world's most exclusive boutiques for £1000 or more for two - first saw the

light of day far from Zanotti's swish Milan atelier... in Ashington.

❝ This day I was doing some bins along the back lane behind Woodhorn Road, near the football ground. One of them still had a black bag stuffed with rubbish in it, and as I lifted it out it burst, showering foul-smelling bin juice all over my trainers, absolutely soaking them. Now I've not got much sense of smell, but even I could tell that they stank. It was eye-watering.

As luck would have it, the next bin up the street had a pair of slippers in it, and they were in my size. Slugs had been crawling over them in the night, so they were a bit glittery, but they weren't as bad as my bin-juice-soaked trainers! I put them on, and continued with my round. As I lugged my Karcher up and down the back lane, I couldn't believe how many admiring looks my stylish, slugged-up slippers got from the local women.

Anyway, one of them must have got straight on the phone to Giuseppe Zanotti in Milan, because next time I

Bum deal: Smart Alec McQueen saw potential in Brian's bum display.

looked in *Vogue*, there was a 12-page photo-feature on his latest dapper collection of glittery cloth shoes... and every £1000 pair looked exactly like the ones I'd paraded up and down the Woodhorn Road catwalk just a week previously.

Now I can't prove that he stole my idea, and if he took me to court I'd no doubt have to retract this statement, and I would, but the man's a thief, pure and simple.

Leaf through the ads in any men's style magazine and there's one thing practically all the models have in common. Whether they're selling fancy watches, designer shoes or expensive aftershaves, chances are they'll be wearing a vest. And to discover how this apparently humble garment became de rigueur in the exclusive world of à la mode fashion, we once again have to go back to the streets of Ashington.

" I used to clean the bins at a fish and chip shop down by the docks in the Port of Blyth. This one time, I'd just got a new pressure washer and I didn't really know how to work the nozzle properly. I pointed it at the bottom of the bin and turned on what I thought was a gentle spray but was actually the most powerful jet the washer could deliver. The water rebounded off the bottom of the bin, accompanied by a substantial quantity of rancid fish-heads, guttings and tails. By the time I managed to shut the nozzle off I was soaked from the waist up. The smell of rotting cod was so strong, even the manager of the chip-shop was retching into his sleeve.

I hurriedly took my shirt off and threw it in the bin - there was no way that

> ## I couldn't believe how many admiring looks my stylish, slugged-up slippers got from the local women

was ever going to be wearable again, even if I washed it - and for the rest of the day, I did my round in my vest. It was a difficult day as I was constantly batting off seagulls attracted by the smell of my hair. But as it happens, they weren't the only birds who were getting excited when they saw me.

Because, in the middle of the afternoon, just as I was tipping over my final wheelie bin of the day to drain the swill into the gutter, I felt someone tap me on the shoulder. I looked round to see a woman with immaculately coiffed hair, Jackie Kennedy sunglasses and a four-grand Cocoa Chanel handbag. It was none other than *Vogue* editor Anna Wintour. Standing behind her was the world famous photographer Mario Testino, who was squinting at me through a rectangle formed from his fingers and thumbs.

"Me and Mario were just on our way to a fashion show down the coast in Seaton Sluice when we saw you washing out that bin," Wintour gushed. "We really liked what you were doing, rocking that vest. It's definitely going to be this year's big thing in haute couture fashion."

With that, Testino started snapping away while I posed round the bins. Anna enthused, encouraging me to pout down the lens, exclaiming that the rugged, raw and exciting shots of me in my sweat-stained and seagull-spattered singlet would be ideal for the centre spread

> ## I was constantly batting off seagulls attracted by the smell of my hair

Bin-go: *The humble origin of most of Brian's cutting-edge cast-off couture.*

in the next edition of *Vogue*. To say I was thrilled would be an understatement. This was the big break into the world of fashion that I'd been dreaming about for years.

But like all the other fashionistas who had crossed my path, Wintour turned out to be all mouth and trousers. Sure, Testino's snaps appeared in the next issue of her magazine just as she had said, but with my face airbrushed out and supermodel David Gandy's photoshopped in its place. They'd also replaced the backdrop of Blyth docks with the harbour at Monte Carlo. That would have been annoying enough, but there in the small print at the bottom of the page came the unkindest cut of all. It read: 'Vest by Karl Lagerfeld.' "

Brian says that intellectual property theft is all part and parcel of the fashion industry, and unless you get your designs on the catwalk first, chances are some other designer will lift them and claim the credit. And over the years, Lillicrap has unleashed on the world many a fashion innovation for which he has never been publicly credited, including...

★ The nineties rappers' craze for wearing a backwards baseball hat, which Brian originally started

doing after his own cap kept getting knocked off when leaning into wheelie bins to clean the crud out of the corners

★ The rolled-up jacket sleeves made popular by *Miami Vice's* Don Johnson, which Brian first did on his shellsuit top to prevent the cuffs getting fouled by rotten food and animal waste

★ The Beverly Hills penchant for wearing shoes with no socks, originated by Brian one day after he got caught short with a wet number 2 in a lay-by whilst out on his bin rounds and was forced to improvise

And now set to launch his debut collection, Brian is determined that the name Lillicrap will soon be famous in the fashion world, spoken of in the same breath as Jean Paul Gaultier, Ralph Lauren and Pierre Cardin. And he is hoping that the movers and shakers from the most influential salons will be at his show, and that his designs will be taken up and eventually filter down to the high street.

"It'll be on at Ashington Miners Welfare at some point in November, but I'm not sure when, as there are a few allotment society shows to work around," he told reporters. "I can't afford models, so it will be just me on the catwalk showing off my collection. And they're will be a game of bingo after each design to keep everyone entertained while I change into my next creation."

"It'll be a fiver to get in, but that will include a pie and pea supper and the bingo. And there'll be a raffle for a meat platter with tickets at 25p each or £1 for a strip of five," he added.

Street style: *Could Blyth join Paris and Milan as an international fashion capital?*

That's Zanotti fair!: *Slug slipper influenced Giuseppe's shoe collection.*

mr. LOGIC

HE'S AN ACUTE LOCALISED BODILY SMART IN THE RECTAL AREA.

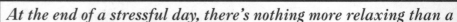

"SPANISH FLU MY ARSE!" ~ GREER

1918 pandemic "just bad cold" says Greer

by our Men's Things Correspondent **Billy Pintpot**

THE 50 MILLION men who died of Spanish Flu during the 1918-19 outbreak didn't have the flu at all, just a bad cold, says academic harridan Germaine Greer.

Speaking at the Hay-on-Wye Literary Festival, the Australian feminist, 77, told her audience: "Whilst the 50 million female victims of the H1N1 virus definitely had the Spanish flu, they didn't make a fuss. They simply got on with it and died."

"In contrast, all the men just had a bad cold and were making a big song and dance about nothing," she said. "If they'd really had the Spanish flu, they would have known about it, let me tell you."

Flu are you kidding?: Greer (inset) suggests male Spanish Flu victims were making a fuss about nothing.

The Lonely Beautiful Princess What Went to the Olympics on a Pink Unicorn Pony

Once upon a time there was a lonely beautiful Princess called Princess Tiara what had been picked to ride her pink unicorn pony called Moondust at the showjumping at the Olympics at Bolvaria...

Oh Moondust. Doing the olympics is like a dream come true and I only hope that we go and win a gold medal and I find a handsome prince to stop me being so lonely too.

Neigh!

Next day in Bolvaria...

And next to ride in the showjumping at the olympics is Princess Tiara on her pink unicorn pony Moondust.

Come on Moondust. I know you can get round without knocking any of the fences off.

Moondust cleared the first fences dead easy...

Well done, Moondust.

You've cleared the waterjump too and there is just two fences to go.

I know you can do it, there is just one more fence to go and we'll of won the gold medal.

But...

Oh no, look! It's a wicked witch and she's casting a evil spell on the last fence.

I'll see to it you don't win gold, Princess Tiara. *Cackle! Cackle!*

She's maked it went all overgrown with brambles and that. You'll never clear that Moondust.

But Moondust had other ideas...

I forgot you was a magic unicorn pony Moondust... you done a rainbow to get over the last fence.

Curses!

Its a clear round and the gold medal at showjumping goes to Princess Tiara and Moondust.

Hooray!

The head olympic judge come over to give her gold medal to her...

Here is your medal for you, Princess Tiara.

Ta very much.

But even though she was very happy Princess Tiara's eyes was shedding a tear because she was still so lonely even though she was so beautiful...

Sob. I might of won the gold medal but I am still so lonely.

Suddenly...

PING!

Wow. The head olympic judge has went and turned into a handsome prince.

That's right Princess Tiara...

...I'm crown prince Mario of Bolvaria and that wicked witch turned me into a judge and the only way I could turn back to a prince was when I put a gold medal for showjumping around the neck of a beautiful princess.

OMG!

Will you marry me Princess Tiara and be the queen of Bolvaria and live in my castle?

Yeah, alright.

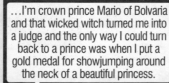

And Princess Tiara married handsome Prince Mario and the best man was Moondust and they lived happily ever after and the witch was banished.

Hip hip hooray.

185

copyright Jordan 2019

Letterbocks

email: letters@viz.co.uk ★★★★★

WHY is it when bob-sleighers are awarded their medals in the Winter Olympics, the bloke on the back gets one too? I mean, come on, he's a fucking passenger both metaphorically and literally. And don't get me started on the four-man bob. They're handing medals out like bully beef these days.

Tarquin Palatinate, Goole

I'M beginning to think that some of these so-called *"Readers' Wives"* films on the adult channels are a bit of a con and the women aren't even married. In many of them, the 'wife' is getting shagged senseless in her home by Ben Dover or whoever, but you never see any wedding photos on top of the telly or on the display cabinet. Whatever happened to the sanctity of marriage?

Bobby Shaftoe, Newark

HOW come Barclay-card won't let me pay my Barclaycard bill with my Barclaycard? It seems a bit suspicious to me, to be honest. Don't they trust the validity of their own credit card?

Hector Roachford, Derby

HOW come the fugitives on Wanted posters are never smiling? They may have looked glum when their picture was taken, and with good reason, but now they're out and about and probably on the piss somewhere, they'll probably be grinning like Cheshire cats, and hence more difficult to recognise. The police should force criminals to smile when having their mug shots taken.

Bradley Golightly, Devon

CALL me paranoid, but how come Nelson Mandela came out of the Big House after 27 years and didn't even have to wear a tag? I only did 18 months and had to wear one. Alright, he was a sound bloke and all that, but someone was definitely pulling strings somewhere.

Reg, Dartford

WHY don't clowns take a leaf out of the history books and bind their feet from birth like Chinese ladies did in the past? Surely that would solve the problems caused later on in life when shopping for shoes as their feet would be a much more standard size.

Rory Walker, email

PEOPLE always say I'm lucky because I've reached the age of 45 and not once been to a funeral. But it's not that I haven't been struck by tragedy. 16 years ago my brother and his whole family perished in a house fire, but their funeral was on the day that Kettering Town played in the FA Trophy Final. We lost 3-2. How tragic is that?

J. Navan, Kettering

IF Doctor Frankenstein was such a genius for creating his monster, how come it had such a shitty haircut? All that vulcanisation and scary electrical charges were all well and good, but would it have been such a big deal to have nipped him round to the barbers and given him a nice short back and sides before he released him on the world? Dracula always had his barnet well sorted before he went out of an evening.

Toby Moray, Dring

I DON'T know why NASA wasted all that money locking astronauts in some specially built dome for a year in order to see if they could survive the confinement of a long space voyage to Mars. They should just send my mate Steve - he hasn't left his house for two years. The spaceship would have to have access to the XXX-Hot-Milfs channel, though, and a steady supply of tissues.

Chengdu Charlie, Edinburgh

I READ somewhere that the biggest fear a writer has is a blank page. I'm surprised that with their supposed fertile imaginations they couldn't come up with something more scary than a bit of paper. What about being attacked by a polar bear or perhaps falling down a really deep well full of giant, man-eating frogs? I'm no Jeffrey Archer but even I could come up with that one.

George Rucksack, Poole

WHEN our local high street became badly congested with traffic, the council took the decision to pedestrianise it. Overnight, the problem was remedied and the cars, lorries and buses disappeared. Perhaps the Transport Minister should take similar action to solve the problem of our grid-locked motorway network.

T. O'Neill, Glasgow

I GOT a random phone call today in which some strange woman started asking me about my having had an accident in the last three years. I don't know which of my mates grassed me up, or maybe someone spotted me throwing the trousers over the garden wall, but calling me up about it is bang out of order.

D. Smints, Carlisle

WE recently had new neighbours move in next door, so I did the polite thing and went round to introduce myself. I asked if they were going to have a housewarming party to which they replied yes. They had it the following Saturday and I didn't receive an invite, so I put a brick through their front window.

Robin, Leeds

THESE street beggars have got a ruddy nerve. I've got a £200,000 mortgage, two credit cards maxed out and I owe £10,000 hire purchase on a car that's now worth jack shit. Yet these scruffy idle bastards want ME to give THEM money! If anything they should be helping me out, for fuck's sake.

M.J. Darke, Bristol

WHILST on a joyless shopping trip in Bolton recently, I managed to fart out the opening bars to 70s classic *The Boys are Back in Town*, note perfect, in WH Smiths. So satisfied was I at this musical achievement that I asked the manager for a copy of the CCTV footage, but was told to fuck off.

Rich Snowdon, Astley Bridge

IF goose feathers are supposed to be all warm and great for bedding, how come geese fuck off to warmer climes for the winter because they can't handle the cold?

D. Attenborough, London

JOE PESCI THE CAT

THE FUCK YOU LOOKIN' AT?

HEY- LOOK AT THAT FUNNY LOOKING CAT!

FUNNY? WHAT DO YOU MEAN FUNNY? FUNNY HOW?

LIKE I AMUSE YOU?

ANY OF YOUSE FUCKS COMES ANY CLOSER AN' I'LL NAIL YOUR FUCKIN' BALLS TO THE WALL.

CITY COUNCIL

LET'S PUT HIM IN THAT WHEELIE BIN FOR A LAUGH!

HUH? HE CAN'T TALK TO US LIKE THAT!

JESUS, YOU FUCKIN' WISEGUYS NEVER LEARN, DO YOU?

SHORTLY AFTER...

EXCUSE ME, SIR - WE'VE HAD A REPORT ABOUT A DISTURBANCE IN THE AREA ...

OH, YEAH? WHY DON'T YOU GO FUCK YOUR MOTHER?

PAT PAT!

GET HIM!

-Tayler-

WHY is it that things always seems to kick off during a boxing weigh-in? Surely this would be the last opportunity for both boxers to settle their differences, shake hands and call the fight off.

Duddley Fenwick, Perthfordshire

WHY are the Daleks from *Dr Who* so bitter and angry all the time? You'd think with all their fame and money they'd be having a great time flying around the Galaxy. But all they do is bleat on about exterminating things and chasing Dr Who all over the place. They should do my night shift at the chicken factory and see how lucky they are.

Neil Johnson, Durham

WHILE shagging my wife the other night, I accidentally called out the name of my bit on the side. Fortunately, they're both called Sharon, so she was none the wiser.

Andy B, South Shields

I CAN'T decide who I would rather have sex with, Rachel Riley from *Countdown* or Victoria Coren Mitchell from *Only Connect*. I suppose the only fair way to decide would be if they came round my flat and had a naked wrestling match, and I would have sex with the winner.

James Millar, Sutton

FOLLOWING my recent holiday to Thailand, I feel I must warn other travellers about the dangers of being hoodwinked by these so called 'ladyboys'. I paid a ladyboy for sex in good faith, only to discover to my horror that she was in fact just a normal lady with a vagina and everything.

Jason Carne, Prague

PLUTO has been downgraded and is no longer classed as a planet because it is too small, yet a recent space probe confirmed that Jupiter is made entirely of methane. Surely a lump of rock, however small, is more like a planet than just a massive fart in space.

Nick, Weymouth

I'VE just seen a small child run at top speed into a plate glass window in the Bluewater Shopping Centre Apple store, thinking it was the way out, causing him to bounce off it and land on his arse. Not the funniest thing I've ever seen, but fucking close.

Madgerald, Purley

MY 20-month-old son looks like exactly the sort of immature bastard who would pin me down and fart on my head when I'm too old and decrepit to defend myself. So to even things out I'm doing the same to him whilst I'm still stronger than him. I'd advise your readers in a similar situation to get their retaliation in early, too.

Dr. Flexure, Shrewsbury

IF anyone ever has the need to say 'Baked Beans' in an Australian accent, then I find it helps if you pronounce it 'Biked Beans' as it comes out with the correct accent. For added authenticity, you could add 'mate' on the end of it, or mention something about how you catch crocodiles.

Tim Buktu, Timbuktu

IT'S no wonder women sit down to piss. I've just tried it and it's much easier.

A Mann, email

I'M thinking of getting a Red Hot Chilli Peppers tattoo on my arm, but the only problem is, I don't like their music very much. I'm not sure whether to scrap the idea or just get it done anyway and hope their music grows on me.

Jack Todd, Leighton Buzzard

I REMEMBER fondly how my dog used to fart and then skulk across the room hanging her head in shame, which was only right as it really stank the place out. Sadly she died some years ago and I now have a cat. However, when he fires a salvo of foul, putrid-smelling marsh gas, he makes no move but slowly turns his head to give me a withering look as though it's my fault.

Col Percy Fawcett, Durham

I FUCKING hate mushrooms.

Rob Flynn, Cromer

＊ *That's as may be Mr Flynn, but was there any need to swear? A letter reading 'I hate mushrooms' would have got your point across just the same, and you would not have caused offence to our readers with your foul language.*

BALD FOR A DAY

BALDNESS. It happens to the best of us, and Gregg Wallace. But if **YOU** woke up one morning to find yourself suddenly hairless, how would **YOU** spend 24 hours? We rounded up four of our fave celebs and asked them one simple question… What would **YOU** do if you were *Bald for a Day*?

Professor Brian Cox, synthpop scientist

BEING bald for a day would be a career-ender for me. I earn my crust by being constantly awestruck by the majesty of the universe, and this wide-eyed naiveté is only possible because I have a thick, tousled head of hair, like a cheeky errant schoolboy. If I woke one morning to find my locks had vanished, I would instantly lose all my child-like optimism, and become a bitter, jaded husk of a man, droning on flatly about how space is nothing more than a meaningless, desolate vacuum in which we are all doomed to die. On the plus side, though, my fringe wouldn't keep getting in my eyes when I look through my telescope.

Ray Mears, small screen survivalist

AS a seasoned survival expert, I know that having a full head of hair is absolutely vital in the wild. This is why bald animals – such as bald eagles – are dying out, whilst more hirsute beasts – such as cats or normal eagles – are ten a penny. So, if I awoke to find myself bald for a day, I would simply fashion a toupee out of bracken and moss, glue it to my head with sap from a nearby tree, and then quietly wait out my hairless 24 hours in a foxhole or ditch where I would be sufficiently protected from hairier predators.

Richard Dawkins, blasphemous boffin

I WOULD use my 24 hours of hairlessness to prove once and for all that the Bible is full of shit. As soon as I awoke to find myself bald, I'd head straight to the nearest circus and go on the 'Test Your Strength' machine. When the God-botherers saw that I was just as strong without my hair as I was with it, they'd quickly realise that bit in the Bible about Samson was utter bollocks, and this would subsequently make them question every other aspect of their pathetic, primitive "faith". Within hours, the Catholic Church as we know it would have crumbled into the dust, and its legions of disenchanted followers would now kneel before I, Great Dawkins, Supreme Bald Prophet of Rationality.

LIKE most other sane people, I'm sick of getting stuck behind tractors, waddling along at 23mph and causing road chaos. Is it not time the manufacturers souped them up a bit? If we can put a man on the moon, surely we can tweak these lumbering hulks and get them going faster. Traffic would flow better and we might get some work out of these lazy farmers.

Chobby Barlton, Seaham Harbour

The Railway Children 2017

HERE COMES THE CUNT NOW.

ALASKA is the last great unexplored wilderness of America. This sparsely populated frontier country, where temperatures can fall to a blood-freezing minus 40° and below, is home to a host of frightening predators - giant grizzly bears, ravenous timber wolves and fierce mountain lions all roam these remote, inhospitable badlands. And when these terrifying animals come into conflict with Alaska's human inhabitants, it's time to dial 911 and call in...

This is Anchorage, Alaska, home beat of Wildlife Enforcement Officer Jim Mitchum. He's spent the last thirty years in the frontline of the war between man and beast. And when rogue animals attack, he's ready and waiting to go into battle…

PEST FORCE ALASKA!

Another day, another emergency call, and Jim hightails it over to the quiet Anchorage suburb of Little Fairbanks, where homeowner Audrey Vanadium has made a shocking discovery.

Thank goodness you're here. Come in.

Hmm. These droppings are too small to be from a full-grown grizzly or a wolf, Mrs Vanadium.

Do you know what I think you've got here?

What?

Alaskan State Wildlife Enforcement Officer Jim Mitchum has been called to a quiet suburban home in Anchorage, where a housewife has made a shocking discovery.

Hmm. These droppings are too small to be from a full-grown grizzly or a wolf, Mrs Vanadium. Do you know what I think you've got here?

What?

You got yourself a mouse!

Oh my God!

Mice infestations are responsible for millions of dollars worth of damage in Alaskan homes each year. The ravenous rodents nibble through wires, causing electrical short circuits and housefires…

They also get into foodstuffs, where they spread germs that can cause nausea, stomach upsets... *and even death!*

But after three decades manning the frontline of the war between humans and animals, Jim knows exactly what to do.

I'm going to put down a trap, right next to the hole.

CORNY BREX

Coming up next on Pest Force Alaska: Jim sets the trap, and the householder can't believe what he's using for bait!

Oh my God! I don't believe it!

Anchorage, Alaska. With temperatures regularly plunging to a marrow-freezing minus 40°, it's no surprise that the wild animals are desperate to get indoors where it's warm. But when the critters move in, so does veteran State Wildlife Enforcement Officer Jim Mitchum. It's his job to serve an eviction notice on the wilderness state's animal invaders.

Jim's responding to an emergency call from a woman in Little Fairbanks, whose kitchen is under attack from a mouse….

And the homeowner gets a surprise when Jim reveals what he's going to use as bait to trap his quarry…

Oh my God! I don't believe it!

188

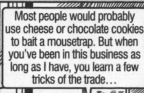
I'm just going to put a little bit of peanut butter on here, see?

Peanut butter?

Most people would probably use cheese or chocolate cookies to bait a mousetrap. But when you've been in this business as long as I have, you learn a few tricks of the trade...

JIM MITCHUM
ALASKAN STATE WILDLIFE
ENFORCEMENT OFFICER

Mice will eat cheese and chocolate cookies, sure, but what they really can't resist is good ol' peanut butter.

I've left the trap by the hole. I'll be back tomorrow to see if we've caught anything.

With the mousetrap set, all Jim can do now is wait, and he returns home for some well-earned shut-eye.

ANCHORAGE CITY LIMITS
DANGER! WOLVES, BEARS, COUGARS

Coming up next on Pest Control Alaska...

Right, let's see what we've caught.

Scream!

PCA

Yesterday, Alaskan State Wildlife Enforcement Officer Jim Mitchum was called to a home in the sleepy Anchorage suburb of Little Fairbanks to deal with a dangerous mouse. Bright and early the next morning, he's returning to check his trap.

ANCHORAGE CITY LIMITS
DANGER! WOLVES, BEARS, COUGARS

Sometimes a mouse isn't killed outright. That's why I like to check my traps first thing in the day. I don't like to see any animal suffer, even vermin.

JIM MITCHUM
ALASKAN STATE WILDLIFE
ENFORCEMENT OFFICER

Homeowner Audrey Vanadium who made the emergency call is waiting for him.

Hi, there.

Come in.

Right, let's see what we've caught.

Scream!

PCA

Jim's plan has worked. There's a mouse in the trap, and it's stone cold dead.

Well, this little fella won't be giving you any more trouble.

PCA

It was a routine callout, but even after thirty years in the job, a clean mouse takedown is always very satisfying.

JIM MITCHUM
ALASKAN STATE WILDLIFE
ENFORCEMENT OFFICER

This job's over, but there's no time to rest, because the emergency calls never stop coming in to...

...Pest Force Alaska!

ANCHORAGE CITY LIMITS
DANGER! WOLVES, BEARS, COUGARS

Next time: Jim heads north, deep into grizzly bear country, where a homeowner has discovered a nest of silverfish under her kitchen lino.

Aaaargh!

Get back!

189

ALDRIDGE PRIOR

HE'S A HOPELESS LIAR

I'VE BEEN QUOTED OUT OF CONTEXT

Panel 1: EEH ALDRIDGE, I'M SO HAPPY FOR YOU SON... FULCHESTER REGISTRY OFFICE. TO THINK THAT YOU'RE ACTUALLY GETTING MARRIED TODAY!

Panel 2: JUST LOOK AT YOU! ≥SNIFF≤ MY LITTLE BOY IS GETTING WED... CAN IT REALLY BE TRUE? OH YEAH, IT DEFINITELY IS, MUM. SWEAR TO GOD.

Panel 3: I CAN'T WAIT TO MEET THIS GIRL YOU'RE MARRYING.... WHAT DID YOU SAY HER NAME WAS?. MILEY SOMETHING? MILEY CYRUS, MUM.

Panel 4: YEAH, SHE SAYS SORRY THAT SHE COULDN'T MEET YOU BEFORE, BUT SHE'S HAD THIS REALLY HECTIC SCHEDULE WITH THE NEW ALBUM AND THE EUROPEAN TOUR. BUT YOU'LL MEET HER TODAY— HER ROLLS ROYCE WILL BE ARRIVING ANY SECOND.

Panel 5: WELL I CERTAINLY HOPE SO! I'VE HAD TO TAKE OUT A PROVVY LOAN TO PAY FOR THE RECEPTION! AND YOUR AUNTIE PAT AND UNCLE DEREK HAVE FLOWN ALL THE WAY FROM NEW ZEALAND TO BE HERE TODAY!

Panel 6: SO GOOD OF YOU TO COME, PAT AND DEREK. THOSE FLIGHT TICKETS MUST HAVE BEEN TERRIBLY EXPENSIVE! AH WELL, WE COULDN'T MISS OUR NEPHEW'S WEDDING DAY— EH ALDRIDGE?

Panel 7: YOU SHOULD HAVE SAID—MY MATE ROB WOULD HAVE FLOWN YOU OVER FROM NEW ZEALAND FOR FREE. HE'S ONE OF THE PILOTS FOR MARINE ONE, THE AMERICAN PRESIDENT'S HELICOPTER AND THEY LET HIM USE IT AT WEEKENDS.

Panel 8: HE'S A GOOD BLOKE, IS ROB. AMAZING PILOT. THIS ONE TIME, HE FLEW MARINE ONE UPSIDE DOWN OVER MY BACK GARDEN AND CUT MY LAWN WITH THE COPTER BLADES.

Panel 9: I CAN'T HELP NOTICING THAT NONE OF THE BRIDE'S FAMILY SEEM TO BE HERE YET... YEAH, THEY ALWAYS TAKE AGES TO GET ANYWHERE. TAYLOR'S DAD HAS ONLY GOT ONE LEG, YOU SEE.

Panel 10: "TAYLOR?" I THOUGHT YOUR FIANCÉE'S NAME WAS MILEY. ERM, NO, IT'S TAYLOR SWIFT. WELL, ANGELINA JOLIE, ACTUALLY. GWYNETH PALTROW.

Panel 11: ANYWAY, HER DAD ONCE TOOK LSD IN THE 1970s, AND HE THOUGHT THAT HIS OWN LEG WAS EATING HIM. SO HE CUT IT OFF WITH A HACKSAW. IMAGINE THAT, EH? CUTTING OFF YOUR OWN LEG 'COS YOU THINK IT'S EATING YOU!

Panel 12: EXCUSE ME, IT'S TEN PAST ONE ALREADY AND I'M OFFICIATING AT ANOTHER WEDDING STRAIGHT AFTER YOURS. IS THERE ANY SIGN OF THE BRIDE? YEAH, HANG ON, THIS IS PROBABLY HER ON THE PHONE NOW...

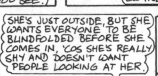

Panel 13: HELLO? YEAH, YEAH, I'LL TELL THEM.

Panel 14: SHE'S JUST OUTSIDE, BUT SHE WANTS EVERYONE TO BE BLINDFOLDED BEFORE SHE COMES IN, 'COS SHE'S REALLY SHY AND DOESN'T WANT PEOPLE LOOKING AT HER. ACTUALLY, SHE'S ALLERGIC TO BEING LOOKED AT. IF ANYONE LOOKS AT HER, SHE COULD DIE.

Panel 15: DON'T BE SILLY, ALDRIDGE, THE WEDDING HAS GOT TO BE WITNESSED! AND WE'VE COME ALL THE WAY FROM NEW ZEALAND...

Panel 16: ALL RIGHT, ALL RIGHT I'LL GO AND FETCH HER IN... I'LL BE BACK IN TWO SECONDS.

Panel 17: HIS PHONE WASN'T TURNED ON. IT HASN'T EVEN GOT A BATTERY IN IT...

Panel 18: FULCHESTER REGISTRY OFFICE

Panel 19: LATER. DING DONG DING DONG. SAINT CYRIL'S CHURCH

Panel 20: ...IF ANY PERSON PRESENT KNOWS OF ANY LAWFUL IMPEDIMENT TO TREVOR AND EUNICE BEING JOINED IN HOLY MATRIMONY... ...LET THEM SPEAK NOW OR FOREVER HOLD THEIR PEACE.

Panel 21: YEAH, I DO. SHE'S ALREADY MARRIED TO ME. WELL, SHE'S MARRIED TO MY BROTHER, ACTUALLY... ...BUT WE WERE BORN SIAMESE TWINS, SO LEGALLY SPEAKING SHE'S MARRIED TO ME AND ALL. AND THAT'S A TRUE FACT, THAT IS.

D.J. '16

Commuter wards off passengers with bag

A 24-year-old woman has successfully used her bag on the aisle seat to prevent anyone from sitting next to her on the train for the full duration of her commute to work.

Lizzie Heaton, a London mobile phone shop assistant, yesterday placed a bag containing some sandwiches and a copy of *Take a Break* magazine on the adjoining seat throughout her entire 33-minute trip from Kew Bridge to Waterloo.

bag

She told reporters: "I was sitting by the window, and it occurred to me that if I put my bag on the next seat, no-one would sit next to me. And they didn't."

"I pretended that I didn't notice other people coming down the carriage looking for somewhere to sit by staring intently through the window at something in the middle distance. It was really brilliant."

A Network Rail spokesperson explained that placing a bag on the aisle seat was a perfectly legitimate tactic for travellers who wish to maintain an un-used space next to them. He said: "It certainly seems that this passenger has discovered a loophole in the system. Using luggage in this way definitely seems like a good idea."

Inter sitty: Train traveller Lizzie Heaton yesterday

"We've checked the various railway by-laws dating back to the 1950s and there's nothing that says a passenger can't heap all their crap on an aisle seat for the purposes of preventing someone else who has bought a ticket from sitting down and taking the weight off their feet."

burns

However, Miss Heaton's tactic is understood to have gone down less well with her fellow commuters, with one of them even going so far as to tut and shake his head when she wasn't looking.

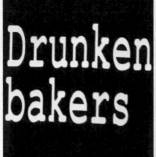

Heaven's Above!

A HULL MAN who sent up a camera drone to check his roof for loose slates after the December storms says he has seen a vision of HEAVEN. Skidby-based brush salesman *Burton Coggles* lost control of the £35 flying device shortly after launching it in his back garden and watched helplessly as it flew into the sky and out of sight. He told us: "It wasn't responding to the controls and it kept going higher and higher until it was a tiny black dot. Then it vanished into the clouds."

"I thought that was the last I would see of it."

However, the next morning the 49-year-old father of seven found the drone crashed on the path by his front door. "It must have just come straight back down again when the batteries ran out," he said.

"I took it inside to see if it had managed to film anything during its flight. I was expecting a few unremarkable shots of seagulls flying past or perhaps a blurry aerial view of the Humber Bridge or the docks," he told us. Instead, when he plugged the memory card into his computer, an extraordinary image appeared on the screen... Heaven!

shafts

"Although it was only a small thumbnail, I was able to clearly make out fluffy clouds, shafts of ethereal light and loads of cherubims, seraphims and them angels with their halos and wings everywhere," said Coggles. "As you can imagine, I was trembling with excitement as I clicked on Play."

"Unbelievable though it sounds, the drone had clearly flown up into the clouds and right into the kingdom of Heaven. It had even gone over the top of the Pearly Gates," said Coggles. "You could see Saint Peter trying to swat it down as it went past, but it was too high for him to reach, even though he was stood on a stool. In the end it hovered all around the celestial city for about ten minutes, videoing everything, even God Almighty himself!"

Vision of Hereafter for Humberside drone man

The 'In' cloud: Coggles saw A-list celebrities eating ambrosia on drone video.

"He looked just like he does in the paintings, with a big white beard, sandals and a sort of toga made from a sheet. And Jesus looked a bit like Robert Powell or Mike Rutherford out of Genesis," he told us.

brims

Amazingly, the drone didn't only capture pictures of Heaven. For its on-board microphones even managed to pick up some of the sounds of the next world. " Above the buzz of the drone's motors, I could hear harps and the ethereal singing of the choir eternal," said Coggles. "It was a beautiful, angelic sound, even coming out of the tinny speakers on my laptop. And when God spoke, he had this deep, booming voice like Orson Welles or Brian Perkins off Radio 4."

"As luck would have it, it must have been the day Lemmy died, because he turned up for his final reckoning in front of the Lord at the exact same moment my drone flew past.

I recognised him from his black cavalry hat, moustache and unsightly boils," he told

Angels delight: The sound of the choir eternal filled brush salesman's heart with indescribable joy.

us. "He was standing there, taking swigs from a bottle of Jack Daniels whilst God went through the book of his life, turning the pages and tutting to himself."

helmets

According to Coggles, God judged the Motorhead frontman harshly for his bad language, hard-drinking lifestyle and numerous extra-marital affairs with rock groupies. "The Lord was very wrathful about all the sins that Lemmy had committed during his life as a heavy metal wildman, not to mention his large collection of Nazi memorabilia, and sent him to burn in the lake of fire for all eternity," he continued.

girl

On the video, Coggles was able to spot many other late celebrities who had made it into Heaven after living good lives. He told us: "The drone managed to get a great aerial shot of Marilyn Monroe, Lady Di, Mother Teresa, Michael Jackson, Florence Nightingale and Jimmy Hill all sitting together on a cloud eating ambrosia. They had gossamer wings and shining halos." Coggles also saw his late parents and grandparents, who waved at the camera. "They looked very happy," he said.

Although he has never been a particularly religious man,

Coggles says his privileged peek into the Paradise that awaits us all on the other side has made him think again about his beliefs. "Before my drone went up into Heaven, I'd never really thought about the afterlife or what happens when we die," he told us. "But now that I've actually seen God, albeit on the screen of my laptop, it's certainly given me pause for thought, I can tell you."

"It's got me thinking that there might be something to this religion business after all."

Sadly, the footage of God, Heaven and the angelic host was lost later that day when Coggles accidentally used the memory card out of the drone to back up his PlayStation. "I was at level eleven on Sonic the Hedgehog Two and I only had the Death Egg and Egg Gauntlet zones to go, and I must have picked up the wrong card off the side," he told us. "I could have kicked myself when I realised what I'd done."

"But it doesn't make any difference. I know what I saw on that computer," he added.

What role do the stars of the smash HBO show see for remote-controlled flying machines in the future?

GAME OF DRONES

IT'S the saucy swords'n'sorcery series that has taken the world by storm. And now, as the sixth series of George RR Martin's epic serial *Game of Thrones* gets ready to hit our screens, we visited the set and interrupted filming to ask the stars of the show to what use, in their opinion, drones will be put in the future.

"It's easy to imagine a day whe McDonald's staff will no longe have to come out of the restaura to deliver Filet-O-Fishes™ to th grill order parking spaces whei the customers wait for them."

"In the future, a drone carryir a bag of food and a cardboar tray of drinks, will emerge fro a special sliding hatch right ne to the food collection windo exactly four minutes after th order has been placed. The guided by GPS technology, it w make its way to the correct ba and deliver the wrong order, alor with an insincere computerise message saying 'Sorry for yo wait'," Headey added.

"Of course, that's providing the remote control for the drone isn't at the other side of the room," he added. "Other specialist drones could be used to fetch the Radio Times, Doritos and tins of lager from the fridge."

WE found actress **EMILIA CLARKE**, who plays Mother of Dragons *Daenerys Targaryen*, queueing at the catering van.

"I'VE never really thought about it," she told us. "I suppose they could be used to help people get dressed in the morning. They could just stand there with their arms in the air while the drone hovered above them, holding their vest in some sort of solenoid-operated claw mechanism, which could open and drop it over them."

"Of course, someone else would have to operate the remote control, unless the drone was completely autonomous. But that technology is still probably further in the future," she speculated, before getting to the front of the line and ordering a breakfast in a bun with extra beans and brown sauce.

ACTOR **JEROME FLYNN**, who plays Lannister bodyguard *Bronn of the Blackwater*, was coming out of one of the set portaloos, doing up his trousers, when we asked him about his views on the future of drones.

"I suppose the hovering technology could be pressed into service to cut the lawn. I can imagine a future where the drones' propellers are replaced with whirring blades and the machines are flown upside down an inch above the grass to cut it," he told us.

"Of course, these devices wouldn't need to be remotely controlled, as the owner could simply hold onto a handle at the back whilst pushing it up and down the lawn. And it would be orange," he added. "I'd give it ten minutes if I was you."

WE caught up with US star **PETER DINKLAGE**, who plays *Tyrion Lannister*, in the make-up caravan, where he was having a scar put on his face using rubber glue. Dinklage told us he could imagine a role for drones around the house in tomorrow's world.

"Nowadays, if you want to turn the telly over and you've left the remote control on the other side of the lounge, you've got to get out of your chair and go and fetch it," he said. "But in the future, a remotely operated drone will go and fetch it for you."

DISHY **LENA HEADEY**, who stars as *Cersei Lannister* in the series, was enjoying a crafty, between-takes ciggie with some lighting technicians when we quizzed her about drones.

"Although they are merely novelties now, I could imagine drones being of great benefit to mankind in the future," she said.

ACTOR **AIDAN GILLEN** wa having a piss round the bac of the soundstage when we four him. And the actor, who plays th Machiavellian **Lord Baelish**, ha some startling thoughts to sha about the future uses of dror technology.

"Barbers could use them their shops to hold that mirr up behind the customers' heac when they've finished cutting the hair."

"It would speed up the who hair-cutting process, leavir the barber's hands free to brus the hair off the back of yo neck and down your collar wh: simultaneously lifting that rubb car mat thing off your shoulde The savings made this way cou be passed onto the customers," said, whilst shaking the drips off.

would have limited use in this field, except in a very particular set of circumstances where a monk had committed a crime and gone on the run," she told us.

"Whilst he could easily ditch his habit and sandals, disguising himself in civilian clothes and losing himself in a crowd, a police drone would easily be able to hover high in the air and spot his tell-tale tonsure," she added. "Then ground-based officers could move in and taser the bastard."

SUAVE, debonair actor **CHARLES DANCE**, who appears as Lannister clan patriarch **Lord Tywin**, was on the phone having an almighty bust-up with his wife, ex-wrestler Klondyke Kate, when we interrupted to ask him for his views about drones.

"This is a subject that concerns me deeply," he told us. "They could be put to use by trainspotters, who currently risk life and limb in pursuit of their hobby. At the moment, in order to spot a number on a train, they are often forced to lean out over the platform edge and squint through their glasses. They are only ever one slip away from disaster."

"But in the world of tomorrow, train-spotting camera drones equipped with on-board number recognition software could zoom around stations and marshalling yards with the freedom of a bird, spotting numbers such as 35627, 39674B or 575528 in less than a millisecond, while being controlled from the safety of the tragic railway enthusiast's bedroom in his mum's house," he said.

TOMBOY **Arya Stark** actress **MAISIE WILLIAMS** was relaxing between takes, chomping her way through a family-size bag of pickled onion Monster Munch, when we asked her to prognosticate about drones.

"When I was growing up, I always wanted to be a policewoman, so I've always been interested in crime and detection. I believe drones

ROLY-POLY actor **JOHN BRADLEY**, who plays Night's Watch stalwart **Samwell Tarly**, was escorting six giggling prostitutes up the steps of his backstage Winnebago when we buttonholed him to ask how he thought drones might shape the future.

"In my opinion, it is only a matter of time before drones take over from guide dogs. Blind people could walk down the street holding onto a hovering drone, which could act as their eyes, leading them where they want to go, negotiating obstacles and taking them safely across the road," he surmised.

"And the good news is, it wouldn't even put guide dogs out of business," Bradley continued. "Labradors are so intelligent that they could be trained to operate the drones remotely via a video link from control centres miles away, perhaps even on another continent such as North America or Asia."

Sky News

£10m drone makeover for Beeb current affairs flagship

Flying tonight: £1m drones will add aerial shots to evening news broadcasts.

THE Ten O'Clock News is to start using drone footage in its broadcasts. Ten studio-based hovering cameras, costing £1 million each, will buzz around the lighting gantries, providing viewers with live aerial shots of their favourite newsreaders as they read that day's bulletins.

A BBC spokesperson said the decision had been taken to bring the news department into line with all the corporation's other programmes.

"Just about every show on the BBC uses drone footage these days," head of Current Affairs Jane Fightingships told the Edinburgh Television Festival. "Countryfile, The Antiques Roadshow, Top Gear... you name it, if it's on the beeb it'll have drone footage plastered all over it like a mad woman's shit."

occasional

"Of course the Ten O'Clock News won't be filmed completely from an overhead drone," she continued. "That would be ridiculous. We're just going to intercut the occasional shot from a camera circling fifteen feet above George Alagayah or Huw Edwards in amongst the more familiar studio-floor-based footage."

snooker

Ms Fightingships admitted that there had been some teething problems with the new technology. She said: "During a practice run-through last week, one of the drones hit a microphone boom and crash-landed on newsreader Nicholas Witchell' head and his ginger hair got tangled up in the rotors. As

On the hair: Props tangled with carrot-top Witchell's barnet

the operator revved it to try and get it airborne again, it just got worse, and in the end they had to cut it out with scissors."

stymie

A clearly rattled Witchell read the news later that evening wearing a baseball hat pulled down over one side of his head to hide a bald patch, said Ms Fightingships.

Meanwhile, news bosses have asked lady presenters including Sophie Raworth, Emily Maitlis, Fiona Bruce and Mishal Husain to wear high-necked tops when the studio drones are operating. A senior producer told us: "Newsreaders often have to report on serious and distressing subjects."

"We don't want the gravity of these stories to be diminished by viewers getting a cheap thrill by trying to look down their bras," he added.

Viz DRONE BREACHES PALACE SECURITY

SECURITY procedures at all royal residences were being reviewed last night after a downmarket adult grin-mag managed to fly a **DRONE** into Buckingham Palace.

Viz editor *Hampton Doubleday* was able to pilot the drone, purchased for £20 on the high street, through a pantry window on the east side of the palace. Controlling it from the street, he then hovered the machine unchallenged around the corridors, staterooms and halls of the royal residence.

security

And despite invading the Queen's privacy, the magazine editor said he had "no regrets" after highlighting the shocking lack of security.

"I couldn't believe how simple it was," said the 58-year-old editor. "Nobody questioned the presence of the intruding machine in the two hours I spent flying it round. I was able to photograph butlers, priceless treasures and even some minor royals who were in the palace," he added.

train

Shockingly, Doubleday was even able to manoeuvre his flying spy in the palace directly into the Queen's private bedroom.

"Nobody said a word as I flew the drone into her Majesty's boudoir," said Doubleday. "A butler even opened the door for it."

Controlled from outside the palace gates, the drone spent the next half hour buzzing round the Queen's

The Queen's breach: Viz editor Doubleday (inset) was able to fly camera drone (left) through gaps in Buckingham Palace (top) gates.

We flag up lax security by flying drone into Queen's bedroom!

bedroom, photographing the contents of her wardrobe, her underwear drawer and her en-suite bathroom.

fire

"Fortunately Her Majesty was not in residence at the time, as she was opening a supermarket in Wales. But if she had been, I could of

Alarming: RC device photographed Queen's bedside table.

photographed her in bed, in the bath, or even sitting on her thunderbox," Doubleday told us.

praetorian

Conservative MP for Fulchester South, Sir Anthony Regents-Park called the intrusion "a shocking breach of palace procedures," and said that a thorough investigation must be held to highlight the unacceptable lapse in security.

"If it is this easy for a downmarket four-letter magazine to infiltrate the most tightly guarded house in the land, imagine how easy it would be for the likes of Isis to do the same," he thundered. "And what if, instead of a camera, there was a dirty bomb strapped to the drone? The consequences simply don't bear thinking about," he added.

body

Sir Anthony went on to thank Viz Comic and editor Doubleday for bringing this deficiency in security to light.

"As a nation, we cannot thank them enough," he told a packed House of Commons. "And I ask everyone in Britain to send Viz Comic a cheque for £50 for the service they have done highlighting the gaping holes in Royal security," he continued, to loud cheers from both sides of the floor.

operator

When order was restored, Speaker of the House John Bercow suggested that cheques should be made payable to Viz Comic, and that the cheque guarantee card number should be written clearly on the back.

"Or appreciative Britons may prefer to send cash to Viz Comic, PO Box 841, Whitley Bay, NE26 9EQ," he said, to excited waving of papers and cries of "Hear, hear!"

UK grumble ac

VETERAN stickr *Ben Dover* announced ambitious plan to s using drones to sh his adult movies. perennially pri national treasure, hopes that the rem control hovering came will add a new dynamic dimension to hardcore productions

"We'll be able to get some a that I just can't manage by m' said Dover, who writes, d shoots, edits and distributes a own videos.

"When I was younger, I wa more flexible and I could g camera right down into the p you could see everything," h us. "These days, my back's and it's even a chore for bend down and tie my laces the cinematography is suffer a result."

bollocks

Dover's drone-mounted cameras will fly up close performers, swooping be legs, avoiding bollocks and g hitherto unimaginable shots animalistic hardcore action.

Dover admits that the u the hovering gadgets on a set is not without its pot problems, he told us: "Ther risk that, during a close-up

Drone

AMISH elders Pennsylvar yesterday g the thumbs up for t members to play drones. The traditiona Christian sect, who s all modern technol made the excep because the rem control flying gadg "were such good fun."

"I had a go with one and it was Amish leader Jonas Swartzent told *The Plain Living Gazette* went right up over the barn, b the woodshed and did a loop loop. I landed it right on top c chicken coop. It was awesome."

faith

However, Swartzentruber said were still strict limitations on th of drones by followers of the which follows a strict doctri

use r/c technology to shoot scud

Bone-ons to Drone-ons

Flight of the grumble bee: Adult video producer Dover intends to use radio-controlled hovering cameras to capture cocks and fannies from new angles.

owndraught from
ans could cool an
's ardour. Also,
igh-pitched whining
might drown out
rmers' unconvincing
s, groans and gasps."

d there's also the
mare scenario that, during
ney shot, a glob of flying
could hit one of the
s and bring it down."

dinner

these are risks Dover
lling to take. He
s: "In many ways,
graphy is just like
e film-making. The
s natural history
have raised the bar
l of us. The public
xpects much higher
ction values than they used to
e old days. Thanks to HDTV
3lu-ray, Beautifully composed
s and imaginative camerawork
e order of the day, whatever
f movie making you are in."

"The only difference between me and David Attenborough is that he films lions, wildebeests and iguanas whilst I film single mothers from Leeds with tattoos on their tits," he added.

K, say Amish

*vout and about: Some Amish
ople flying a drone, yesterday.*

le living that rejects all forms of
nology.

y mustn't put cameras on them,
when they're out flying them
must wear a straw hat, braces

and a shirt with no buttons on."

"And when they go to buy new batteries from Maplins, they have to go in a horse and cart," he added. "And have a beard."

Break-in News
Thief drones set to revolutionise burglary business

WE ARE all agreed that new technology is a wonderful thing. But sooner or later, there's a chance of it falling into the wrong hands and getting used for illicit purposes. Mobile phones, the internet and GPS sat-navs are all now routinely used by criminals to arrange, carry out, and cover up their despicable crimes. And it appears that drones could be the next tool in their arsenal.

For according to the National Union of Intruders, Housebreakers and Ratboys, home burglaries could be completely automated within the next few years. The professional body says that by 2020, criminals could be using drones to break into your house, steal your stuff and deliver a shit onto the living room carpet.

"Gone are the days when burglars had to tramp the streets with a swag bag, a jemmy and the turtle's head," said NUIHR spokesman Nosher Bent. "If Amazon can deliver your new telly with a drone, we can take it away just as easily using the same technology."

felonious

"Within the next five years, my felonious members will be able to turn over a gaff and leave a dollop on the rug in half the time it takes now, and all without leaving the comfort of their own home," added Mr Bent. "Thanks to drones, the future's looking bright for tea-leaves."

franciscan

But some older members of the burglars' union were less keen to embrace the changes in working practices. 56-year-old housebreaker Nobby Fletcher told us he was finding it difficult to adapt to the new technology.

benedictine

"I've been turning over drums in the time-honoured way for forty years," he told us. "I tried to do my first job with a drone last week, and it was a farce."

"I got it out of the box and I couldn't understand the instructions. They may as well have been in Chinese for all the sense they made," he said. "I eventually got it going and tried

Flight fingered: House breakers could be using drones by 2020, says burglars' union.

to fly it through a window of a flat in Cricklewood but it kept going upside down. Then one of the neighbours called the police."

shaolin

Mr Fletcher said he would be sticking to his traditional burgling techniques. "Breaking in and shitting on the floor by hand was good enough for my dad and my grandad," he continued. "I learned my trade at their knees."

"Drones are just another passing fad. At the end of the day, you can't beat sneaking round in the dark with a crowbar and a mole at the counter," he added.

buddhist

But Inspector Frank Slippers of the Metroploitan Police advised the public to be vigilant. "We would ask anyone who sees any drone hovering suspiciously to call the police," he said.

FIVE YEARS AGO we didn't know what they were, because they hadn't even been invented. But now they have and they're the must-have fad gadget of 2016. They're **DRONES**, and they're literally everywhere, buzzing round our heads 24-7. *But how much do you really know about these hovering electronic marvels?* **Prepare to lift off and get stuck eighty foot up in a fucking tree as we take an aerial view of...**

10 Things You Never Knew About DRONES

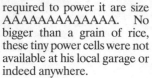

1 **ALTHOUGH** they've only been in the shops for a couple of years, the first drone was invented by Renaissance genius Leonardo da Vinci, when he took his earlier invention of the helicopter and mounted four of them on a pair of crossed coat hangers. Amazingly, the device worked first time, rising vertically to a height of 100 feet before suddenly veering off to the left, hitting the Leaning Tower of Pisa and crashing into a pond.

2 **DRONES** aren't the first things to hover above the ground. Mother Nature has been making things that hover for hundreds of years, including humming birds, wasps and those hawk things you see at the side of the motorway looking for mice.

3 **THE** drone was actually invented by Sir Christopher Cockerell way back in the 1950s. He designed the device - which he called a "hovercraft" - to take aerial photographs of the fruity piece next door sunbathing in her garden. But when he tried it out, due to the excessive weight of its giant engines, it only went up about four inches off the ground, not high enough to get over the fence. Eventually, Cockerell adapted his design to carry fare-paying passengers to France to buy carloads of cheap wine. But only when it wasn't too windy.

4 **GO** into a shop in Scotland and ask for a drone, and you might not get what you're expecting. For "drone" is also the name given

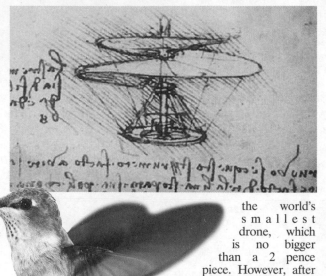

to each of the three hollow tubes that stick out of the top of a set of bagpipes, allowing the traditional Scottish instrument to make its characteristic fucking awful racket.

5 **BRITISH** astronaut Major Tim Peake took a small radio-controlled drone with him on his recent mission to the ISS. However, when he reached the orbiting space platform, Peake was devastated to realise that he had brought AA batteries for the device when it actually took AAAs. Ironically, it didn't matter in the end, because in the weightless vacuum of space Peake's drone hovered in mid-air without even needing to be switched on.

6 **ONLINE** retailer Amazon insist that by 2020 they will routinely be delivering packages using autonomous, self-piloting drones which will land on special pads placed in their customers' gardens. But they won't.

7 **THE** world's smallest man, Calvin Phillips, recently treated himself to

the world's smallest drone, which is no bigger than a 2 pence piece. However, after unboxing it, Phillips was unable to get his flying toy airborne, as the batteries required to power it are size AAAAAAAAAAAAA. No bigger than a grain of rice, these tiny power cells were not available at his local garage or indeed anywhere.

8 **ON** Christmas morning 2015, Britons unwrapped an estimated 15 million drones. By lunchtime, over 11 million of them were stuck in trees, wedged in gutters or tangled in television aerials.

9 **BY** tea time, so were the other 4 million.

10 **EVEN** though they give up all their earthly belongings and chattels when they enter a monastery, monks have owned drones for centuries. But these

drones aren't the remote control electronic gadgets the rest of us are familiar with... they're BEES! Drones are stingless male bees who gather in large groups and all attempt to mate with a single female at the same time. A bit like premiership footballers in hotel rooms.

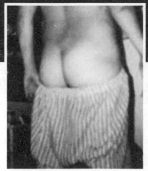

Micro-Drones, My Arse!

MINIATURE flying drones the size of pinheads could soon be helping doctors diagnose bowel conditions, according to a report in this week's British Medical Journal.

Engineers at the University of Fulchester are in the process of developing tiny micro-drones which will be able to fly up a patient's arse to spot polyps, warts and internal piles. At present, doctors can only identify such abnormalities using long probe-like cameras inserted into the rectum, an uncomfortable procedure and one not without risk.

diagnosis

"These little endo-flying machines are going to make diagnosis of these conditions a whole lot safer," said project leader Professor Johnny Kwango.

she wrote

"It's a bit like that film The Fantastic Voyage, but instead of being piloted by a tiny Donald Pleasance and Raquel Welch, these drones will be remotely controlled by a medical professional," he added.

Spy in the Brown Eye Set to Revolutionise Medicine

Funding for the project came in the unlikely form of sponsorship by soft drinks manufacturer Red Bull, who are better known for putting their name to extreme sports. But Red Bull spokesman Hyman K Oysterburger said that supporting bowel research was a breath of fresh air to his company.

midsomer

"Putting our name to snowboarding events, motocross jumping shows and air races is all well and good, but we wanted to lend support to grass roots medical research too," he added.

Hairy caecum: Drones will fly up alimentary canal.

he told reporters. "And as medical research goes, this is pretty exciting stuff," he added.

of crows

"These little ass drones are going to have our logo all over them. And the surgeon who flies them is under instructions to do a few barrel rolls while examining the intestinal walls, and maybe show off with a couple of three-sixty loop the loops," he added.

"Whatever, it's gonna be one hell of a show of rectal aerobatics."

SLAM!

FLUSH!!

199

P vs David Hamilton vs A Drogba............

WALK FROM Land's End to John O'Groats and you'll hear the same old argument every single step of the way: *Who's the best Diddy?*

For some, the only sensible answer is New York gangsta rapper **P DIDDY,** who keeps the planet's toes tapping with his hardcore hip-hop hits, which include *Bad Boy For Life* and *Shake Ya Tailfeather*. Others, though, will aggressively avow that the correct response to the question is septuagenarian broadcaster **'DIDDY' DAVID HAMILTON,** who has been bringing his own brand of pint-sized charm to Britain's small screens and wireless sets since the late fifties. Whilst others would contend that the real champ is football ace **DIDDY A DROGBA,** who netted over 100 goals for Chelsea during his illustrious career at Stamford Bridge.

But there can be only ever be one winner, and it's high time this decades-old dispute was finally put to bed. Here we weigh up the pros and cons of the world's three favourite Diddys, in order to decide once and for all which one is the greatest...

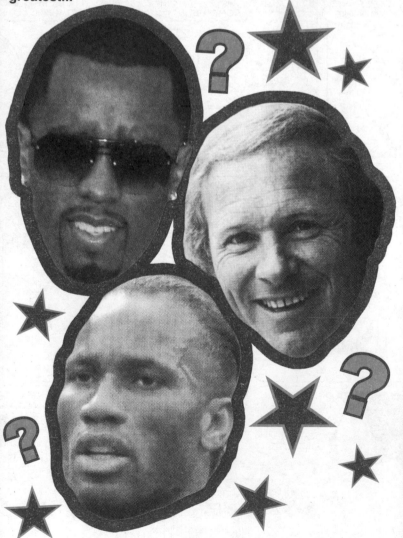

P

THE ARTIST born Sean 'P Diddy' Combs is officially the world's richest rap with *Forbes* magazine estimating his fortune at a wallet-boggling $750 million. bad for a humble, working class lad born on the mean streets of Harlem, NY. Ho ever, hot on Diddy's gold-plated heels is none other than fellow gangsta rap icon Dre, whose bank balance currently stands at a cool $700 million. This means t one bad investment from Diddy would see him swiftly toppled from the pinnacle the hip-hop wealth charts - a humiliating blow that could see the *Bad Boy For Life* star turn to drink and debauchery, haemorrhaging cash at an alarming rate, and leaving him penniless and diddy destitute within months.

WITH his sharp suits, slick shades and X-rated hip-hop lyrics, Diddy is widely garded as the King of Cool among today's young people. But his legions of ador admirers would cringe and turn bright red if they knew that, behind closed doc their hero can regularly be found pushing foul-smelling parcels of excrement out through his anus. If this humiliating dark secret ever got out, the New Yorker's street credibility would understandably be left in tatters.

ROUND

HE MAY be Sean John Combs to his dear old mum, but his armies of adoring fa know the 46-year-old rap legend by a myriad of other monickers, including P Did Diddy, Puff Daddy, Puffy and Swag. None of these nicknames appears to have b bestowed upon him by the distressingly-toothed English comedian and singer-so writer Ken Dodd, but we can't be completely sure. Fairness dictates that we give the Bad Boy mogul the benefit of the doubt here, and consequently he nets half marks in this round.

ROUND 4: ALL

EVER since Tupac Shakur's murder in 1996, rumours have abounded that lor time rival P Diddy had a hand in the as-yet-unsolved drive-by killing. Howev that's all they are: rumours. With absolutely no hard evidence whatsoever t Diddy was in any way involved in 2Pac's fatal shooting, the *Shake Ya Tailfeather* star chalks up a pitiful score in this round.

ROUND 5: AFTER DINNER SF

DESPITE boasting more than 25 years of glittering showbiz experience, p forming on some of the biggest stages on the planet and shifting countless r lions of albums and singles, P Diddy has NEVER spoken at a charity after-din event alongside Neil Dudgeon, the actor who plays DCI Barnaby in the ITV drama series *Midsomer Murders*. As such, it's a disappointingly low-scoring final round for the hip-hop mogul.

ASK the artist formerly known as Puff Daddy if he fancied a game of footb and he'd turn up at the park wearing a full-face crash helmet, ridiculous shoul pads, white tights tucked in his socks and carrying a rugby ball. When the ga kicked off, he'd run backwards, threatening to throw the ball whilst shouting numbers. Had he ever turned out for Chelsea FC, he would have been immediately red-carded for hand ball.

P 10

DIDDY WIN? Diddy 'eck! It's a hip hop humiliation for rap s P, as he is roundly trumped by both his nickname-sakes. T singer may have reached number 19 in the charts with his 1997 s gle *Victory*, but this performance has failure written all over it, pro ing once and for all that when it comes to Diddys, he's a real Dud

NEXT WEEK: SMITH vs DE SADE vs MARK &

HE BEST DIDDY?

DAVID HAMILTON

A DROGBA

ROUND 1: NET WORTH

NCE his broadcasting career was launched in the late 1950s, 'Diddy' David milton has fronted more than 12,000 radio shows and 1,000 TV programmes. ese have included big money quiz shows, such as ITV's *All Clued Up*, and flagship tish series such as *Top Of The Pops* and *Seaside Special*. And that's without men-ning the publication, in 2012, of his football-based autobiography *A Fulhamish* e. There is no concrete information on whether Hamilton's combined earnings m these various projects might equal - or even top - $750 million, but with hard evidence either way, we must give the diminutive DJ the benefit of e diddy doubt in this round. **7**

TOP Premiership footballers are paid silly money these days, and during his 9 years playing for Chelsea Drogba was thought to have trousered a whopping salary of £1 million a month. Factor in lucrative endorsement deals for football boots, fizzy pop and crisps, and the Ivory Coast centre forward could easily have amassed a fortune every bit as impressive as his Diddy namesakes over his career. However, footballers are notorious spendthrifts, spunking cash on cars, watches with all dials on, and designer suits. If we conservatively estimate that he has bought 20 top-of-the-range Range Rovers a week since 2004, not by any means out of the question, Drogba could now be nursing a massive overdraft. A poor opening round. **1**

ROUND 2: STREET CRED

NE quick YouTube search will uncover literally tens of clips in which the minuscule adcaster can be seen fronting *Top Of The Pops*, surrounded by swarms of adoring s. As if that wasn't enough to confirm Hamilton's unshakable popularity with the fash--conscious youth of today, he recently teamed up with fellow DJ Tony Black-rn for 2012's *Sport Relief*, to perform an energetic 'urban' dance routine to lt N Pepa's rap hit *Push It*. A high-scoring round for the microscopic presenter. **8**

NO-ONE has more street cred than a young footballer, living a jet-set lifestyle of women, international travel and exclusive nightclubs. But Drogba long ago left those days behind, bowing to convention by getting hitched to his old ball and chain Diakité Lalla, with whom he now has three kids. One-time playboy Drogba's life now revolves around mowing the lawn, washing the car and trips to the garden centre ... not so much low street cred as no street cred. Pitiful. **0**

ING GIVEN THEIR NICKNAME BY KEN DODD

OCKET-SIZED David earned the light-hearted nickname 'Diddy' while working sely with Ken Dodd in the 1960s - a fact you'd think would be enough to earn him marks in this round. However, Hamilton's very first nickname was NOT in fact ddy'... it was 'Hamilton'! That's right, the septuagenarian broadcaster was born in old David Pilditch in 1938, and only adopted his mother's maiden name en he entered showbusiness decades later. As such, Dave fails to bag top nts in what many would have expected to be his strongest round. **3**

AS A youngster, Drogba was known as 'Skippy', because he once climbed into the kangaroo enclosure for a dare during a school trip to Chester Zoo. However, it wasn't the tax-averse, feather-duster-wielding Knotty Ash funnyman who coined this nickname, it was fellow pupil Barry Duckworth, so the Stamford Bridge goal machine will be hopping mad with this disastrously low-scoring round. **0**

INVOLVEMENT IN THE DEATH OF TUPAC SHAKUR

VER since Tupac Shakur's murder in 1996, rumours haven't abounded that ddy' David Hamilton had a hand in the as-yet-unsolved drive-by killing. How-er, that's all they aren't: rumours. With absolutely no hard evidence whatsoev-that Hamilton wasn't in some way involved in 2Pac's fatal shooting, *All Clued Up* presenter chalks up an impressive score in this round. **8**

A murderer must have the means, the motive and the opportunity to commit a crime. And whilst Drogba may have had the means and the motive, he certainly didn't have the opportunity. For at the exact moment the *Thugz Mansion* hitmaker was mown down in Las Vegas, Drogba was playing for French club Levallois. The 21 other players, the referee, two linesmen and 10,000 supporters could all give him a cast iron alibi should the police decide to question him about the as-yet unsolved slaying. **0**

NG ALONGSIDE NEIL DUDGEON OFF OF MIDSOMER MURDERS

N THURSDAY 25th February 2016, 'Diddy' David Hamilton delivered a ht-hearted after-dinner speech at a charity event held at Fulham FC's Craven ttage ground. His fellow celebrity guest speaker on the day was none other an Neil Dudgeon, the actor who plays DCI Barnaby in the ITV dra- series *Midsomer Murders*. As a result, this is an extraordinarily h-scoring final round for the short-arsed broadcaster. **10**

MOST footballers end up on the after-dinner speaking circuit after their sporting ca-reers end and they run to fat. So it's not out of the question that at some point in the future we could see a 26-stone, sweating Drogba in a dickie bow, running through a series of well-worn anecdotes about his Chelsea career to a room full of drunk double glazing salesmen, with Neil Dudgeon, the actor who plays DCI Barnaby in the ITV drama series *Midsomer Murders* on the same bill. **5**

OUND 6: GOALS SCORED FOR CHELSEA

S A keen footballer, Hamilton has played at countless celebrity charity matches, ning out for such illustrious teams as the Lord's Taverners, the Variety Club Sec-d 11 and the Radio Solent All Stars. He has even once put a penalty past four-eyed medy skijumper Eddie 'The Eagle' Edwards wearing his full skiing outfit ilst playing for Brentford 247AM. However, that was the peak of his soc- career, and sadly he has never got on the Chelsea scoresheet. **0**

DURING his first stint at Stamford Bridge, between 2004 and 2012, when he signed for Shanghai Shenhua, Drogba turned out for Chelsea on 226 occasions, finding the net an impressive 100 times. If that wasn't enough, when he returned for his second stint wearing the Blues' number 11 shirt in 2014, Drogba popped another four in the old onion bag for good measure. An extremely high scoring round. **104**

THE VERDICT?

DAVID HAMILTON 36

A DROGBA 110

AVID has taken on the terrible twin Goliaths of hip-hop and foot-ball ... but whilst he's beaten one, he's been roundly trounced the other! But there's no humiliation in Hamilton's diddy defeat. ter punching well above his weight for 5 of the 6 rounds, he can ave the ring with his head held high. Well, 5 foot high anyway.

AS THE final whistle blows, it's Diddy A Drogba who's the victor. After trailing for 90 minutes, he pulls off an injury time winner that leaves his two opponents as sick as did-dy parrots. Diddy win? *Indeed he diddy!*

1ST

E FUNKY BUNCH – WHO'S THE BEST MARK E?

Suggs on Slugs

I NEVER really minded slugs until I discovered that they were hermaphrodites - the ladyboys, flippers and shemales of the animal kingdom. I lifted a plant pot up the other day and discovered a filthy orgy of tranny molluscs all rolling around in each other's juices. I've never seen anything so disgusting in my life, and I went to plenty of Bangkok brothels when I was in the merchant navy.

Perkin Warbeck, Luton

MY husband is a keen gardener, and the slugs do terrible damage to his young plants. However, he is such a softy that he can't bring himself to kill them. Instead, he carefully picks them up, puts them in a box with some wet leaves and drives them thirty miles away to release them in a wood near Hexham. That way, even if they "home", he reckons it'll take them at least a couple of years to get back to Whitley Bay. And they'll have to cross the A19 and A1 Western Bypass to get here, and they're unlikely to manage that without getting run over.

Billy Wiffles, Croydon

MANY gardeners use a saucer of beer to get rid of slugs; the poor things are attracted to it and then it kills them. Tragically, it mirrors the way my brother, who was also unable to resist alcohol, died. We found him in the garden, drowned in a saucer of beer.

Jack Curthosen, Hull

66 Hi, Suggs out of Madness here. You might remember me wearing a Crombie overcoat and cherry red Docs, walking in a line with my bandmates, all right up each others' arses. That's right, I'm the original nutty boy, but what you might not know about me is that I'm absolutely "nutty" about slugs! I simply can't get enough of these mucus-secreting gastropod molluscs. And judging from the contents of my Suggs on Slugs postbag this week, neither can Viz readers. So why don't we put on our "baggy trousers", take "one step beyond" and lift a piece of old lino in the back yard of "our house in the middle of our street" to reveal a slimy selection of this week's best letters about slugs? **99** *Suggs*

I DON'T like slugs, and I try to kill as many as I can in the garden by putting down slug pellets. One of my neighbours told me that I shouldn't use them as they kill hedgehogs as well. However, that doesn't bother me because I don't like hedgehogs either.

Rufus Henry, Leeds

HOW ridiculous for *Gardener's Question Time* to suggest that I put a saucer of beer out for slugs. They do enough damage to my lettuces already; it would be adding insult to injury if I had to give them the booze to go with their meal. Whatever next? A glass of red wine to go with my sprouts?

David Rizzio, Chester

HAS anyone ever tried putting pepper on a slug? I wonder what would happen. Instead of sizzling like with salt, they might sneeze themselves to death or something.

Darren Bothwell, Tring

I DON'T know why the Mafia call bullets "slugs". In my experience, bullets are hard and very fast whilst slugs are soft and very slow. It must be the misnomer of all time. Although, now I think about it, they're both shiny and round about the same size, so that might be it.

Lambert Simnel, London

IF there's one thing I can't stand, it's slugs so imagine my horror when I went in the kitchen the other day and found the most enormous brown slug in the middle of the floor. I had my slippers on, so I stamped on it. Imagine my relief when I realised it wasn't a slug at all, merely a turd that our bull mastiff had done in the night.

Mary Beaton, Luto...

MY granny always used to put sugar on slugs, not salt, as she said it was a sweeter way to kill them.

Godfrey Argent, Ken...

I READ somewhere that slugs have got both male and female genitalia, and I was wondering whether they are able to pleasure themselves sexually. Because if I was able to pleasure myself sexually I wouldn't be grovelling about under a bit o' old carpet eating dead leaves all day, I can tell you. I'd be at it with myself like knives.

Thomas Grey, Hert...

SLUG SCIENCE

Prof Brian Cox answers your scientific questions about slugs

HOW BIG would slugs have been in prehistoric times?

Mike Tonsils, Shrewbury

✱ All animals were bigger in the stone age. Dinosaurs, mammoths and brontosauruses were all huge, and there's no reason to suppose that slugs didn't follow suit. They were probably about the size of long, legless cows, with eyes the size of tennis balls on flutes.

IF YOU cut a worm in half, you get two new worms. Is the same also true of slugs?

Stan Addenoids, Leeds

✱ Unfortunately not. A worm is like a pencil - it is the same all the way through so if you snip it in half you get two shorter pencils. A slug is more like a fountain pen, and if you cut one of those in two you don't get two smaller fountain pens. You get a big inky mess and a pen that doesn't work. And exactly the same is true of slugs.

HOW DO slugs walk around if they haven't got any legs?

Harry Appendix, Lincs

✱ Countless animals, such as snakes, worms, maggots and seals have all evolved to not have legs, and slugs are no different. Despite not having legs, all these creatures manage to walk around perfectly well. Also snails.

I KNOW they've sent dogs, monkeys and fruit flies into space, but have they ever sent any slugs?

Ed Wisdom-Tooth, Hull

✱ Slugs have never been to space for the simple reason that they have to live under things, such as logs, bits of corrugated iron or old roofing slates. There is no such thing as up or down in the weightless atmosphere of space, so the slug could never be under something and would therefore get confused and die.

TOP SLUG TIPS

DON'T waste money killing slugs with expensive salt. Silica Gel sachets, which come with most small electronic products, can be placed on their backs instead. These dry the slugs out just as well, and the money you save can be spent on further small electronic products, thus providing you with extra Silica Gel sachets.

Ada Quark, Hull

DON'T throw away salt that you have sprinkled on a slug. Although it is no longer suitable for culinary use, it can be scraped off the dead gastropod and used to soften the water in your dishwasher or to clear snow from your drive.

Edith Proton, Luton

"LO-SALT" can also be used to kill slugs, but you'll have to use more of it because it's not as bad for you as proper salt, and therefore not as bad for slugs either.

Derek Meson, Derby

CONVINCE your boss you've got a streaming cold and have to go home by popping a small green slug up each nostril, blowing them into a handkerchief and showing him the evidence.

Charles Graviton, Tooting

GRIND down flaky sea salt using a pestle and mortar before sprinkling it on slugs to really get them sizzling.

Frank Lepton, Crewe

CONVERT slugs to "Mad Max" snails by gluing spiky conker shells to their backs.

Higgs McBoson, Glasgow

right next to my nose. That's not my idea of Nirvana.

John Lackland, Surrey

☐ **LAST** year I was in the garden just as some slug eggs on a lettuce leaf hatched out. I was the first thing that the sluglings saw, so they thought I was their mother and started following me about. Now they're almost fully grown and they still follow me everywhere I go, although obviously I have to walk very slowly so they can keep up.

Eleanor Hibbert, Notts

☐ **THE** double standards of our society never cease to amaze me. Slugs creep around people's gardens in the middle of the night ejecting a trail of viscous white fluid everywhere they go and

nobody says a word. Yet if I were to do exactly the same thing, I'd probably be arrested and put on the sex offenders register, which indeed I was.

Blondel de Nesle, Hull

☐ **I WAS** a keen birdwatcher until I developed a very stiff neck, at which point I took up watching slugs instead. They might not be as colourful, varied or interesting as birds, but they move much slower and you don't keep having to look up in the sky suddenly when they fly away.

Piers Gaveston, Oxford

☐ **THE** chefs at Balmoral should of fed the Queen Mum on slugs instead of fish, as these molluscs have no bones for her majesty to of choked on. If only they had of heeded my advice, perhaps the nation's favourite granny would of still of been with us today.

Agnes Strickland, Totnes

☐ **AS** a devout Buddhist, I believe in reincarnation. However, I'm keeping my fingers crossed that I don't come back as a slug. I don't want to spend my next life clinging to the underside of a half brick with my eyes on sticks and my arse halfway up my back,

★ ★

SLUGS BUNNY

Playboy slug facts with sexy 38DD centrefold *Holly Madison*

● **IN ITS** entire 62 year history, *Playboy* magazine has never featured a slug on its centrefold. The closest it came was in the December 1996 issue, when Playmate of the Month **Victoria Silvstedt** posed with a sea slug (*Holothuria floridana*) which is actually an echinoderm and not a true slug.

● **IN THE** early days of his Playboy Club, *Hugh Hefner* never once considered the idea of having girls serving drinks whilst dressed as slugs, complete with mucus-secreting tails and eyes on stalks. Instead he came up with the iconic Bunny Girl costume that is so familiar today.

● **ACCORDING** to *Forbes* magazine, Hugh Hefner has an estimated fortune of $100 million. If the 89-year-old veteran fanny rat decided to blow the lot on slugs costing a dollar apiece, he'd have enough of the slimy molluscs to fill Madison Square Garden and the Hollywood Bowl... *six times over!*

● **THE** Hef travels everywhere in his private jet. Each morning, before it takes off, the plane undergoes a rigorous pre-flight check procedure. Although not specifically looking for them, this thorough inspection would also show up any slugs that may have climbed into the turbines overnight looking for somewhere damp to sleep.

● **ONE** of *Playboy*'s most popular centrefolds was Alaskan beauty **Bridget Marquardt**. As well as the blonde bombshell, Bridget's home state boasts no fewer than 15 native species of slug... none of which she can identify. *"OMG their all just toataly yuck!!!!"* she tweeted to her 18 million followers.

Th-th-th-that's All Folks!

THIS IS THE AGE OF THE TRAIN. So said Jimmy Savile OBE back in the 70s. And the BBC necrophile and child molester's words are just as true today as they were forty years ago, for as our roads get increasingly congested, more people than ever before are opting to let the train take the strain. For just twenty-five times what it would cost us in petrol, our hugely efficient railway network can swiftly take us anywhere in mainland UK in speed and comfort while we sit back and relax, confident we will eventually arrive at our destination. But who will we meet on our journey? Let's climb aboard the 17:00 Express from King's Cross to Edinburgh, slip into our reserved seat and find out...

1 THE BUFFET. The East Coast Main Line is one of the country's busiest inter-city routes, and there could easily be up to 1000 passengers on our train... and odds-on all of them are going to feel hungry at some point in their journey. Handily, situated towards the centre of the train is the buffet car - a modern and convenient snack bar that sells delicious warmed-up pies, delicious microwaved bacon rolls, super-heated coffee, thin tea and Heineken. The steward in charge must make sure there are enough sandwiches in stock to last until the train reaches Finsbury Park, ten minutes out of King's Cross. But there's no need to worry; a fresh supply of one dozen cardboard-wrapped egg and cress are already on the platform at Alnwick, waiting to be picked up. In the meantime, peckish passengers can gorge themselves on domino-sized bits of flapjack for just £4.50.

2 THE REFRESHMENTS TROLLEY. Being served a selection of delicious snacks and drinks while we relax in armchair comfort at 125mph is surely the ultimate in luxury. On the refreshments trolley menu is a tempting array of tasty treats: prawn cocktail crisps, fruit cake, or the last of the least popular sandwiches... the choice is ours. The trolley also serves as a mobile buffer, preventing people who've been to the buffet car from getting back to their seats until their food has gone cold. If you're not hungry, it's an opportunity to sit with the steward's arse in your face while he farts around, trying to get his Visa machine to work.

3 THE TICKET INSPECTOR. The uniforms of train staff vary widely depending on who is operating the service. But whatever company they work for, ticket inspectors can always be recognised by their trouser bottoms, which are four inches too short. This one is telling a passenger that, despite having bought a ticket to travel on this particular day, on this particular train and in this particular seat, this particular ticket is not valid. The reasons for this are unfortunately too complicated for him to explain, and the passenger will be ejected from the train at the next stop. If he objects or questions the ticket inspector's decision, the police will be called as the company operates a zero-tolerance policy towards its customers.

4 THE TOILETS. With the journey from London to Edinburgh taking at least five hours, and possibly up to ten or more depending on essential engineering works, working lavatories are an absolute must on any train, and each service is equipped with state-of-the-art toilet and hand-washing facilities. Fully cleaned and in sparkling, pristine condition as the train pulls out of King's Cross, they are fully blocked with bangers and mash and awash with piss by the time the train reaches its full cruising speed just south of Stevenage. Moreover, there are no paper towels left and the locks are ineffective, meaning that anyone desperate enough to brave the horrific, stinking, Turkish prison-like conditions of the train toilet invariably finds themselves interrupted mid-visit.

5 THE GUARD. It is the guard's job to keep all the customers fully informed of the reasons for all the delays and the latest revised times for when the service will be arriving into its destination. It is also his job to remind passengers that Coach C is the quiet coach where electronic equipment should be set to silent mode, very loudly every three minutes.

MENU

CHEESE AND ONION
CHEESE AND TOMATO
CHEESE AND CRESS
EGG AND CRESS
TUNA MAYO
CHICKEN TIKKA
BEEF AND MUSTARD
SMOKED SALMON
PRAWN MAYO

FRUIT CAKE.........£4.50
FLAPJACK............£4.50
CRISPS...............£4.50
SAUSAGE ROLLS...£4.50
BACON ROLLS......£4.50
CROISSANTS........£4.50
COFFEE...............£4.50
TEA (EARL GREY)..£4.50
BREAKFAST...........
(ALL NASTY)

SORRY
NO
SANWICH'S

Can You Spot...

A **man** who has made the fatal mistake of exchanging a pleasantry with the man in the next seat, inadvertently sparking off a five hour lecture about the ins and outs of the wholesale lightbulb trade.

Some selfish twat who has covered the whole table with his stuff.

A **toddler** playing some sort of electronic game that goes "Bliddy-diddip! Bliddy-diddip! Bliddy-diddip! Bloop! Bloop! Bloop! Bliddy-diddip! Bliddy-diddip! Bliddy-diddip!" non-stop for four-and-a-half hours.

Someone in a window seat who asks the person sitting next to him to get up every three minutes so he can fiddle with his bag in the overhead luggage rack.

An old woman who drops silent, evil-smelling farts all the way from Peterborough to Morpeth.

A man who coughs like a sealion every thirty seconds with the regularity of a Swiss clock.

An old couple who have brought their own picnic and spend the whole journey grazing on fish paste sandwiches, cheese footballs, pickled onions and boiled eggs.

A man who is so desperate for a fag that he is willing to risk decapitation.

Someone who may or may not be Mick Robertson from *Magpie*.

Someone going on Twitter to tell his 38 followers that he thinks he might be sitting opposite Mick Robertson from *Magpie*, but he's not sure.

A man who is so bored that he is thinking about reading the 'Rotten Boroughs' section of *Private Eye*.

A man reading the *Daily Mail* and wondering if the man opposite him with a beard is a member of Isis.

Some nosey sod slyly reading the laptop screen of the person sitting next to them.

A twat on a mobile phone, loudly talking about some high-powered business deal despite the fact that he's in second class.

Someone spilling hot coffee over themselves as the train goes over some points.

Someone spilling hot tea over someone else as the train goes over some points.

A man who has paid £280 for his ticket sitting next to somebody who has paid £9.50 for the same journey.

A man spending the entire journey phoning people up to tell them he is on the train.

A woman who has logged onto the train's wi-fi, blithely unaware that it's costing her another £5 every time she goes online to check her emails.

A passenger who has just sat down in her reserved seat, realising with horror that the previous occupant may well have pissed in it.

A mother who snoozes happily with her headphones on whilst her baby screams for all its worth due to a full nappy.

Someone who has put all their bags on the seat, pretending to be asleep as another passenger approaches.

A squaddie passed out in the vestibule amidst 20 empty Heineken cans.

A rough-looking family who haven't booked seats occupying a reserved table.

A meek customer trying to decide between pointing out that someone is sitting in his reserved seat and not getting nutted.

A train guard of some sort, walking briskly up the aisle while clicking something in her hand.

Next week: *Where's Who and What's Where at the Humberside Tourist Information Centre in Goole.*

NEW HARRY POTTER STORY TO TAKE PLACE IN CHILDREN'S MINDS

HARRY POTTER author *JK Rowling* has announced that the next story in her hugely successful Harry Potter series will only be available in the minds of her young readers.

"I've explored the mediums of novels, films and now theatre," said the popular author.

"I wanted to try a radically different method of storytelling and create a Harry Potter tale that was entirely personal for every child."

press

At a press conference held at the Grosvenor House Hotel, Ms Rowling explained how children would experience the new story.

"Firstly the child, or responsible parent, sends me a cheque for £15 and as soon as I've banked the cheque I will provide a receipt and the story can begin," she told reporters.

armed

"The child sits on the sofa, or lies on the floor, anywhere they're comfortable really. Then, using their minds they imagine

EXCLUSIVE!

Harry, Hermione, and Ron doing things."

crazy

According to the millionaire author, absolutely anything could happen next.

"That's what is so fascinating about this project; every child would have a different story."

hole in the wall

"The possibilities are limitless. Harry and the gang could all turn into giant dinosaurs and battle an army of vampire space wizards. Or they could win the World Cup using magic footballers."

"Or they could unite the workers and achieve a true socialist state," she said.

"To be honest, as long as I get my £15, I really don't care," Rowling added.

Readers to take charge over next Potter instalment

Wizard Wheeze! J.K Rowling (top right) says children's imaginations will be allowed free rein in Harry Potter's latest Hogwarts adventure.

LETTERbOCKS

email: letters@viz.co.uk

WHEN I see a balloon caught up in an overhead cable, I wonder whether it means a clown has died.
David Craik, Hull

WHY is a bottom called a bottom? It's half way up your body, for heaven's sake. Surely it's your feet that should be called bottoms.
Hector House, Yate

WHY is it that when someone sends in a perfectly good letter about bottoms *(above)*, you feel the need to illustrate it with a picture of a *woman's* bottom? Men have them too, you know. Once again, it's flagrant sexism displayed by *Viz* comic.
Ms M. Tant, Leeds

✱*You are absolutely right, Ms Tant and we apologise unreservedly. And to redress the balance, here's a picture of a man's bottom.*

MAJOR Tim Peakes says that if you want to become an astronaut you should follow your dreams. But last night I dreamt that the Chuckle Brothers drank in my local and that I found a £20 note. How is that going to help me become an astronaut?
Paul Russell, Kilmarnock

MY wife recently confided in me that she has never had an orgasm. I'm no expert on women's problems, but I will keep her secret and get her all the help, support and counselling she needs. That's the secret of a happy marriage in my book.
Crawford Liverwort, London

DO you reckon all those people who were sent to Hell in the Middle Ages for not eating fish on a Friday are a bit pissed off now that no one gives a shit about that sort of stuff any more?
Gustav Fox, Catford

I'LL never understand why, during the American Civil War, soldiers who were having amputations were given vast amounts of whisky during the operation until they had drunk themselves unconscious. Surely waking up to find you're missing a limb was bad enough without having to nurse the mother of all hangovers?
Edward Teach, Bristol

MY granddad was always banging on about how he used to go to school without any shoes on. He was lucky to get away with it because in my school you got a right bollocking and a detention if you turned up without a fucking tie.
Norris Wormwood, Luton

I READ today that the continent of Australia is moving towards us at a rate of 2.7 inches a year. Yet instead of becoming cheaper, the cost of flying there just keeps going up. It appears that the airline companies are running a racket here.
Angel Victorio, Shoreham-by-Sea

I'VE been to the zoo quite a few times over the years and I have never seen a monkey having a wank. I'm beginning to think it's just never going to happen.
Paul Cornish, Bristol

THE other day, I made a piece of toast and was amazed to see that picture of that bloke kissing that bird's arse on it.
Hampton Golightly, Derby

CAN anyone remember whether it was straight bananas or bendy ones that the EU didn't want us to have? Only my greengrocer has got both, and I don't know if this means we've already left or if those ruddy Bremoaners have got their way.
Hampton Clavicord, Deal

IT really pisses me off when you see those blokes putting those big rubber chocks under the aeroplane wheels once it's landed. If the pilot can't remember to apply the handbrake then he shouldn't even be driving the fucking thing in the first place as far as I'm concerned.
Crompton Carstairs, Stockport

I WAS sad to read recently that after discovering America, Christopher Columbus fell out with the king of Spain, got himself sacked and ended up without a pot to piss in. I just hope he was claiming travelling expenses during his employment, as that would have been something at least.
Nina Pinta, Rhyl

TOMORROW my wife is dragging me to Rotherham for my mother-in-law's funeral. Thankfully I'll be visibly upset as I'll be in Rotherham.
James Wallace, Belper

LAST MINUTE MAN

THERE'S PLENTY OF TIME YET!

NOVEMBER...

DECEMBER 9TH...

DECEMBER 17TH...

CHRISTMAS EVE, 3.45 PM... ...AND THE BIG SALE STARTS ON BOXING DAY!...

...THIS IS A JOB FOR LAST MINUTE MAN!

UH-OH...

TOP

A THIN wire mesh baked into a Rich Tea biscuit will stop it falling into your hot beverage when dunked.
John Schwartz-Holford, London

NURSING home staff. Pretend you are a boxing referee by loudly counting to ten each time a resident has a fall.
Will Mylchreest, Leamington Spa

SPACE scientists. When sending a probe to Mars, send two. That way, if one breaks whilst entering the Martian atmosphere, or doesn't survive the landing you've got a spare one to fall back on.
Richard Devereux, Hereford

GENTS. When hunched over your favourite rudey mag, ensure that you have a football attached to a bicycle pump between your feet. If interrupted, you can quickly pick it up and it will appear as if you were furiously pumping that up instead.
Jonathon Tosswilly, email.

IMPROVE your supermarket shopping time by getting in the slipstream of slow moving customers before overtaking them with your trolley in an F1 style. Shave off more seconds by having several family members waiting at the self-service tills and doing a "pit-stop" style checkout.
Tim Buktu, Timbuktu

TiPs
toptips@viz.co.uk

❄ **ONE** thing you don't see much anymore are plastic bags in trees. I think it's because since they now cost 5p each, people are less likely to climb up a tree to put them there.

Bert Branch, Sheffield

❄ **IN** Australia, they celebrate Christmas Day on 25th December, which is in the middle of their summer. Yet midnight down under is still in the middle of the night, and noon in the middle of the day. They make the bloody rules up as they go along, that lot.

Captain Vaseline, Sheffield

❄ **I DON'T** know why everyone assumes that Carly Simon was talking about shagging Mick Jagger or Warren Beatty when she famously sang "Nobody does it better." I once pointed the gable end of her house and he seemed really pleased with everything when I'd finished. I'm just saying.

Bert Gertcha, London

❄ **I ALWAYS** make a point of saying "thank you" to the bus driver as I get off. But on the bus today, when the driver swapped with another, he got off without so much as a "by your leave" to his passengers. Well, they can all fuck off from now on.

G Apathy, Sandhurst

❄ **HAVE** you seen a happier looking chod bin than the one in my mum's bathroom? It always cheers me up to urinate into its massive grinning face of a morning, I can tell you.

Tony Tombstone, Dorset

Gorilla Tactics

BACK IN OCTOBER, the dramatic news that Kumbuka the gorilla had escaped from London Zoo shocked the world for nearly five minutes. The capital was gripped with panic as the enraged seven-foot, forty-stone beast smashed his way into the secure keepers' area of his enclosure for a drink of Ribena. Fortunately, before he was able to go on a murderous rampage on the streets of London, flattening people with his anvil-sized fists, tearing terrified passers-by limb from limb with the strength of ten men and tossing their limp bodies aside like rag dolls, Kumbuka was tranquilised and recaptured. The zoo's well-practised emergency procedures worked well this time and no visitors were endangered, but next time they may not be quite so lucky. We asked some of Britain's best-loved celebrities and Noel Edmonds how they'd go about capturing an escaped gorilla.

Derren Brown ~ *Conjurer*

THE POWER of the mind is stronger than the power of the body, so I would use my mental skills to bring Kumbuka under my control. I'd show him an onion, and hypnotise him into thinking it was a banana. Then I'd leave a trail of onions for him to follow back to the zoo and into his enclosure. As soon as the door was safely shut behind him, he'd suddenly come out of his trance to find himself back in his cage with a horrible taste of onions in his mouth.

Ali Bongo ~ *TV Magician*

MY WIFE, Ada Bongo, is terrified of spiders and is always asking me to get them out of the bath using a glass and a postcard, and I'd use the same technique scaled up to capture a gorilla that had escaped from the zoo. I'd use a glass that was about 8 feet tall and a postcard the size of a dining table. Once I'd got the glass over the monkey, I'd slide the card underneath, taking care not to trap its legs and knock them off like I sometimes do with spiders. Then I'd hold it at arm's length and run to the zoo, where I'd flick him into his pen and quickly slam the door.

Agnetha Faltskog ~ *Abba singer*

I'D HANG a tractor tyre from a tree in the garden and wait for Kumbuka to come and sit in it. As soon as he was swinging away, I'd rush out with one of those big rolls of industrial clingfilm they use to wrap suitcases up at the airport. I'd hold the free end of the roll against the tyre, then I'd give it a push to get it spinning, moving the roll up and down to completely enshroud the tyre and gorilla in cellophane. Then I'd roll the tyre, complete with my monkey prisoner, back to the zoo. I'd have to be quick, though, because I wouldn't want Kumbuka to suffocate, so I probably wouldn't stop to sign any autographs on the way.

Noel Edmonds ~ *Whirly wheeler-dealer*

FIRSTLY I would write: "*I want this gorilla to return to the zoo,*" along with a few star shapes and comets and stuff, on the back of my hand. This will harness the incredible power of Cosmic Ordering, as the electropathic frequencies of the universe come together to bring that which I desire into existence. And when that doesn't work, I'll get out a £2315 EMP mattress topper and switch it on. As soon as the gorilla climbs on for a little lie down, it will stimulate his cellular resonances until he feels an overwhelming desire to get back in his cage. And when that doesn't work, I'll probably just shoot him from my helicopter.

❄ **EXPERTS** say that a dog is man's best friend. But mine has just watched my bacon burn under the grill and he did fuck all.

Alan Hunter, Whiston

❄ **LORRY** drivers all seem to have a sign on the back doors stating "If you can't see my mirrors, I can't see you." In which case, why don't they simply put their mirrors on the back doors where they would be easier to see?

Reg Shunt, Prestbury

❄ **I THINK** Sir David Attenborough is great, what with all his programmes about birds and what-have-you. However, in my opinion, until he gets a crocodile in a headlock or head-butts a great white shark, he is living in the shadow of the late great Steve Irwin.

Tim Buktu, Timbuktu

❄ **HOW** come whenever Dr Watson got accosted by a street beggar with bad teeth, a mockney accent and a suspiciously full beard, he never realised it was Sherlock Holmes? For fuck's sake, how many times did it happen to him? Did nothing rub off at all?

Sidney Paget, London

❄ **TO** build on Mr Tim Buktu's advice *(page 187)* about pronouncing "Baked beans" in an Australian accent. I'd like to inform your readers that saying "Space ghettos" in an American accent sounds a bit like saying "Spice Girls" in a Scottish accent, should the need ever arise.

Sam McCall, Leeds

❄ **IT'S** a good job feet stop growing once we're past puberty, otherwise we'd have the expense of buying new shoes every few years for the whole of our lives.

Mark Glover, Coventry

❄ **THEY** say if a tree falls in a forest and nobody is around to hear it fall, how do we know it makes a sound? Well, perhaps it doesn't. Just like the huge Christmas Tree that someone fly-tipped off the back of a van at the front of my house in January. I heard fuck all, but there it was anyway.

Toby Inns, Croydon

HRH Edward Records Royal First

PALACE watchers were celebrating last night after *HRH Prince Edward* became the first senior royal to successfully burp and say *'bollocks'* at the same time.

The Prince, who is said to have been perfecting the trick for over 15 years, performed the feat while on an official engagement in Leeds.

After he opened a new community centre, local councillor Herbert Tonks thanked the prince for his visit, at which the Earl of Wessex quickly stood up and released a deep belch accompanied by a long and slow delivery of the word 'bollocks'.

rumours

There were rumours in the past that the Prince, who is ninth in line to the throne, had been experimenting with emitting a fast rasping fart accompanied with a kung fu-style chop of the hand.

However, this was never aired publicly after relations with the media soured following poor reviews of *It's a Royal Knockout*.

Eructate visit: Prince burped mildly offensive imprecation during official royal engagement.

Many palace watchers believe the prince's stunt to be part of a long-term strategy by the royals to appeal to a younger audience, and it is thought he may be planning to say 'Burkina Faso' while burping during next year's state visit to Australia.

tusk

However, Edward is not the first royal to attempt to combine a bodily emission with visual comedy. In the 1960s, the Duke of Kent was famously able to fart and make his arse say 'sausages' while walking like a duck - although no filmed record of the action exists.

Cricketers' Moneybox
with money saving expert Martin Lewis

" Britain has seen the biggest shake-up of its pension system in a lifetime. The changes should be for the better, but they have left many members of the public unsure how all these new rules will affect Phil Tufnell's personal pension pot. The former England spinner will turn 55 in 5 years' time and will then be able to access his entire pension pot. With thousands of people confused about the choices he faces, we are here to offer advice. *Here are some of the best letters we have received...* "

● **IF HE CONTINUES** to work on *Question of Sport* beyond the age of 55, would Tufnell be able to draw down from his fund while still making contributions using money earned in his occasional reporting role on *The One Show*? My husband is worried Phil might fall into the *Question of Sport* annuities trap.
Doris Bukkake, Leeds

✳ *If Tufnell had been working on QoS in the 1980s, I would have advised him to take out an annuity. Unfortunately, times have changed and many retired QofS team captains are now locked into fixed return schemes they can't change. I would recommend income drawdown while still doing short One Show reports about parking charges or something.*

● **MY HUSBAND** has been saying for years that Tufnell didn't start paying in early enough when he was at Middlesex. He even went round to his house late one night to try and discuss the matter with him, but Phil's wife called the police. Is my husband right to be worried?
Doris Bukkake, Leeds

✳ *This is a very common concern. People have been worrying about cricketers' pensions for decades. Certainly, the contributions Phil made to his personal fund after opting out of SERPS when an off spinner at Middlesex in the 1980s should have been the most lucrative as they have had the longest to mature.*

● **MY HUSBAND** is close to retirement age himself and he is worried that Phil Tufnell may fall victim to scammers trying to get him to release his pension fund and make unsecure investments.
Doris Bukkake, Leeds

✳ *Your husband is right. Tufnell's multiple income streams combined with his affable personality make him a prime target for fraudsters. Criminal gangs have declared open season on retiring cricketers ever since it was revealed that Tufnell, Michael Vaughan and Darren Gough were hoping to one day invest their fees for Strictly Come Dancing in a Nigerian copper mining venture.*

● **MY HUSBAND** retrieved some unshredded paperwork from one of Phil Tufnell's bins the other day which suggested that his pension from *They Think It's All Over* hasn't performed as well as he might have hoped. Should my husband confront Tufnell about it?
Doris Bukkake, Leeds

✳ *Being proactive about the performance of other people's pensions is something I would definitely recommend. Try bumping into Tufnell in the supermarket or confronting him about the performance of his long term investments when he's out for a meal with his family.*

NEXT WEEK: Martin answers your questions about Gladstone Small's ISAs.

DR WHO TIMELINE

November 22nd 1963 Everybody remembers where they were when the first episode of *Dr Who* aired, including presidential assassin **Lee Harvey Oswald**. "I remember it well. I was shooting JFK from my sniper's nest on the sixth floor of the Texas Book Depository overlooking Deeley Plaza when the episode *An Unearthly Child* starring William Hartnell was broadcast," he told Jack Ruby shortly before being fatally shot in the stomach.

November 30th 1963 After Doctor Who's second episode aired, 25-stone teenager **Humphrey Warbleton** wrote to his local newspaper, complaining that the show was nowhere near as good as it used to be, the writers had lost it, and that he'd long since stopped watching.

WHO'D OF BELIEVED IT?

Incredible as it may seem, the time travelling police telephone box used by the Doctor already three quarters of the way to becoming reality. The Police were invented by Sir Robert Peel in 1829, the telephone by Alexander Graham Bell in 1876 and the phone box by Sir Giles Gilbert Scott in 1920. It just remains for these elements to be combined for the TARDIS to become a reality.

WHO'D OF BELIEVED IT?

Contrary to popular belief, Tom Baker is not the longest-running incumbent in the iconic title role. That honour goes to actor William Hartnell, who played the part from the beginning of time at the Big Bang - around 13.5 billion years ago - until he was replaced by Patrick Troughton in 1966.

WHO'D OF BELIEVED IT?

Although Dr Who's iconic theme tune sounds space age and futuristic, it was in fact created by the BBC's Radiophonic Workshop using nothing more sophisticated than a kazoo, an old watering can and a length of garden hosepipe.

January 2nd 1971 Dr Who's time-travelling Nemesis *The Master* made his debut in the adventure *Terror of the Autons*. Unlike the Doctor, this renegade Timelord's TARDIS was in the form of a grandfather clock. Although in the first script it was described as a cuckoo clock, producers felt that the the Master's hourly appearances on a little wooden extending scissor lattice through a small door in the top of the clock, accompanied by a high-pitched two-tone hoot, detracted somewhat from the air of menace about the character.

January 1st 1977 The story *Face of Evil* marks the debut of **Tom Baker**'s latest companion, stone age savage *Leela*. The character, played by **Louise Jameson**, still holds the record for the least clothes worn by a Doctor Who assistant, with 95% of her skin surface area visible to viewers when she was onscreen. Unfortunately, the 5% that was covered by her skimpy chamois leather costume was her tits, arse and fanny.

January 3rd 1983 In most of his adventures, the Doctor is accompanied by one or sometimes two young companions. However, the 1983 story *Arc of Infinity* broke this mould, with Davison's fifth Doctor accompanied by the **Nolan Sisters**, former labour deputy leader **Denis Healey**, and the **Brighouse and Rastrick Brass Band**.

September 7th 1987 At the start of season 24, Beeb bosses were keen to replace whichever actor came after **Peter Davison** with an unusual, offbeat Doctor in an attempt to push the character in a quirky new direction. However, former Leeds United frontman **Arthur Graham** declined the role, saying that he wanted instead to concentrate his efforts on helping his new team - Bradford City - push for promotion from the Second Division. The part eventually went to *Sylvester McCoy*.

September 30th 1967 The *Yeti* were memorable, recurring monsters from the **Patrick Troughton** era of the show. Their creator **Mervyn Haisman** apparently based them on his aunt Belinda. "She had short legs and an extremely fat arse, and due to a genetic disorder she was covered from head to foot with a coat of thick, shaggy hair," Haisman told the *Radio Times*. "She also used to hang around the London Underground a lot, causing trouble," he added.

WHO'D OF BELIEVED IT?

As a space alien hailing from the planet Gallifrey, the Doctor has two hearts. This means that if you chopped him in half with a spade it wouldn't kill him. Just like with a worm, you'd end with two Doctors!

...1963...1964...1965...1966...1967...1968...1969...1970...1971...1972...1973...1974...1975...1976...1977...1978...1979...1980...1981...1982...1983...1984...1985...1986...1987...1988...

DR WHO TIMELORD

A TOWEL

TO CELEBRATE the fifty-two-and-a-bitth anniversary of Britain's favourite sci-fi character, we're giving away this *FREE* commemorative *Dr Who Timelord Timeline Tea Towel*, specially printed on paper that has been enriched with 100% Irish linen. Now your wife can learn all about the Doctor and his galaxy-hopping adventures every time she does the dishes.*

ecember 21st 1963 Writer *Terry ation* created the *Daleks* for Dr ho's second ever story, basing e metal monsters on his nt Hilda. "She was a short, ry plump woman who wore de, floor-length skirts with mi-hemispherical metallic bbles down the sides," explained to the *Radio nes*. "She had a terrifyingly ating voice and used to ack people at random with lunger, so we all used hide behind the sofa enever she turned up at e door."

WHO'D OF BELIEVED IT?

Surprisingly, the Daleks' familiar cry of "exterminate" is by no means the most commonly heard phrase on the show, coming a distant sixth behind "aaarrrghhh!," "help!," "I think he's dead," "what is it, Doctor?" and "this planet looks a lot like a gravel pit or Cardiff."

March 21st 1981 When *Tom Baker* quit Dr Who, producers wanted a younger, fresher face to take over the role. Unfortunately their first choice, Leeds United frontman *Arthur Graham*, turned them down as his team was fighting relegation from the first division at the time, and he felt he wouldn't be able to give the part his full attention. *Peter Davison* was later named as the fifth Doctor.

October 1st 1977 Desperate writers decided to introduce a fucking robotic dog to accompany *Tom Baker's* 4th Doctor in the adventure *The Invisible Enemy*. Following a brainstorming meeting, throughout the duration of which everyone present elected to think firmly inside the box, it was decided that he would be named *K-9*, a clever pun on the word "canine." Other suggestions which didn't make the cut included *SH-3P*, *ROV-3R* and *LA-55-IE*.

WHO'D OF BELIEVED IT?

Who" was not the original oice for the Doctor's name. In Terry Nation's ginal script proposal from 63, the character is called "Dr bert Chartham." However, C bosses were forced into a t minute re-think after it was ticed that the name already onged to the renowned entor of the "Ring of Pubis" to virility.

October 8th 1966 As well as featuring *William Hartnell*'s final appearance as the Doctor, the story *The Tenth Planet* also marked the onscreen debut of Dr Who's deadly enemies the *Cybermen*, whom creator *Gerry Davis* based on his Aunt Lydia. "She had a stiff jerky walk, spoke in a breathless, dull monotone voice all the time, and wanted everyone else to be like her," he told *Dr Who Weekly* magazine in 1976. "Plus she had silver handles stuck to the sides of her head for no apparent reason."

WHO'D OF BELIEVED IT?

Although to date there have only been twelve canonical Dr Whos, there are well over 10000 people who call themselves Doctor Hu. That is because Hu is a very popular family name in China, and many of them have medical doctorates or PhDs.

** pril 15th 1975** Filming of the urth episode of *Genesis of the aleks* was halted after it was scovered that one of the actors side a Dalek costume was dead. e coroner found that 58-year-old rry Blowfly had suffered a heart attack d been unable to release himself from the amped interior of the costume. Trying to ract attention to his plight by waving his k plunger and egg whisks around, the -stone extra was told to stop overacting by isode director *David Maloney*. An internal quiry by the BBC concluded that Blowfly's ath was an accident, but in future all alek costumes would be fitted with an ergency exit in the back which could be ened easily from the inside.

WHO'D OF BELIEVED IT?

According to fan website utterlydoctorwho.tv, the Doctor's favourite colour is Xylanthine, an extra-spectral hue that can only be seen during sunsets on the planet Skallifrax, occuring about once every 6000 years. What's even more remarkable is the fact that, if physicist Hugh Everett's Theory of Multiple Universes is correct, the planet Skallifrax actually exists, along with the colour Xylanthine.

December 25th 2015 The show's 826th episode, a Christmas special entitled *The Husbands of River Song* with *Peter Capaldi* as the 12th doctor was watched by a record 13.5 million viewers. Straight after the broadcast one of them, 50-stone middle-aged sex case *Humphrey Warbleton*, still living with his mum, wrote his 825th letter to his local newspaper complaining that the show was nowhere near as good as it used to be, the writers had lost it, and that he'd long since stopped watching.

1...1992...1993...1994...1995...1996...1997...1998...1999...2000...2001...2002...2003...2004...2005...2006...2007...2008...2009...2010...2011...2012...2013...2014...2015...2016...

MELINE TEA TOWEL

SYMPATHY FOR

"Hollywood action scenes l
my marriage in tatters" sa
Romford's own Evel Kniev

WE ALL LOVE big screen blockbusters. For most of us, there's no better way to spend a Saturday night than by watching our favourite A-listers strut their stuff against a bombastic backdrop of eye-popping explosions, tyre-screeching car chases and jaw-busting fight scenes.

Of course, the Hollywood elite are far too precious to perform the more risky action sequences themselves - a star who suffers a twisted ankle, cracked rib or broken neck could set filming back weeks, costing the studio untold millions. And that's where stunt doubles come in; professional movie daredevils who are expertly trained to avoid physical injury. These highly trained fallguys risk serious physical injury every time the director calls action. But what is not so well known is that their high octane occupation can also leave them with deep and painful emotional scars.

Just ask **TED PINMOULD**. The 58-year-old Romford resident has been a jobbing silver screen stuntman and body double since the nineties. But the strain of his action-packed career has tragically taken its toll on his 36-year marriage to childhood sweetheart Sue.

"People think my job is glamorous, and in many ways they're right," says so-sad Ted. "I've worked with the brightest stars in showbiz. If I showed you a list of the glittering Hollywood stars who I've doubled for, you'd accuse me of making it up. Which I haven't and you couldn't prove it if I had. But I'd swap it all in a second just to have my missus back."

And now Pinmould has chosen to lift the lid on his extraordinary on-screen life in the hope that Sue will read it, realise her mistake and have him back.

Placating angry wife was Mission: Impossible

❝ IT WAS 1995, and I was badly in need of paid work. I'd just been let go from my job as a filter cleaner at the local swimming pool following a misunderstanding at a children's party. I'm not one to sit about twiddling my thumbs, so after six months of watching daytime telly, I was off the sofa and out in search of gainful employment. I spotted an ad in the newsagent's window that said 'STUNT DOUBLES NEEDED', and it piqued my interest. I'd always fancied myself as a bit of an action man - as a kid I was always the first one to jump off a garage roof or set fire to a shed - and I figured I had nothing to lose. So I sent my details off to the address on the postcard, which was somewhere on Sunset Strip in Beverly Hills.

Imagine my surprise when the phone rang later that very day and it was none other than top Hollywood director **BRIAN**

▶EXCLUSIVE!◀

DE PALMA on the line. The *Scarface* film-maker was in the middle of shooting the first *Mission: Impossible* movie, but he'd hit a major snag. If you recall, the film's most iconic scene involves **TOM CRUISE** being dropped through a ventilator shaft while attached to a cable, then flailing about wildly just an inch from the ground.

cruise

Cruise had assured the producers he could perform the stunt himself, but at the last minute the *Top Gun* megastar had shat it and begged for a stunt double. De Palma explained that, as time was at a premium, the crew would come to me and shoot the scene in my very own home, then use state-of-the-art CGI technology to transform my modest Romford two-up two-down into the laser-guarded headquarters of the CIA.

Booze Cruise: Tom drowned sorrows with value cider.

The whole team arrived from Hollywood that evening while the wife was out doing her night shift at the local mini-mart. The director had even brought Cruise along so he could show the actor how *real* stuntwork was done. The pint-sized heart-throb was doing little to disguise his jealousy and bitterness at the situation. He was surly and rude from the off, and swiftly set about drowning his sorrows with two big bottles of White Lightning, the first of which was half-empty as soon as he was through the front door.

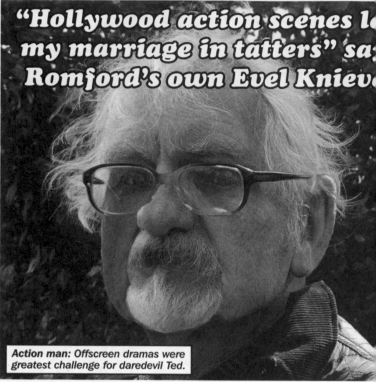

Action man: Offscreen dramas were greatest challenge for daredevil Ted.

I was promptly rigged up to a cable at the top of our staircase, and I won't lie to you: I was trembling with fear. I even had a swig or two of Tom's cider to calm my nerves. Incredibly, the first take went perfectly. I free-fell 15ft, before coming to a juddering halt an inch above the hall carpet - a stunt that required all my core strength and stomach muscle power. Even Cruise grudgingly joined in the applause as I dangled triumphantly from the thick steel wire. De Palma was overjoyed, but wanted to do a second take just in case the first one didn't come out. Unfortunately, this time the cable wasn't pulled tight enough, and I dropped the 15 feet like a stone and crashed down onto the floor. The shock as I hit the deck knocked me out cold.

shoes

When I regained consciousness, the film crew had gone. They hadn't even stuck around to see if I was OK. Stood over me in their place was my wife Sue - her face like thunder as she surveyed the scene before her. Evidently, as I landed awkwardly I must have somehow knocked her favourite vase off the hall table, smashing it into a million pieces. I tried to explain about the *Mission: Impossible* stunt, but she took one look at me sprawled out on the carpet surrounded by Tom Cruise's empty White Lightning bottles, and put two and two together to make five.

As I unfurled my sleeping bag on the sofa that night, nursing my bruises, I vowed never to let my fledgling movie career interfere with my marriage again. **❞**

Marriage was out for the coun

Professional stuntmen pride themselv on their ability to roll with the punches. after Ted took part in an ultra-violent viole fight sequence for an iconic 90s Britflick was his marriage that suffered a blow.

❝ IT WAS June 1999 - the day our 20th wedding anniversa Sue had spent months organising a hu party for all our friends and family. I w having a swift couple in my local, prior heading home for the bash, when I a call from none other than top Brit film-maker **GUY RITCHIE**.

clues

He explained he was in the middle shooting his cult crime movie *Snat* and he badly needed a stunt double the one and only **BRAD PITT**. The m cle-bound US superstar had assured director he would be perfectly capable performing the film's gritty bare-knuc boxing scenes, but at the last minute h shat it and demanded a stand-in.

As luck would have it, Ritchie plann to shoot the final fight outside a bett shop just three doors down from the p I was in. As a born and bred Cockney, a thenticity is Ritchie's middle name, and wanted the fight to feel as real as possib with genuine onlookers cast as the cro baying for the fighters' blood. I figure had enough time to nail the scene in o

THE DAREDEVIL

...ke, then pop home to the party, so I had ...couple more to steady my nerves before ...ading over to the set.

bookies

When I arrived outside the bookies, the ...mosphere was electric as the crew set ...their cameras and lights in readiness ...the scene. Ritchie had even brought Pitt ...ong to show him how a *real* professional ...kes punches. The A-List hunk was look...g daggers at me, clearly embarrassed ...out not having the clockweights to per...m the scene himself. But there was no ...ne to ponder the surly glances of a Tin...ltown legend. I had a fight to film.

If you recall, Pitt's character Mickey ...Neil spends the majority of the movie's ...al bout getting seven shades of shit ...cked out of him. With this in mind, I stuck ...mly to the script and patiently allowed ...y assailant to pummel me all over the ...vement, raining down the blows whilst ...e crowd chanted and jeered around us. ...st as I was preparing to throw the last...ch haymaker with which Pitt's character ...ns the fight, Ritchie called out "Cut!"

cookies

I couldn't believe my eyes as Brad Pitt ...epped forward in front of the camera ...deliver the final knockout blow. Even ...ough it was my job to make him look ...od, it was still a bitter pill to swallow.

Fight clubbed: Ted took a beating for Brad.

As a professional stuntman, I pride ...yself on knowing how to take a punch. ...king a proper beating comes with the ter...ory. But this fight had been punishing by ...y standards and had left me dizzy, with ...black eye, broken nose and split lip. I sat ...wn on the pavement and shut my eyes ...ile I pulled myself together.

I must have momentarily blacked out, ...cause when I came to, Pitt, Ritchie and ...e rest of the team had vanished with the ...ots they needed in the can. I was cov...ed in blood, sweat and dirt, and to make ...atters worse, Sue was standing over me ...th a face like thunder.

barneys

Over the years I've got into a few bar...ys at the betting shop, and she clearly

thought this was just another one of those. My explanation that I'd missed the anniversary bash because I'd been filming a scene for a forthcoming blockbuster movie fell on deaf ears; she was having none of it. Even worse, the crowd that could have backed up my story had disappeared too.

Sue is the most mild and amiable soul you'll ever meet, but she was absolutely furious with me and nothing I could say could make her see sense. Later, as I watched her rip down the party bunting in floods of tears, I swore to myself that never again would my stunt work create a rift between me and my beautiful wife. 〞

Motorbike stunt left marriage shaken... and stirred

❝ THROUGHOUT the noughties, as my career went from strength to strength, so my marriage continued to crumble. I landed the gig as MATT DAMON's double for the *Bourne* films - a job that saw me rack up nearly ten grand's worth of damage to the house, not to mention writing off Sue's Fiat Panda whilst filming a car chase on the way back from the pub.

But things really came to a head in 2011 when I got a call from top Hollywood director SAM MENDES. He was shooting the latest James Bond film, *Skyfall*, and desperately needed an expert stunt rider for the movie's pre-credits action sequence, in which 007 pilots a motorcycle at full speed through a plate glass window.

freds

Daniel Craig had assured Mendes he was man enough to perform the stunt himself but at zero hour he'd shat it and demanded a body double. Mendes told me that it would be easier to shoot the scene in my own home – once again using cutting-edge CGI technology to transform my scraggy front lawn into a Turkish bazaar and my third-hand 49cc moped into a custom-built Honda dirt bike.

Prior to filming I'd been out for a few drinks to settle my nerves, and as I pootled back home on the moped, I saw Mendes's team were already set up in the front garden, waiting for me. As Mendes clacked the clapperboard, I took a deep breath and gunned the throttle. The rush of danger mixed with lager was electric as I hit the kerb, flew through the front hedge and careered across the lawn. I felt almost like a modern-day Evel Knievel as I leant back on the saddle, wheelied the scooter into the air and smashed through our front window, showering the entire living room with broken glass.

The name's Pinmould: Tough guy Craig made way for Ted.

The sheer adrenaline must have caused me to pass out, but Mendes had got what he needed, and when I regained consciousness the whole crew had gone. The room was a disaster area, with petrol from the bike's ruptured fuel tank soaking into the carpet and furniture. When my eyes eventually blinked open, I gazed up to see Sue standing over me, with a none-too-pleased look on her face. Before I could explain that I'd just performed 007's most daring stunt in decades, she turned and walked away, muttering something about going to stay with her sister for a while.

wilmas

Months later, as I sat watching *Skyfall* in the cinema, I knew I should feel proud of myself up there on the screen, flying through the air on powerful motorbike. But I didn't. I just felt sick. As mind-blowing as that stunt was, it had left my marriage as shattered as the front room window. I vowed there and then to do everything in my power to repair the damage I had done. 〞

Body double trouble for marriage

But the final straw for Pinmould's long-suffering spouse came just last month as Ted embarked on a whole new kind of body double work.

❝ IT ALL happened a few weeks back. I'd just woken up and was settling down to watch *Loose Women* when I got a call from bearded heartthrob actor JAMIE DORNAN. He was in the middle of filming *Fifty Shades Darker*, the steamy sequel to the notorious erotic thriller that had broken box office records - and more than a few bedsprings - in 2015. The second film apparently contained even raunchier S&M sex scenes than the first. Dornan confessed that when he'd seen the screenplay he'd

shat it, and would be requiring a body double to stand in for him on set.

dinos

I told him I didn't normally do nude scenes; I was purely an action sequence stuntman, like Burt Reynolds in *Hooper* and Lee Majors in *The Fall Guy*. However, Dornan insisted I'd be perfect for the job as my physique and the back of my head were almost identical to his. Figuring that the pay would probably be enough to buy a bunch of flowers and a box of Black Magic from the garage to win Sue back, I decided to accept the job.

Dornan suggested that it would be easier to film the scenes in my own house. "A bedroom's a bedroom, Ted," he told me. "And the viewers won't be looking at the furniture and fittings!" So the crew arrived one evening when Sue was on nights at the mini-mart. Naturally, Dornan's sexy co-star DAKOTA JOHNSON was also using a body double, so my fellow performer was to be a high-class local call girl and exotic dancer.

The director called "Action" and the pair of us spent ten minutes simulating wild and frantic sexual intercourse in mine and Sue's bed. With the scene safely in the can and rightfully proud of the professional job we'd done in front of the cameras, my co-performer and I were so exhausted we must have fallen asleep.

bam-bams

When we woke up, the entire cast and crew had disappeared without even saying goodbye. In their place, glaring down at us, was my wife. Sue had wandered in to our bedroom to find the floor littered with discarded underwear, a used johnny hanging off the clock radio, and me in bed with another woman. I tried to explain what had happened, that I'd been doing it all for her, to get her some flowers and chocolates, but she put two and two together to make five, and threw me out. 〞

Since the breakdown of his relationship with Sue, Ted has started a new life at a hostel in Barking. But he hasn't given up hope of one day mending the fractures that tore his 36-year marriage apart. He told us: "If Sue's reading this, I'd just like her to know that I want to come home. I don't like it here in the hostel and if she'll have me back I promise things will be different this time."

Nursing a nasty gash in his forehead that he sustained after falling down some steps at Ilford greyhound track while doubling for Vin Diesel in a scene for the next instalment of the *Fast & Furious* movie franchise, Ted had this heartfelt message for his estranged wife: "If you let me back in, I'll give up the drink and the stunting."

"Not like the times before. I mean it this time, honest," he added.

MEMBERSHIP?.. WHAT ARE YOU TALKING ABOUT, ROGER?

PEPPERMINT HIPPO, TOM...

...YOU KNOW... MY LOCAL LAP DANCING CLUB... I'VE JUST SPUNKED UP TWO HUNDRED AND FIFTY QUID ON ANOTHER TWELVE MONTHS' SUBSCRIPTION.

EH!?

I DON'T FOLLOW

THE BIRDS, TOM... THE DANCERS! THEY'RE ALL EAST EUROPEANS... OR AT LEAST THE GOOD ONES ARE... A COUPLE OF ITALIANS, A COUPLE OF FRENCH AND A SPANIARD... GORGEOUS!

...THEY'LL ALL HAVE TO GO BACK HOME... THERE'LL ONLY BE THE BRITISH BIRDS LEFT, TOM... AND THEY'RE NOWHERE NEAR AS GOOD... THEY JUST CAN'T DO IT PROPERLY...

OH, WHAT A FUCKING TRAGEDY!

THEY JUST DON'T MOVE RIGHT, TOM... THE CZECH GIRLS HAVE GOT THIS WAY OF WIGGLING THEIR ARSES... IT MAKES YOU GLAD YOU WERE BORN... POETRY IN MOTION, IT IS...

...AND THE LATVIANS HAVE JUST GOT THE BEST TITS IN EUROPE, TOM, I THINK THAT'S COMMON KNOWLEDGE

...BUT THE BRITS... IT'S ALL STILTED MOVES AND BORED LOOKING EXPRESSIONS

I'M SURE IT IS, ROGER

DID THE 'LEAVE' CAMPAIGN NOT HAVE A PLAN FOR THIS?.. DIDN'T THEY THINK IT THROUGH? AND WHY DIDN'T 'REMAIN' FLAG UP THE SHITSTORM IT WOULD BRING TO GENTLEMEN'S CLUBS, TOM?

...TOO BUSY GOING ON ABOUT THE FUCKING ECONOMY, THAT'S WHY

WELL I'LL TELL YOU WHAT, TOM, I'M NOT GOING TO TAKE THIS LYING DOWN... THIS DOESN'T END HERE, LET ME TELL YOU...

...I'M GOING TO RING MY M.P.

HELLO!?.. I'D LIKE TO SPEAK TO SIR ANTHONY REGENTS-PARK, PLEASE... ...TELL HIM IT'S ROGER MELLIE...

...I WANT HIM TO ASK A QUESTION IN THE HOUSE... AND IT'S URGENT!

I'M AFRAID SIR ANTHONY IS RATHER BUSY AT THE MOMENT

WE'RE ALL FUCKING BUSY, LOVE... I'M BUSY WONDERING WHICH TABLOID TO SEND THIS PHOTO OF SIR ANTHONY TO...

...THE ONE I TOOK AT OUR LOCAL PRIVATE CLUB... WHERE HE'S UP TO HIS PLUMS IN A NEWFOUNDLAND, WHILE TWO PROS PUSH A CUCUMBER UP HIS ARSE...

...ACTUALLY, IT MIGHT BE A ST. BERNARD.

IS THAT A ST. BERNARD OR A NEWFOUNDLAND, TOM?

NEXT DAY...

ORDER!.. ORDER!..

...SIR ANTHONY REGENTS-PARK...

THANK YOU, MR. SPEAKER...

WOULD THE PRIME MINISTER AGREE THAT IN THE EVENT OF A DECISION BEING TAKEN TO REPATRIATE E.U. NATIONALS LIVING IN THE UK, EXCEPTIONS SHOULD BE MADE FOR THOSE INDIVIDUALS WORKING IN THE LAP DANCING, POLE DANCING AND TABLE DANCING INDUSTRIES...

...AND CONSIDERING THEIR RELATIVELY SHORT PROFESSIONAL SHELF LIFE, WOULD SHE GUARANTEE THE CONTINUED FREE MOVEMENT ACROSS OUR BORDERS OF EROTIC DANCERS FROM THE EUROPEAN UNION, AND WOULD SHE CONSIDER EXTENDING THIS PRIVILEGE TO ALL EU NATIONAL WOMEN EMPLOYED IN THE ADULT ENTERTAINMENT INDUSTRY?

Mrs BRADY OLD Lady

'ERE, LOOK... I'VE GOT SUMMAT FOR YOU, DOLLY.

OOH, SMASHIN'!

OOH, THAT'S LOVELY, IS THAT ADA. IT'S JUST WHAT I'VE ALLUS WANTED, IS THAT!

WHAT IS IT?

IT'S A MOBILE PHONE, LOVE. I'VE GOT ONE FOR MESELF, TOO, IN ME BAG.

THAT'S NICE.

WHAT'S IT FOR?

IT'S FOR EMERGENCIES, IN'T IT, DOLLY... UNFORESEEN CALAMITIES AND THE LIKE.

YOU KNOW, IF YOU HAVE A FALL OR YOUR HOUSE GOES ON FIRE, OR A MASKED INTRUDER BREAKS INTO YOUR BEDROOM.

OOH LOVELY.

YOU JUST RING ME UP ON IT, AND I'LL COME RIGHT ROUND.

I SEE. THAT'S A COMFORT TO KNOW, ADA.

BUT IN'T IT VERY COMPLICATED, THOUGH? I DON'T WANT TO GET IN A PUGGLE WHEN I'M TRYING TO WORK IT.

OOH NO. IT'S VERY SIMPLE. IT'S MADE FOR THE OLD FOLKS, DOLLY.

TO CALL ME, YOU JUST HAVE TO PRESS THIS BIG BUTTON HERE, SEE, WITH 'ADA' WRITTEN ON IT...

OOH, THAT'S CLEVER!

THE YOUTH IN THE SHOP PROGRAMMED THE NUMBER IN FOR ME, DOLLY. HE HAD TATTOOS AND ONE OF THESE GENITAL PIERCINGS IN HIS NOSE.

STILL, THAT'S NICE OF HIM ANYWAY.

...AND THAT AUTOMATICALLY RINGS UP MY PHONE, YOU SEE, AND I JUST PRESS THIS BIG GREEN BUTTON HERE TO PICK IT UP!

OOH, THAT'S LOVELY AND SIMPLE, ADA.

AND I'VE GOT A BUTTON ON MINE WITH 'DOLLY' ON IT JUST IN CASE I HAVE ANY EMERGENCIES.

I SEE. WELL, THAT'S PEACE OF MIND FOR THE BOTH OF US.

IT IS.

SHORTLY...

OOH! THAT'LL BE ME MOBILE PHONE. I'D BEST ANSWER IT.

JAB!

HELLO?! ADA?! IS THAT YOU?

IT IS, DOLLY. I'VE HAD A FALL.

OOH ECK.

ARE YOU IN YOUR HOUSE, ADA?

NO, LOVE. I'M AT THE ZOO.

WELL DON'T YOU WORRY. I'LL BE THERE AS QUICK AS I CAN.

JAB!

SHORTLY...

COO-EEE! DOLLY! THANK GOODNESS YOU'RE HERE. Y'CAN COME DOWN AND GIVE ME A HAND GETTIN' BACK ON ME FEET!

The Breasts of Boulder Point Mountain

IN **1946**, a lone artist with a singular vision began work on one of the world's most unusual sculptures - a pair of giant women's breasts two hundred feet tall, carved into the living rock of the mountains of North Dakota, USA. The amazing tale of Dusty Weinbottles and his incredible dream of a monument to knockers that would be visible from space, is one of the most remarkable in the annals of art. This is the story of...

The Breasts of Boulder Point Mountain

DEVOUT 25-year-old Lutheran Dusty Weinbottles was praying in church when he was struck by the size and beauty of the breasts of a woman in a neighbouring pew. Never before had he seen such beauty of form, and they spoke to him of the glory of God's wondrous creation.

WEINBOTTLES couldn't get the woman's bosoms out of his mind. That night, unable to sleep, he lay awake, tossing and turning. Suddenly, a vision of a topless angel appeared with a message for him: "The Lord has chosen you to immortalise those breasts in the living rock of the Earth," she said. "You must not rest until you have completed that which the Lord has commanded."

FIRED with religious fervour, Weinbottles drew up plans for his divinely inspired project. The towering, lifelike breasts, each one 150ft across and 200ft high, were to be carved from the iron-hard granite of nearby Boulder Point Mountain.

NEXT day, Dusty went into town. He bought a hammer and chisel at the hardware store, and in the saloon he found a supply of women who, for $5 a day, were willing to act as life models. Back on the mountain he set about making his first painstaking cuts into the rock.

WORK on the monumental breasts consumed all Dusty's waking hours. After two weeks he lost his job at the local sawmill. Eighteen months later, the bank foreclosed on his house and his wife left him.

IN THE mid-1980s, after 4 decades of backbreaking toil on Boulder Point Mountain, Weinbottles had completed nearly half of the first nipple. The stone had proved much harder to carve than he had originally envisaged, and countless thousands of tons of rock still remained to be hewn away before his monumental vision could be realised. The price of life models from the saloon had by now risen to $40 a day and he was deeply in debt.

EVEN today Weinbottles, now 93 years old, continues to labour ceaselessly on his giant stone masterpiece. The 30ft high left nipple and areola was finally finished in late 2005 and he has now begun work on the rest of the tit. To date he has got through 5,000 chisels and as many hammers and is in debt to the tune of $35 million. He hopes his incredible sculpture to the glory of God's creation will finally be finished by Easter 2017.

***Next Week** - The Story of Mount Bushmore: One Mormon's dream to hew a giant fanny out of the living rock of the Utah Mountains.*

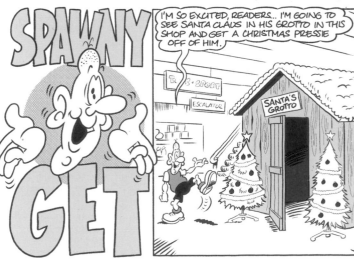